THE SCIENCE OF LIVING THINGS

General Editors

J. M. PARRISH, M.A. (Oxon,)
JOHN R. CROSSLAND, F.R.G.S.

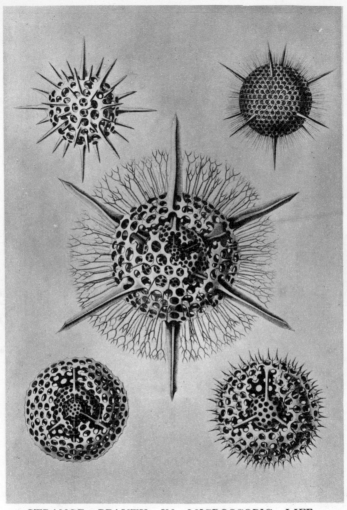

STRANGE BEAUTY IN MICROSCOPIC LIFE.

The radiolaria, which float in the upper layers of the deeper oceans, are found in the ' plankton ' that forms the main diet of certain whales. They can be seen only under a powerful microscope.

Courtesy of the Natural History Museum.

THE SCIENCE
OF LIVING THINGS

BOTANY: ZOOLOGY
ANATOMY: PHYSIOLOGY

Advisory Editor

PROF. SIR FREDERICK KEEBLE
C.B.E., F.R.S., Sc.D., *Adviser in Agriculture to Imperial Chemical Industries. Lately Sherardian Professor of Botany, University of Oxford.*

Edited by

A. H. G. ALSTON, B.A. (Oxon.)
of the British Museum (Natural History)

ODHAMS PRESS LIMITED
LONG ACRE, LONDON, W.C.2

INTRODUCTION

THE science of living things—the systematic collection and arrangement of the fascinating and often astonishing facts that lie behind life on land, in the sea and in the air, human, animal, bird, plant and insect, called Biology—possesses for us a significance and importance unequalled perhaps by any other branch of scientific inquiry. For it is the story of life itself, a subject of such breadth and depth and rich variety that it is concerned with everything that has being, from minute, invisible organisms, such as the yeast that helps to make our beer, to the complex miracle of the human body and the propagation of the human race. It is a study that ranges back through æons to the first germ of life and its evolution to plant, reptile, beast and man ; that is diligently seeking solutions of our most modern problems, investigating the newest theories of heredity, eugenics and the diseases that attack man or the animals and plants on which his life depends. It is, in fact, a subject that is the close personal concern of every human being.

Biology, then, is concerned with the life story of each living thing. It studies its construction, how it grows, is nourished, breathes and propagates ; the adversities it meets in its struggle for existence, how it is equipped to fight them, and how far it succeeds ; its relations to other members of its special kingdom of the universe, its ancestors, and its evolution from primitive forms. And, in the study of plants and the study of animals, that is, Botany and Zoology, the biologist is concerned with how they enter into man's affairs, whether to his benefit or to his detriment.

Although this book is written on a definite plan, beginning with the most simple forms of life, and passing on to the most complex, it is by no means essential to start at the beginning and work straight through the subjects to the end. The reader to whom this method does not appeal is advised to select the subject that has the greatest interest for him, and to make that his starting-point.

The book is divided into three main parts, preceded by a brief survey of the progress of biological knowledge and the

scientist's methods of sifting his evidence. The first main
section, Botany, discusses the structure of plants, the families
into which they are divided, their struggle for survival, and
their history from the dim ages of the pre-historic world.

In the second division—Zoology—animal life is dealt with
on the same lines. Here again the study begins with the
most primitive types of creature (in *The Humblest Citizens
of the Animal Kingdom*) and gradually reaches the more
complex. The marvels of beauty, size and strength which
have their place in the article on *Birds, Beasts and Fish* are
rivalled by the truly astonishing feats of organisation among
the ant and other insect communities that are revealed in
The Social Life of Animals. Finally, the ancestry is traced of
some of the animals we know to-day, and we meet the
monsters of that pre-historic world of which science has built
up for us so vivid a picture.

With the third section we reach the supreme achievement
of creation—Man—and here the delicate and skilful adjust-
ments of the mechanism of the human body are explained,
Anatomy telling us how our bodies are built, and Physiology
showing how they work. This section is concluded with a
discussion on Heredity.

DISCOVERIES THAT AWAIT THE ENTHUSIAST

To help the reader whose interest lies specially in one
subject to find a path through the maze of books available,
suggestions are added to each section for the next stage in
reading. A brief concluding section contains advice to both
amateur and intending professional on how to follow up
the study. The reader who is attracted to Biology as a profession is told how best to find a proper training, and where
the various fields lie in which a qualified biologist may find
a market for his services. The amateur who has discovered
the endless fascination and stimulating pleasure to be derived
from the study of living things for its own sake, will learn
of the rich and varied sources he may tap in his determination
to add to his knowledge. " What more felicitie can fall to
creature than . . . to be lord of all the workes of Nature ? "
asked Spenser. How much a true understanding of both
himself and his " subjects " can add to that " felicitie " is one
of the discoveries that await the enthusiastic student of Biology.

CONTENTS

HOW SCIENTISTS HAVE LEARNED ABOUT THE LIVING WORLD

by GEOFFREY TANDY, B.A.(Oxon.), of the British Museum (Natural History)

WE read in the first book of Moses called Genesis: "And out of the ground the Lord God formed every beast of the field, and every fowl of the air; and brought them unto Adam to see what he would call them : and whatsoever Adam called every living creature, that was the name thereof. And Adam gave names to all cattle, and to the fowl of the air, and to every beast of the field. . . ." This may no longer suffice as a literal account of what happened, but it is certainly a simple and direct expression of man's need to make order of the world around him. This need to make order is real and deep-seated in every human being. It may well be that the order made by a particular person is neither far-reaching nor satisfactory to any person but himself, but order we must have. The psychologists speak of rationalisation and mean much the same thing as making order. The reasons we give for our actions may not be, and often are not, those which really moved us, but the need to feel that we are consistent to ourselves, even if we appear wildly inconsistent to other people, is something everybody can recognise.

The kinds of order which men make of the world of living organisms depend very much on the view which they take of their own place in it. Man is still disposed to regard himself as the lord of creation and the most important animal in the world. If his view of himself be conditioned by the account of the creation of the world set out in the early chapters of the book of Genesis, it is not surprising that he should take such a view. In any case, our knowledge of what it is to be alive must, in the last resort, be derived from the knowledge of ourselves as living things.

In the ordinary affairs of everyday life, we make a large number of assumptions concerning other living organisms which are curiously ill-founded if we stop to consider them. For instance, we assume that it is cruel to put a live lobster

11

into boiling water, but never bother about treating a live cabbage in the same way. Even if we can salve our consciences about the lobster, we shall be pretty certain that to put a living cat or dog into boiling water is cruel and, indeed, punishable by law. What reasons have we ? Well, of course most of us have no reasons : we just feel that it must be so. Nevertheless, the process of thought must be something like this : " How it would hurt me to be put in boiling water ; what a terrible noise I should make about it ; how I should writhe and scream ; a scalded cat makes a terrible noise indicating extreme pain and discomfort ; the lobster makes less, therefore he feels it less ; the cabbage makes none, therefore it feels nothing at all." The conclusions *may* be entirely correct, but the only way to be sure what the cabbage feels about it, is to be a cabbage. Ridiculous as this may sound, it contains a principle which no honest inquirer into the affairs of living organisms must ever forget.

MISTAKES THAT MOVE MEN TO INQUIRY

IT is impossible to get adequate understanding of the present state of our knowledge and views about the living world without consideration of the history of the natural sciences. We may be disposed to laugh in a good-humoured, condescending way at the biological notions of our predecessors ; at the quest of the alchemists for the Philosopher's Stone which would transmute base metals into gold ; at the beliefs that the sun goes round the earth or that madness was due to possession by devils. We should remember, however, that they are all part of a continuous process and fitted into the general scheme of the times, when they held sway in men's minds, as well as our notions fit our scheme. The fact that our notions never do quite fit is one of the most powerful influences which move men to continue the inquiry.

Moreover, the belief in an underlying order which awaits our discovery is so strong as to make men suspect that any scheme which contains apparent discrepancies must be wrong and to lead them to investigate the discrepancies in the hope of resolving them. Such investigations have played a great part in the establishment of present ideas of the atom and the nebulæ. Men say : " like begets like," and proceed happily in the belief until someone of an inquiring turn of mind points to an animal or plant which does not always conform. The nonconformist is then examined in the hope of discovering how such an exception to such a well-established rule can be possible. Much of our knowledge of the facts of inheritance has been gained by attention to such matters.

It is not in the least easy to put ourselves in the mental places of our ancestors. It is so difficult that we are very apt to think of the science of our own time as altogether unprecedented and, indeed, unexcelled. This is true enough in a measure, but we must not allow ourselves to forget that many of the fundamental ideas of to-day are the same as they were two thousand years ago. We cannot now escape from the conclusion that this earth is populated by an enormous number of different kinds of living organisms.

It has, for a long time, been customary to speak of a *species* of plant or animal. Many attempts have been made to define this term and some of the attempts will be considered elsewhere in this course. At this point we need do no more than realise that the fundamentals of the notion have been common property among human beings for a very long time indeed. Most of us can recognise a number of different kinds of living organisms without setting ourselves up as scientists. It is when the number of kinds becomes very great that the specialist comes in. Even then the difficulty of spotting differences is not enormous. When we wish to incorporate our knowledge of resemblances as well, the task becomes very great. To make a system which will express our knowledge of the relation of one kind to another, whether by blood or otherwise, is something which yet remains to be done to the satisfaction of even the majority of naturalists.

WHAT IS LIFE?

WE do not yet know how to draw up a satisfactory definition of what we mean by life, but the inability to make a definition of a horse—that is to say, a form of words which will describe a horse and no other animal—does not mean the inability to recognise a horse when we see one. This is a point which is very often overlooked, so it is worth mentioning. We do know a great many things about living organisms which are not true of non-living material. We know that living material can become dead, and when it has done that, nothing can restore it to life again. We know that the living protoplasm of all organisms is a watery substance ; so watery that it contains 98% of water—more than milk contains. We know that every substance in protoplasm is found in some form in non-living material ; but that living organisms are able, from non-living materials, to make substances such as sugars and proteins which we are not able to make artificially, in laboratories or elsewhere.

It is far from easy to see how any satisfactory verbal definition of life can ever be framed, since the more we know about such a complex dynamic condition, the less easy it is to make any form of words sufficiently inclusive. It is not impossible to imagine that the process will, some time, be expressed in a mathematical equation, but such a form would appeal, in all probability, to a limited audience. For nearly all biological purposes, and for all ordinary practical ones, we can get on perfectly well without a definition of life ; it suffices if we are agreed that such and such things are living.

BIOLOGY'S DEBT TO THE PAST

To fix on any point in the history of human knowledge and say that it is the beginning of any thing is, considered broadly, an entirely impossible and futile task. Everything that we know stands on a set of antecedent activities, and if we take any point as a beginning it is only because, if we are to begin at all, we must begin somewhere. It has become a pretty well-recognised convention in any historical review of biology to begin with due acknowledgments to Aristotle and to trace his influence until the period during the Dark Ages, when Aristotle was considered as the final and absolute authority for any statement. At this time it was held that what he did not know was not knowledge and anything which could not be proved from his writings needed not to be considered. This is the usual picture of science in Europe until the wind of the Renascence, that over-sentimentalised, over-rated Revival of Learning, began suddenly to blow towards the end of the fifteenth century.

If we wish to take the figure of a man who set to work to study living things in what we should now call a scientific way, we cannot take a better than Leonardo da Vinci (1452–1519). No attempt is here made to do justice to that most astonishing, many-sided genius. He was certainly, as the common phrase runs, in advance of his time. If he had dared to publish the results of his investigations in the anatomy and physiology of our own and other species, he would very likely have got into serious trouble with the authorities.

Many of the drawings and observations which he made from his dissections could scarcely be bettered to-day. It is hardly reasonable to suppose that before his day men were in a state of complete and blind ignorance concerning the multitude of species with which we share this earth. It is certain, none the less, that since then the collection and communication of observations on living organisms has happened in far greater measure than in any other period of which we know.

THE SPONGE "AN ANIMAL LIKE YOU AND ME"

OUT of all this arises a further point : that our knowledge assembles round the familiar objects, and words which are used in these connections become less adequate as we extend their scope. Those who have never considered the matter in detail may feel pretty confident that they know the difference between a plant and an animal. "What! not know a cow from a cabbage! Why, of course I do, and so does everybody else with any sense." True, maybe : but what is a sponge, a sea-anemone or a mushroom? What reasons have we for thinking any of them is either plant or animal? A. P. Herbert put the case for the sponge in his biological compendium *The Wherefore and the Why* :

> The sponge is not, as you suppose, a funny kind of weed.
> It lives below the deep, blue sea,
> An animal like you and me,
> Though not so good a breed.

The development from this beginning is by no means the whole story, but it is most true that no botanist would now claim a sponge as a plant, whereas it was so considered by naturalists right into the last century. It is very likely that the standards of the eighteenth-century naturalists are still pretty widespread. For most people, the habit of staying rooted in one place is the cardinal feature of a plant. Nowadays we judge almost entirely on the methods by which the organism gets its living. An organism which is able, by the use of energy from the sun, to build up complex substances from simple non-living material and does not devour the results of the work of other organisms is wholly plant. Organisms which take other organisms, or fragments thereof, into their bodies and there break them up and use the energy thus obtained for their own life-processes, are wholly animal. There are, as we might expect, any number of examples of the combination of the two habits—some of them very difficult to classify.

As long as man had to depend on his own unassisted vision, he was greatly restricted, both in the number of organisms which he could, and in the details of those which he did know. Kipling, in a story called *The Eye of Allah* (*Debits and Credits*), deals with the attempts of a group of men in a fourteenth-century monastery to convince the abbot that the use of a simple microscope would not bring them into conflict with the ecclesiastical authorities. The artist had used it to get himself new patterns and the physicians wished to use it to investigate human diseases : the abbot smashed the instrument because, being wise in his generation, he saw that the time was by no means ripe for such work. Whether the Arabian physicians communicated any knowledge of microscopy to the physicians of the Crusading armies may be left an open question for our purposes. It was not until the second half of the seventeenth century that microscopes came into general use for scientific purposes, and from then onwards our knowledge of minute plants and animals and of the minute structure of the larger ones has been growing steadily.

WHAT WE OWE TO THE MEN WHO WERE WRONG

THE scientific work of the sixteenth and seventeenth centuries was dominated by the idea of systematising plants and animals for their " virtues." It was pretty commonly assumed that every living thing must be useful to man, and the students of plants particularly were chiefly concerned with the medical uses of plants. Under all their work also ran the idea that all the different kinds of living things which filled the world were made, in exactly the forms in which they could be observed, by an Almighty Creator at specific moments in time ; that tiger was created tiger and had gone on being tiger in exactly the same way from the beginning. This idea of immutable species dominated the biological sciences until at least the beginning of the nineteenth century.

It is not, therefore, surprising that men hoped ultimately to be able to make a final classification of all living things. The movements towards this end culminated in the work of Linnæus (von Linné). His methods made a very clear turning-point in the progress of biological science. The years 1750 to 1775, when his greatest works were given to the world, mark the end of one era and the first stirrings of the next.

He worked on the famous dictum : " Stones grow. Plants grow and live. Animals grow, live and feel." Thus, for him, were defined the three Kingdoms of Nature ; with the species as unchanging units and man as the crown and pinnacle of the whole edifice.

It would be very misleading to suppose that until the middle of the nineteenth century nobody once thought that species might change. It is frequently observable, in the history of human knowledge, that men's minds are moving in a certain direction, and when a man comes along with what we call a new theory, it is often (though, of course, not always) something for which large numbers of men feel that they have been waiting and are already prepared. The man who sweeps together the results of his predecessors into a whole which men can see, is credited, in consequence, with more than one man's life could possibly produce. This is in no way derogatory to him or his work. He will, usually, be fully conscious of his debt. If we wish to assign blame (a somewhat foolish pastime at best) we must lay it on undiscriminating admirers and followers. Darwin was fully aware that his work was the natural consequence of that of large numbers of other people and, further, that Wallace had come to very similar conclusions independently and almost simultaneously. We also must try to take account of our debt to our predecessors and avoid, as much as possible, the crime of thinking ourselves superior because they did not know what has been found out since they died.

HOW THE SCIENTIST SIFTS THE EVIDENCE

THE remote history of the biological knowledge of the human race is an interesting subject of inquiry and speculation. If we examine the legal code of any human community under the sun, we are certain to find that it contains a great deal of practical biology. Every community has some regulations governing the procreative activities of its members. They will not necessarily be based on what we should call biological knowledge but rather upon a less conscious thing, which we may call race-feeling, or biological wisdom.

We do not need to go to the archæologist or the anthropologist for illustrations. Most people have access to the five books of the Holy Bible commonly called the Pentateuch. Therein will be found the biological wisdom of a pastoral people living in a sub-tropical climate. The prescriptions cover marriage, sanitation, agriculture, dietetics, astronomy ; even fashions in clothing and hairdressing. A point of interest for us is that the priests were the repositories of all this biological knowledge ; in this fact lay much of their power and importance. In the world to-day, we can see that the separation of the functions of priest and biologist has meant a loss of power to the priest. It may very well be that humanity is not yet in a state to pay great attention to those whose concern is less with the affairs of this world in their immediate practical aspects than with those of any other.

The practice of the natural sciences demands a careful consideration of what we mean by evidence. We have already decided that for the scientist, strictly considered as such, the things which he can weigh, measure and otherwise record, are the realities of his business. He is accustomed to speak of these records, of size, colour, shape, behaviour and so on, as the facts of science. These facts can be assembled in such a manner as to have, as we say, no meaning. It is unusual, however, to find anybody going to the trouble to collect facts without a purpose and without selection. It is much more usual to find that the facts have been selected and arranged in order to establish some kind of generalisation ; to exhibit some order unsuspected hitherto, or to support some theory enunciated previously. Everybody is familiar, in greater or less degree, with the procedure in the law courts. A witness is called to " prove " a fact. He will say, for instance, that he saw the prisoner drop something down a drain. A police officer will say that a knife was recovered from that drain, and a medical practitioner will testify that the wound from which such and such a man died could have been made with that knife. A jury will be asked to give a verdict on the evidence.

GROUNDS ON WHICH THE SCIENTIST FORMS HIS BELIEFS

THE scientist is not always able to apply the same rules for the acceptance or rejection of evidence as the lawyers would use. He ought, nevertheless, to be extremely careful not to accept as evidence of many things, something which is only evidence of one ; not to believe that what is true of one organism is necessarily true of others. It is, for instance, commonplace to speak of the " evidence of the rocks : " the study of fossil plants and animals (the science of palæontology) is concerned with the elucidation of such evidence. On such evidence rest a great many of our beliefs concerning the course of the evolution of the living organisms of this world. The word belief is the right one for most of the accounts of the process which are available to us.

It is obvious that no direct eye-witness evidence will ever be available to us. The evidence of the rocks, considered strictly, is evidence that at some period of the earth's history, determinable within wide limits by geologists, there existed plants and animals with certain physical characteristics which we can still see, describe, and compare with those of living organisms. If we wish to say, on such evidence alone, that a Derby winner or a Shire stallion is descended from a little five-toed beast which lived thousands upon thousands of years ago, we are quite entitled to make an act of faith and do so. What we must remember is that we have made the act of faith.

Such evidence is often so convincing that no other conclusion is possible ; just as a murderer is convicted, though nobody saw him commit the crime. The possibility of some other explanation cannot be entirely and absolutely excluded. The evidence is of quite a different kind from that which convinces us that the offspring of a horse and an ass is a mule —usually sterile.

In spite of all these limitations, it is almost beyond doubt that the immense body of scientific literature in existence to-day represents an immeasurably greater knowledge of the world and its inhabitants than has ever been brought together in the history of mankind. This has not come about because man has become so much wiser or more intelligent than he was two thousand years ago. It is highly probable that the intelligent members of the ancient civilisations would have no more difficulty in understanding modern science than the student from India or Japan has to-day. What, then, has put us where we are? Again it is necessary to exercise due caution. In the broad sense, it is probably true to say that nothing could have been omitted without altering the whole structure as we now have it. Nevertheless, some things strike us as more important than others, and if we remember that they cannot stand alone, we shall do no great harm in considering them.

TOOLS OF THE BIOLOGIST'S TRADE

Two things, more than any others, have enabled the students of living organisms to arrive at their present position : the invention of printing and the development of systems of lenses. Standing behind both these things is rapid transportation, but as that is behind the whole of our civilisation as well, we need not consider it here. No worker, in any branch of science to-day, can continue his work for long without access to a library. Moreover, he must keep in touch, either directly or through his library, with other similarly engaged workers all over the world. A hundred and eighty years ago a naturalist could take his library about with him. A botanist with the *Species Plantarum* of Linnæus in his luggage could very quickly tell if he had a species of plant unknown to the science of his day. To-day he would be far from certain until he had been able to consult the library and collections of at least one of the great botanical institutions which are to be found in every civilised country.

Our understanding of the underlying similarity between all living organisms depends on our ability to see things one hundredth of a millimetre or less in diameter. This does not mean that no notion of the essential community of all life had ever been entertained by men before the days of microscopes. It does mean that any knowledge of the structure and mechanism of the cell, which is essentially similar in all living organisms, was impossible without the means of microscopic vision. Early microscopes were usually in the form of simple lenses and the images obtained by their use were very crude and imperfect. Even to-day it is necessary to use the greatest care in distinguishing between appearances really belonging to the object under examination, and those due to imperfections or maladjustments of the instruments. It need not surprise us that the early workers reported observations which strike us as somewhat comic. Nevertheless, some of the seventeenth-century work was wrong not because of faulty instruments, but because the observer had a preconception for which he found " facts " to fit. One of the greatest of these early microscopists—the Dutchman, van Leeuwenhoek—though he made his own lenses and undoubtedly saw spermatozoa, figured them as of two kinds —miniature males and miniature females, because he believed them to be already formed as tiny men and women. These he, in common with most of his contemporaries, believed to be fully formed and to do no more in the uterus of the female than grow in size.

Attention is drawn to this in order to show that a man cannot be in all respects in advance of his time ; not so that we may enjoy a feeling of comfortable superiority to our benighted forefathers. Most of us are willing to believe all sorts of fabulous improbabilities if the story pleases us or if we can gain some advantage by persuading other people to believe it. The story of the germination of wheat, thousands of years old, from Egyptian tombs is such a pleasant, romantic story that no amount of evidence will discredit it in the minds of many people. The belief in a wonderful, superior race called Aryan is firmly established in the minds of millions of people ; for no better reason than that they think they belong to it. Examples of this sort could be multiplied almost indefinitely, but these should suffice to persuade us that even if we are able to avoid falling into error, there is no reason to feel lonely, superior or, least of all, virtuous about it. Anton van Leeuwenhoek was the founder of studies in the microscopic life of the world and for that we should be grateful, if nothing more. His were the foundations on which rest the modern sciences which treat, and often cure, the diseases of ourselves and of the species of plants and animals useful to us.

THE SCIENTISTS SET OUT ON A NEW ROAD

ANY attempt to consider the history of the biological sciences in labelled periods is, for reasons already given, likely to be misleading ; there is always a considerable amount of overlapping. We are very apt to remember the label and forget the accompanying qualifications ; to read the headline and overlook the question mark at the end of the line or the text in small type which is capable of another interpretation. If we say that the botany of the sixteenth and seventeenth centuries was governed by utilitarian considerations, that certainly does not mean that we have had no use for economic botany ever since. It may easily be true to say that we have gained more immediate practical benefits from scientific studies since the cardinal assumption that everything must be of some direct service to man was abandoned. Yet we can be satisfied that the men who carried on their work on this assumption right through to the nineteenth century were much more than victims of a mistaken loyalty. While their principal interests may have been in the virtues of the organisms they studied, they were usually filled with a great desire to amass curiosities. Many of our great museums had their origin in the collections of *materia medica* and curiosities. The collections of Sir Hans Sloane, who was a physician and perhaps the last of the great medical botanists, went to begin the British Museum in 1753. This date may very well stand as the end of the grand period of curioso-medical natural history.

The new period had already been under way for some considerable time, but the magnificent simplification accomplished by Linnæus did a great deal to determine the dominant tone of the biological work of the succeeding century. He provided men with the tools they had been needing for a long time and the work of systematisation proceeded at a great rate. Very quickly the need was felt, and met, for a system which was capable of expressing what naturalists felt were the " blood-relationships " of living organisms. So the purely artificial systems of convenience invented by Linnæus were soon followed by so-called natural systems of classification.

The political events of the period 1750–1850 were all symptoms of the change of emphasis. The French revolutionaries began a new era with their *An premier* ; their new system of weights and measures ; their belief that a new day of progress for humanity had dawned at last. Voyages of discovery brought multitudes of new species of plants and animals to the naturalists of Europe. Large and ambitious encyclopædias of natural history appeared one after another. Yet with it all, it is difficult to resist the conclusion that the drive behind the whole affair was a desire to see the catalogue completed.

This was by no means an unworthy ambition but it had some strange results. Men were quite content, apparently, to say that such an organism, distinguishable from others by such and such features, was a native of the East Coast of New Holland—a stretch of over two thousand miles containing all sorts of climates and kinds of country, from what we now know as tropical Queensland to the temperate regions of Victoria and Tasmania. The organism as a mechanism with its own methods of meeting the surrounding conditions and as a member of a highly complex community, seems to have been scarcely, if at all, considered.

DARWIN CHANGES THE WORLD PICTURE

THE work of Charles Darwin is widely recognised as marking another turning-point in the history of biological thought. Instead of a world-picture composed of units fixed in their essential qualities, he presented one in which the units are liable to change in essentials ; he showed that living organisms must be seen, individually and collectively, as dynamic and not static. Whether he was right in believing that small variations in individuals became fixed in the species because such individuals acquired a better chance of survival thereby, or that man had an ape-like ancestor, need not detain us here. The important matter for us is that, whether he or his contemporaries framed it so or not, the scope of the whole inquiry was changed by his work. Many other great men had a hand in producing the change, but the year 1859, in which was published *The Origin of Species*, is the date of a conversion in the history of biology. We may note in passing that the change consorted very well with the changes in contemporary political and sociological thought, and had undoubted influences outside the strictly scientific fields. The notion of evolutionary progress, towards a goal of perfection, is with us yet—though a little tattered by reason of wars and economic depressions. Expressed as the doctrine of the Survival of the Fittest, it provides justification for all sorts of human villainy.

Since Darwin the dynamic view of the world around us has been increasingly supported by the other natural sciences. The researches of the physicists have shown us that even the atom, at one time believed to be the ultimate, unchanging form of all matter, is a highly complex, dynamic system, exhibiting all sorts of apparently paradoxical relations which do not hold in larger-scale nature. These ideas cannot fail of their effect on biological thought and work. The physico-chemical behaviour of living organisms has been the subject of an increasingly large amount of investigation. More and more, plants and animals are seen as subject to the laws which govern the behaviour of non-living systems. We have also reason to believe that a population of a single species and a population of a number of species are governed by laws similar in character to those which non-living systems obey.

There are hopes that even the data of the species-catalogues can be used to demonstrate that a population of species is only another kind of physical system, essentially dynamic, in which the units are not only active and act upon one another at random, but are also capable of reproduction and variation.

Where all this is leading is a matter of pure conjecture. We have not yet found adequate means of expressing our vision of the dynamic character of the living world in a system of classification. We cannot yet say that a living organism has not some power or characteristic which escapes our analysis and makes matter in a living phase different in essentials from any non-living system. The indications are that it has not ; but it is not yet safe to be dogmatic on that point. Whatever may be the outcome we may be certain of one thing : the prime instrument of the inquiry will be what it has always been—the reasoning power of the human brain.

THE GREEN PLANT:
FOOD FOR ALL THINGS LIVING

by B. BARNES, D.Sc., Ph.D., F.L.S.

THE green plant, owing its colour to the possession of the mixture of pigments known as chlorophyll, is the primary source of food material for almost all the living creatures that inhabit the earth. With the exception of a few kinds of bacteria, green plants are the only organisms which can build up food from simple substances collected from the soil and from the air. These simple substances are not food ; they are the raw materials from which the plant builds up food for its own needs. The green plant is eaten by many animals, which in their turn provide food for the carnivorous animals ; moreover, alive or dead, the green plant nourishes hosts of plants which have no chlorophyll and therefore cannot make the food substances necessary for their sustenance.

As the activities of the green plant are so essential to the persistence of life on the earth, a study of them cannot fail to reveal many points of interest. The structure of the plant must also be considered, since a knowledge of the structure helps to an understanding of the manner in which the plant works ; structure and function are closely inter-related.

We are acquainted with many thousands of kinds of green plants. Some of these are minute, so small that if five thousand were placed in a straight line, that line would measure only one inch ; at the other extreme some of the largest trees rival St. Paul's Cathedral in height, and weigh many tons. Green plants are equally diverse in the situations that they inhabit. Some seaweeds flourish in the Polar seas at a temperature little above freezing-point, and some of our common garden weeds are able to grow slowly and produce a few flowers at almost equally low temperatures. In contrast to these, some simply organised green plants have been observed in a flourishing condition in water much too hot for the hand, and some of the desert plants must pass long hours at comparatively high temperatures. A few plants exist on the surface of rocks under conditions of almost uninterrupted drought, others spend their whole lives immersed in water. No green plants can live their whole lives in perpetual darkness, though for some ferns the amount of light necessary is small. However, our present concern is rather with the more ordinary plants. Of these we may briefly consider three, in order to establish a few general points.

THE LIFE OF AN ORDINARY PLANT

SEEDS of Virginia stock, planted in moist soil in spring, and provided with a moderate supply of water, soon germinate. First we have the seedling, with a delicate upright axis bearing two small leaves of simple outline, with a bud between them. From this bud an upright stem arises, producing leaves, and presently, branches which are very like the parent stem. After the plant has spent a few weeks in the development of leaves and branches, flowers begin to form at the ends of the branches. In due course the flowers wither and are replaced by fruits, the vessels in which the seeds ripen. As this is going on the plant slowly dies. The fruits split, the seeds are set free, and the next generation is ready to begin its development. Thus, the Virginia stock has a short life and matures one crop of seeds ; these remain quiescent during the colder part of the year, and provide the starting points for the next season's growth.

The Snapdragon furnishes our second example. Up to the ripening and liberation of the seeds, development proceeds much as in the Virginia stock, except that the parent plant does not die as the seeds ripen. In the following spring, new branches arise from the bases of the old branches and bear flowers in their turn. Under favourable conditions the plant may live for several seasons and produce several crops of flowers and seeds.

HOW A TREE GROWS

THE seeds of the Sycamore, enclosed in their winged fruits, fall from the tree in autumn and lie dormant all winter. In spring, the seeds germinate, giving young plants with a delicate upright axis and two strap-shaped leaves with a bud between them. A leafy stem grows from the bud and may reach a length of several inches during the first season of growth. It seldom branches in the first year and never flowers. In autumn, growth stops, the leaves drop, and the stem passes

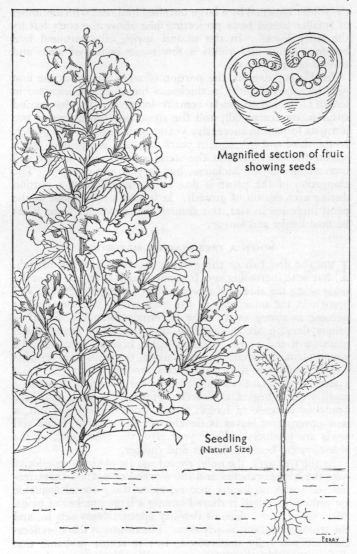

Magnified section of fruit
showing seeds

Seedling
(Natural Size)

PERRY

**THE SNAPDRAGON: A PLANT WHICH
SURVIVES PARENTHOOD**

the winter crowned by a large terminal bud, and with a number of smaller lateral buds projecting just above the scars left by the fallen leaves. In the second spring, the terminal bud becomes active and yields a few more inches of stem and several pairs of leaves.

As this is going on, the portion of stem formed in the first year increases slightly in thickness but does not increase in length ; its lateral buds remain inactive. In the second autumn, the leaves fall, and the stem, now consisting of two portions formed in successive years, again rests for the winter. In the third and subsequent years the story is repeated. Each season the older parts of the stem become more woody and increase steadily in thickness, but they do not elongate. The elongation of the plant is due to the addition of a portion during each season of growth. It is worth notice that as the plant increases in size, the annual increments for some years become longer and longer.

WHEN A TREE REACHES MATURITY

FOR the first two or three years the stem may not branch, but with increasing age, branches begin to appear from the buds along the side of the stem. They elongate, thicken and branch in the same way as the main stem, but they do not become as strong as it. The lowermost branches die off as others develop above them so that the lower parts of the main stem and of its branches again become bare. In the young plant, for twenty years or more, the main stem remains clearly visible as the central axis around which the shoot system of the plant is arranged. As the Sycamore becomes a small tree, it begins to flower. Henceforth, each year, the branches increase in length, fresh branches are put out, a new covering of leaves is developed, and flowers, fruits and seeds are produced. Each year also, the older parts of the shoot system become thicker and thicker.

As the tree ages, the main stem loses its obvious superiority over the larger branches and the marked elongation character-istic of youth no longer occurs, since the material available for growth in length is shared among a large number of twigs. After many years, signs of debility appear, decay sets in, and the tree weakens and slowly dies. The causes of this degenera-tion are not fully understood, but it seems probable that disease caused by the attacks of enemies, together with changes in the living part of the plant, are largely responsible.

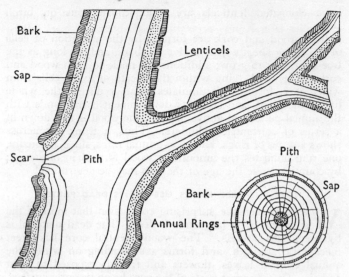

Bark

Lenticels

Sap

Scar   Pith

Pith

Bark

Sap

Annual Rings

A TREE TRUNK IN SECTION

The trunk of a tree consists mainly of dead wood and pith, with only a thin sheath of living and growing tissue in which the sap circulates. The Lenticels are openings in the bark through which air reaches the living cells within and carbon dioxide escapes.

WHAT IS INSIDE THE TREE

ALL trees contain a massive central core of dead wood, running through roots, trunk and branches, and reaching into the bases of the youngest twigs and youngest roots ; these, and the leaves and flowers, consist for the most part of living cells. The dead core is surrounded by a thin sheath of living material, complicated in structure and function, and covered on its outer surface by a layer of dead cork. This forms the bark of the tree, protecting the delicate living sheath from drying up, from mechanical injury and from enemies. The bark is pierced by many openings loosely packed with corky cells ; these openings—the lenticels —convey air to the living cells within and allow carbon dioxide to escape from them. Lenticels are usually most obvious on the thinner branches ; they are clearly visible as small dots on young branches of apple trees, and as horizontal streaks on branches of cherry :

large elongated lenticels are often conspicuous on birch trees.

Both wood and cork are formed by the alteration of cells of the living sheaths just under the bark, and, as long as the tree continues to grow, additions are made to both wood and cork. The wood, lying within the sheath of living cells from which it is formed, accumulates steadily during the whole life of the plant, and since its development corresponds with the annual periods of active growth, the wood is laid down in a series of concentric cylinders. Thus, a trunk cut across shows a series of rings, known as annual rings, since, normally, one ring indicates the amount of wood formed in one year ; by counting these the age of the tree may be determined.

HOW THE TREE MAKES USE OF ITS DEAD PARTS

WE thus reach the surprising conclusion that most of the substance of a large tree is dead. The dead material is by no means useless. The woody central core has great mechanical strength, and forms a scaffolding on which the annual crop of leaves, flowers and fruit is exposed to light and air. The youngest parts of the core lie on its outer surface, where some living cells are mixed with the groups of tiny pipes through which watery solutions move about the plant.

The mass of wood increases as the weight of leaves and branches increases, and, with the steady increase in the diameter of the woody core, more and more space is provided on its outer surface for the increasing number of conducting channels needed for the supply of water and other substances to the leaves, and for the distribution of the food made in the leaves. Most of the material moves up and down in the plant, but there is some movement sideways, especially in the wood. This takes place chiefly in the medullary rays, thin sheets of elements set vertically in the wood and running radially in it and out into the living cells beyond it. In oak, the medullary rays are particularly large and cause the well-known silver grain of the timber, but in many trees they are small and difficult to see without magnification.

So long as the wood is surrounded by an unbroken sheath of living material, it is protected to some extent from invasion by the bacteria and moulds which cause rotting, but this protection seldom remains fully effective for long. Wind tears off branches and exposes portions of the dead and vulnerable wood, animals injure the bark and damage the living sheath below, and this sheath is itself attacked by a number of creatures, which then attack the wood or open a way for others to do so.

Although the living cells of the stem add to the inner surface of the bark during the growing season, the bark does not increase in thickness as noticeably as does the wood. Additions are not made to the bark as freely as they are to the wood, and moreover, portions are frequently lost from the outer surface of the bark by a definite process of shedding. The process is very familiar in the plane tree, since the young bark exposed as the older material falls away is bright yellow and is very noticeable. The bark of the cork oak, which furnishes the commercial product, is exceptional in its thickness and uniformity of texture.

WHAT MAKES THE PLANT STAND UP

YOUNG stems do not contain a solid core of wood. Most of their stiffness is due to a characteristic device which is responsible for the firmness of all young parts of plants. It is common knowledge that the hardness of a pneumatic tyre depends on the balance between the tendency of the inflated tube to expand and the restraint imposed by the outer cover. In young parts of plants we find a similar but more complicated arrangement. The plant is covered by a thin and relatively strong skin which is not very elastic and resists stretching. Inside this there is a mass of soft material composed of many cells pressing against one another and against the outer skin, since they are distended with water. The balance between the outward pressure set up by these cells and the resistance to stretching offered by the epidermis (that is the outer skin of the plant) gives rigidity to the whole system.

It is easy to demonstrate that there are strains in young plant material. For example, if the cylindrical flowering stem of the dandelion is slit into several strips, each strip curls with the skin on the inner and shorter side of the curl. So long as the stem is intact, the skin is stretched and the soft cells within are held under restraint. Cutting releases the tensions, the skin is now free to contract and the soft cells to expand, and curling necessarily follows.

The young and soft stems of most land plants contain some strands of particularly strong material ; these assist in stiffening the stem and they have an important rôle in preventing sudden and localised bending. In general, these strands, which run lengthwise, lie close inside the skin, giving a condition comparable with the arrangement of material in a hollow metal column. This is just the arrangement which offers the most effective resistance to buckling ; in the hollow stems of grasses and many other plants, the efficiency of the arrangement is increased by the partitions which cross the stem here and there. In some plants the centre of the stem is occupied by a pith which, from a mechanical point of view, acts in relation to bending and buckling in the same way that a filling of sand acts in a thin metal tube that is being made into a coil.

The strands of strong material close to the outside of the stem are very apparent in the long flowering stems of the grasses, which are wonderful examples of mechanical efficiency, for the contrast between diameter and length is remarkable. In other stems, such as the square stems of mint, there is a strand of strong material in each corner ; the whole stem may be compared with an erect X-girder which resists excessive bending very well. When it is remembered that one of the main purposes of an erect stem is to hold the flowers and leaves in a good light, the importance of structural devices which check overthrow is at once apparent.

The materials which contribute to the mechanical efficiency of the stem are often of great strength. Linen is made from the strands of the stems of flax, and cordage from similar material from hemp. Some vegetable strands have a breaking strain which is one quarter that of a steel wire of equal diameter. They stretch freely, but their breaking-point lies close to the extreme point to which they can be stretched. Consequently there is little chance that the plant will be permanently stretched sufficiently to cause deformation ; this would be more injurious than breaking, for it would ruin the adjustment of the internal arrangements of the stem, cause the death of some of the parts, and provide a starting-point for disease.

Owing to their elasticity, the young parts of plants move freely in the wind, and, unless the wind is strong enough to cause a break, the plant recovers its form when the wind ceases to bend it. The mechanical strands often lie in the stem close to the delicate strands of minute tubes which are responsible for the transport of liquids about the plant, and they protect them against sudden buckling and injury.

FLOWERS COLOURED BY THE WATER THEY DRINK

THE path followed by water moving in the plant is readily determined. If young leafy stems are cut and placed with the cut ends in water coloured with red ink, reddened veins may be seen in the leaves after an hour or so, if these are held up to the light. The effect is even more obvious if white flowers are present, and the experiment succeeds very well with flowering stems of the white dead nettle. Sometimes, white flowers treated in this way are offered for sale. If the stem is slit lengthwise, narrow red threads are seen, sometimes uniting, and sometimes passing into the leaf stalks and so making connection with the veins in the leaves. Detailed investigation shows that the dye travels only in the small amount of wood present in the conducting strands ; it does not travel in the general mass of soft material composing most of the stem.

If a woody branch is cut and stood in diluted red ink, it is found that the dye travels only in the outermost surface of the wood, showing that it is only the youngest wood that is able to conduct watery solutions. Trees are sometimes killed by making a complete and deep horizontal cut all round the base of the trunk. Such a cut removes the young wood and so prevents the upward flow of water from the roots, thus speedily causing death to all living parts above it.

It is much less easy to trace the paths along which other substances move in the plant. There is, however, little doubt that some of the food substances manufactured by the plant travel in the young wood, and that others are conveyed in special thin-walled tubes. The tubes are independent of and lie outside the woody strands, but, like them, form a continuous system throughout the body of the plant. Where the stem is thick and woody these sieve tubes, so called because the microscope shows that they are crossed at intervals by small perforated plates, lie in the sheath of living material just inside the bark.

It appears then that the stems of plants have two important functions. They support the leaves and flowers, and they provide means for the transport of substances inside the plant. They form a link between the roots which collect water and mineral substances from the soil, and the leaves which take in carbon dioxide from the air, and, after food has been made in the leaves, they provide for its conveyance to those parts of the plant where active growth is in progress, and where, very often, little or no food is being made.

ROOT, LEAF AND CELL: THE ANCHOR, FOODMAKER, AND ESSENCE OF LIFE

UP to this point we have considered only those parts of the plant that are exposed to light and air. Plants usually possess below ground a branching system of roots which anchor the plant to the soil and collect material from it. If young plants are carefully dug up and washed free from soil, they show commonly, but not always, a root system composed of a main root which is a direct downward prolongation of the main stem, surrounded by a number of branch roots. The branches are very like the main root in everything but size, and, if they in turn divide, their branches are smaller versions of the parent. The root system is much less complex than the parts of the plant above soil level, and there is a much greater likeness between the roots of one plant and those of another than between the shoot systems of different plants.

Although the young root systems of many kinds of plants are clearly arranged around a main root, the arrangement may not remain clearly visible in the adult plant, especially if it lives for a number of years. In trees particularly, as the crown spreads, the roots keep pace with it, so that the tips of the youngest branches of the root system lie in the earth beneath the outermost ends of the leafy branches, where most rain drains off from the tree ; these active tips may be many feet away from the trunk of an old tree. Now, the downward growth of the main root is often checked by mechanical obstacles, and also by the further circumstance that, as deeper and deeper levels are reached in the soil, the supplies of oxygen essential to the young root become more and more scanty, and finally cease to be sufficient ; this brings downward growth to an end. Root systems can usually spread sideways better than they can go downwards, and therefore, in old trees, the main root is usually smaller than some of its branches.

Roots branch freely and occupy the ground very thoroughly ; for example, the roots of an average plant of the large sunflower search closely rather more than a cubic yard of soil. In deep, dry soils, which are usually well supplied with air, roots may penetrate to a depth of ten feet or more, and under special conditions, the root system of a plant may be larger than the shoot system. Some of our coastal plants, growing in loose sand, show a few small stems and leaves, but their roots run several feet in all directions.

In limy soils most plants root freely, but in acid, peaty soils root development is often poor, and the plants may have at their disposal some other device which compensates for the disadvantages arising from small roots. Some, like the sundew and the butterwort, supplement the scanty ration of combined nitrogen they obtain from the soil, by catching and digesting insects; others, such as heather, appear to live in association with a fungus, which may provide them with material taken from the peat.

In general structure stems and roots are much alike. Young roots, like young stems, contain a number of conducting strands embedded in a mass of soft cells; as the root ages, the centre is occupied by a solid core of dead wood surrounded by a thin sheath of living cells, protected by an outer layer of cork. Roots have to meet pulls rather than bends, and in young roots we find that the strongest material is nearer to the centre of the organ than it is in young stems; the central disposition of the strongest material is the arrangement which offers the most resistance to pulls.

TUBERS AND BULBS AS UNDERGROUND LARDERS

ALL subterranean parts of plants are not roots. Many plants have their main stem underground, and each spring this stem, which may be much branched, sends up leafy flowering stems which die down at the end of the season. Michaelmas daisies and other familiar herbaceous perennials have this sort of organisation. During the growing season, the food made by the leaves and not used for the current needs of the plant is passed down and stored below ground, being utilised in the next spring in the preliminary stages of growth. Large storage organs are formed by the underground stems of some plants; the bulbs of hyacinths and tulips, the corms of the crocus, and the tubers of the potato are familiar underground stems which act as food reservoirs. All these plants pass at least a part of the year in an inactive condition.

Such plants are usually natives of situations where, for some reason or another, there are special hindrances to growth during part of the year. Some are woodland plants—the blue-

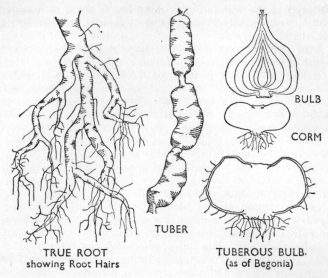

BULB

CORM

TUBER

TRUE ROOT
showing Root Hairs

TUBEROUS BULB.
(as of Begonia)

TRUE ROOT OR UNDERGROUND FOOD-STORE

The tuber and corm are not roots at all, but are underground stems enlarged to act as food reservoirs for the plant. A bulb consists of enlarged, fleshy, food-storing leaves, with, in the centre, a bud from which the flowers spring.

bell is a good example—others, including many of the bulbous plants in cultivation, come from places where there are sharp alternations of wet and dry seasons. The woodland plants, having stored food at their disposal, are able to start growth early in the year, and to produce their flowers, set their seeds and lay in renewed stores before the shade cast by the trees brings activity to an end. Those which live in droughty places can make a rapid start as soon as water is available and complete their work before water scarcity again becomes acute.

THE LEAF: A FACTORY FOR MAKING THE FOOD SUPPLY

FINALLY, in our general survey of the plant, we come to the leaf. The leaves of most plants are thin, flattened objects, usually so arranged on the plant that they present one broad face to the sky. This posture is directly related to the need of the leaf for good light which plays an essential part in the manufacture of food, the essential function of the leaf.

Active leaves always contain a great deal of water, and to this they owe much of their stiffness ; the crisp lettuce leaves so welcome in a salad contain about 95 per cent by weight of water ; the tougher leaves of the trees have about 80 per cent of water. Leaves have the same general arrangement as stems in relation to rigidity, the strong epidermis resisting the expansive tendencies of the softer cells inside. The mass of soft cells inside the leaf is freely permeated by veins ; these have some mechanical strength, and help in keeping the leaf spread out, but their main purpose is the conduction of watery solutions into and out of the leaf. Everyone has probably seen a leaf skeleton ; one is easily made by rotting a leaf for a time in water, and then carefully washing away the soft rotten material. Such preparations show perfectly the complicated conducting system of the leaf and its intimate relation to all parts of the leaf.

HOW THE LEAF FACTORY IS BUILT

THE leaf is covered completely by a well-organised epidermis enclosing a thin layer of softer cells. These are not all of the same kind. Beneath the upper surface, and therefore in the best lit position, lie one, two or more rows of cells which are several times longer than they are broad. The cells are grouped into tightly packed layers with one narrow end of each cell turned towards the upper surface of the leaf. The microscope reveals the presence, inside each cell, of large numbers of small green granules ; these are the chloroplasts and they contain the chlorophyll. The closely packed layers, with the ends of the cells turned towards the light, form the palisade tissue of the leaf, and the lower ends of the cells are often close to the veins.

Between the palisade tissue and the under epidermis, there is a region occupied by cells of rather irregular form. They contain chloroplasts, but they are not packed closely together, for although they touch one another here and there, and although some of them may make contact with the lower ends of some of the palisade cells, there are in this region many air-filled spaces, so that there is a general spongy texture. The spaces between the cells are in communication and they unite also with some rather large air spaces just

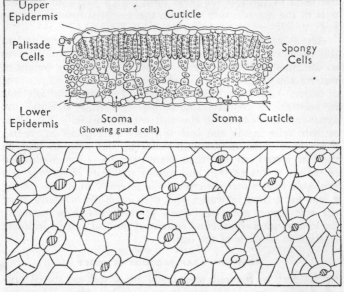

Upper Epidermis

Cuticle

Palisade Cells

Spongy Cells

Lower Epidermis

Stoma
(Showing guard cells)

Stoma   Cuticle

THE DELICATE STRUCTURE OF THE LEAF

The top diagram shows a leaf cut through and highly magnified to display the arrangement of the palisade cells beneath the surface skin.   Below, the under surface of a leaf is highly magnified to show the difference between the ordinary cells (C) and the stomata or breathing pores (S).

inside the epidermis, and communicating with the air outside the leaf through pores in the epidermis.

As a rule, these pores—the stomata—which are not mere holes, but have an organisation by means of which they can open and close, are most abundant on the lower surface of the leaf. The number of stomata in a leaf is not uniform for all plants, but, as an indication of the numbers in which they may occur, we may note that a large sunflower leaf has about 13 million stomata, and that, as an average value, every square millimetre of the under surface of an oak leaf bears 346 stomata. The many and relatively large spaces between the cells inside the leaf provide room for a considerable amount of air, and the abundant stomata allow of the ready exchange of gases between this internal atmosphere and the air outside.

THE CELL: CRADLE OF THE LIFE FORCE

UP to this point we have taken for granted that the plant is made up of cells or of structures derived from cells. We must now pass to a somewhat more detailed treatment of the cell, since we need some knowledge of this before we can study the inner workings of the plant.

Cells are commonly very small objects, though some are large enough to be seen with the naked eye. If we take a ripe tomato which is still in good firm condition, and tear it in halves, we can see without the use of any magnification that the whitish material running into the fruit from the junction of the stalk, and the reddish material of the fleshy wall around the fruit have a finely granular structure. A hand lens of moderate power shows that the granular condition is due to the presence in those parts of many small globules which do not fit very closely together. The globules are the cells. They have a shiny, swollen aspect, since they are distended with water.

Full details can be obtained only by the use of the higher powers of the compound microscope, assisted by the use of fluids which kill the cells without causing them to shrink, and by the application of stains to bring out details. By such methods we find that each cell is surrounded by a thin, firm wall. Inside this, and in intimate contact with the wall, there is a layer of a viscous fluid full of tiny, nearly colourless granules ; the fluid is protoplasm saturated with water. It is not unlike white of egg in its general characters, and, though its exact nature is unknown, it appears to be a very complicated system of complicated substances, and it is the part of the cell in which the mysterious thing we call life has its being. The layer of protoplasm forming the protoplast of the cell completely surrounds a cavity—the vacuole—filled with a watery fluid containing sugars, mineral salts and many other substances in solution. In properly prepared material, stains show that the protoplast includes a rounded object—the nucleus—and that this often includes a smaller rounded body—the nucleolus.

The nucleus is a most important part of the protoplast, for it presides over the activities of the cell, and, though we are not concerned with the subject here, the nucleus appears to be the chief agent in the transmission of inheritable characters. In most cells the nucleus usually forms but a small part of the protoplast, the remaining and larger part being known as the cytoplasm. When chloroplasts are present they are embedded in the cytoplasm and are therefore in intimate contact with the active material of the cell. Cells vary so much in size that it is not possible to give even average figures of their dimensions, but, as some indication of the size of nuclei, we may note that if 2500 nuclei of average size were strung like beads, the string would be an inch long.

Plant bodies are made up chiefly of cells, which may have the simple form just described or which may be much more complex. The complications affect mainly the shape and thickness of the walls. The walls consist of dead material formed by the protoplast, and provide a mechanical framework in which the protoplast lives and works. The walls are pierced by fine pores through which the protoplasts of neighbouring cells remain in communication.

THE CELLS THAT HOLD OR CONDUCT THE MATERIAL

THE conducting strands of the plants, and in particular those of the wood, are not formed of simple cells. The tubular wood vessels are formed by the union, end to end, of several thin-walled cells, with subsequent break-down of the walls between the cells, and thickening of the walls along the sides ; one can get a rough idea of the process by imagining several cylindrical tins piled one on top of another, and then all the lids and bottoms disappearing except those at the two ends of the pile.

As the vessels form, the living contents of the uniting cells disappear so that the vessels contain no living material when they are fully formed. They can conduct material only as long as living cells are close by. This explains how it is that most of the wood of a large tree is dead and unable to conduct fluids. In the tree living cells exist only in the surface layers of the wood, and they die as new cells are laid down outside them. When they die, the vessels in their vicinity lose their power of conduction.

The sieve tubes which are concerned in the movement of the more complicated food substances inside the plant are also formed from elongated cells ; mature sieve tubes contain living cytoplasm but no nucleus. They usually have in close association one or more small cells with specially large nuclei, and it seems probable that these nuclei control the activities of the cytoplasm in the neighbouring sieve tubes.

THE PLANT AT WORK: THE BUSINESS OF GETTING A LIVING

MANY attempts have been made to solve some of the problems of the way in which the plant works, by making chemical analyses of the plant body. It is comparatively easy to analyse the plant and to find what chemical elements are present, but such analyses tell us little of the substances which are actually present in the plant. However, such work shows that the number of chemical elements of universal occurrence in plants is small ; it is made up as follows : carbon, hydrogen, oxygen, nitrogen, sulphur, phosphorus, calcium, potassium, magnesium, iron. In addition, many plants contain appreciable amounts of sodium, chlorine and silicon. The elements do not occur as elements inside the plant ; they are always united with other elements, often in very complicated fashion.

Two tables of analyses follow ; inspection of these will give a good general idea of the position in some common plants.

Table I.—Approximate percentage analyses of common vegetable materials *after* drying

Material.	Carbon.	Hydrogen.	Oxygen.	Nitrogen.	Ash.
Wheat grain	46	6	43	2·5	2·5
Potato tuber	44	6	44·5	1·5	4·0
Beet, leaf	38	5	31	4·5	21·5

Table II.—Percentage composition of three common plant materials

Ingredient.	Wheat grain.	Potato tuber.	Lettuce leaf.
Water	14	75	95
Dry material	86	25	5
consisting of:			
Proteins	12	2	·85
Fats	2	·25	·5
Carbohydrates	68	21	2·0
Ash	2	1	1·0
Fibrous matter	2	·75	·65

Wheat grains and potato tubers are resting structures containing much starch, a carbohydrate plants often store in their resting structures. The figures suggest very clearly how it is that wheat is a better food for animals than are potatoes. The high ash content of the leaves, calculated in relation to their dry weight, is of interest ; leaves commonly contain much mineral material.

The ash contains all the elements present in the plant except carbon, hydrogen, oxygen and nitrogen. The elements found in the ash enter the plant from the soil, dissolved in water taken up by the roots. Much of the solution passes into the leaves of the plant, where the water escapes into the air, leaving the mineral substances behind in the leaves. Some of the accumulation is got rid of by the plant when the leaves fall. At first sight such a circumstance may seem of little moment, yet so complex is the inter-relationship between plants growing under natural conditions that even so trivial a matter as the disposal of excess mineral substances may have its significance. The ash of leaves often contains a fair amount of compounds of calcium, and rotting leaves may sometimes add sufficient calcium to the surface soil to prevent it from becoming acid, even though there may be an acid soil beneath it. The lesser celandine cannot grow well on an acid soil, but it is often found in abundance on the shallow layer of soil kept suitable for its growth by the annual addition of compounds of calcium from fallen leaves.

PLANTS WITHOUT STEM, ROOT OR LEAVES

ANALYSES such as those which have just been given apply to the whole plant ; they tell us little about the composition of its protoplasm. Up to the present it has not been found possible to obtain sufficient quantities of the protoplasm of any of the flowering plants for purposes of analysis. There is, however, a group of lowly organised plants, the slime moulds, whose bodies consist of a naked mass of protoplasm without any cell walls ; these plants have no roots, no stems and no leaves. The protoplasm is not pure, for it always contains a certain amount of rubbish, but it is the best material available. Analysis of this material shows that about 55 per cent of the dry weight is protein, indicating that protoplasm is specially rich in nitrogen, sulphur and phosphorus. Probably most of the nitrates, sulphates and phosphates taken from the soil by plants are used up in making protoplasm.

A MIXED DIET AND DOSES KEEP THE PLANT WELL

THE chemical analysis of plants has led to a number of developments : for example, the modern industry in artificial manures, such as superphosphates and sulphate of ammonia, and to the utilisation of deposits of potash and phosphates in various parts of the world. After it had been shown that plants contained certain elements it was an obvious step to investigate what plants took from the soil, and this work has stimulated much study of the soil and of means to increase its productiveness. Experiments have shown that plants do not flourish unless they can obtain supplies of nitrogen, sulphur, phosphorus, potassium, magnesium and iron, and that some plants need small supplies of other elements as well. It is noteworthy that although plants contain much carbon, they do not obtain this from the soil. Sufficiency, however, is by no means all that is necessary for a plant to flourish. The water in a fertile soil holds, in solution, supplies of all the nitrogenous and mineral substances that the plants need, but if these substances are supplied to the plant singly, and not mixed with the others, they may be poisonous instead of beneficial ; in the soil water, the substances are so balanced that they cancel out one another's poisonous properties and all is well. It has been shown, too, that many plants need, for their best growth, tiny amounts of special substances. For example, broad beans need very small doses of borax or of zinc which appear to produce a stimulating effect on growth out of all proportion to the amount of the dose.

All growing plants contain a great deal of water, so much indeed that it has been suggested that the plant consists of water held in shape by small amounts of a few other substances. When it is recalled that a fresh lettuce leaf contains about 95 per cent of water, the idea does not seem so odd as it does at first sight. Water is of the greatest importance to plants, and this in a variety of ways.

There are some properties of water which fit in well with the special needs of the plant. It dissolves a very large number of substances and so provides a means of bringing material into the plant and of moving it inside the plant. It is transparent to light, and so opposes no serious hindrance to the entry of this important source of energy into the plant. The heat relations of water are of special significance ; it heats up slowly and cools down slowly, and consequently the large amount of water in the plant affords protection against sudden and violent changes of temperature. Further, when liquid water is changed into water vapour, it takes up much heat from the substances with which it is in contact—the porous earthenware butter coolers are kept cool by the water evaporating from them. Plants, too, lose much water vapour and are cooled in the process, without doubt to their advantage in hot weather, when water loss is particularly great.

HOW THE PLANT DRINKS

WE have already noted that water provides the means for the entry of many substances into the plant. In order to understand how entry occurs it is necessary to devote some attention to a matter which, at first sight, has little to do with the plant. Somewhere about 1750, Nollet, a Dutchman, found that when a pig's bladder was filled with alcohol, tied up firmly and placed in water, the bladder swelled, and sometimes burst ; conversely, a bladder of water shrank when it was immersed in alcohol. It was evident that the two fluids were not passing through the bladder at the same rate, and that the water was going through faster than the alcohol. These experiments were the first of many made to discover the power possessed by some membranes to influence the passage of substances through them, and we now know of many sorts of membranes which let some substances pass through them easily, but limit or prevent the movement of others. Such membranes are semi-permeable membranes and they are of great significance in the economy of living creatures.

It is not very difficult to fasten a long glass tube to a thin bag of collodion in such a way that the joint is watertight. If we then fill the bag with a strong solution of sugar and hang it in water, we may make the following observations. First, we note that there is a steady rise in the level of the water in the glass tube and this may continue until there is a column of water several feet high in the upright tube. The rise does not continue indefinitely. It ceases after a time, the level stays constant and then slowly falls, until finally the liquid stands at the same level inside and outside the tube.

At the beginning of the experiment there was water outside, and water and sugar inside the bag of collodion. If samples are taken from the water outside while the experiment is going on it is found that every sample contains more sugar than did the preceding one ; it is understood of course that equal samples are taken. At the end of the experiment, sampling shows that the sugar is now evenly shared in all the water present, both inside and outside the bag.

All the time that the experiment was going on, water was

passing easily through the walls of the bag in either direction, but sugar was passing much more slowly. Consequently, for a time there was a strong solution of sugar inside and a weak solution outside. Under these circumstances, water tended to pass from the weak to the strong solution, and this was shown by the rise of fluid in the upright tube above the bag. As the column rose in the tube it exerted an increasing downward pressure. This acted against the accumulation of water in the bag, since it tended to force water out.

Presently a point was reached where the passage of the water into the bag was just balanced by the amount of water being pressed out, partly by the column in the upright tube, and partly by the resistance to stretching offered by the somewhat elastic collodion bag. Sugar continued to pass slowly out of the bag, so that the two solutions, inside and outside, were approaching a point where they were of equal strength. As this went on, the pressures expelling water from the bag became more and more effective, and the loss of water was indicated by the slow fall of the column. Finally, when the sugar was evenly distributed, levels were the same inside and outside, since the apparatus no longer contained two solutions of different strength, separated by a semi-permeable membrane.

The experiment may be made in another way. A solution of sugar is placed in a bag of collodion which is then sealed up and sunk in water. At first, water passes readily into the strong solution, the bag swells and its wall is stretched. A point is slowly reached where the bag will stretch no more ; then, provided the bag does not burst, nothing appears to happen for a time. As sugar is slowly lost from the bag, internal pressure falls and the bag continues to contract until it is no longer stretched ; when this point is reached, samples will show that the sugar is evenly distributed throughout all the water present. It is evident that in experiments of this kind we are dealing with a balance of pressures.

WATCHING THE ROOT HAIRS GROW

WE return to the plant. Let us suppose that we line a glass pot with blotting paper, fill the pot with clean sand, and push some mustard seeds between the pot and the paper ; we then damp the sand and put the whole thing in a warm place. After a few days the seeds germinate and produce downwardly directed roots. These show a smooth,

tapering tip, and a little behind this is a length of root covered
by long, delicate white hairs. If we watch the preparation
for a few days we see that as the root elongates, the hairs
towards the base shrivel and are replaced by fresh hairs
formed nearer to the tip. The general effect is that as the tip
of the root grows downwards, the zone of hairs also moves
downwards, always keeping at about the same distance behind
the tip.

The microscope shows that each hair is an outgrowth
from one of the surface cells of the root. The hair is part of
the cell, and not a separate structure. One wall covers the
whole and the lining of cytoplasm and the vacuole run out
into the hair. The superficial cells of the fairly young parts
of the root, with the hairs that they bear, form the apparatus
used by the plant to collect soil water. Incidentally, care
must be taken to distinguish clearly between root hairs and
very fine rootlets ; the latter consist of many cells and may
themselves bear root hairs.

Mustard seeds, treated in the manner indicated, give very
clear specimens of root hairs, but when plants are grown in
soil, root hairs are not always easy to find, for they are often
short, and are always closely applied to the particles of the
soil. Since the root hairs have sticky walls it is difficult to
wash away the soil without destroying the hairs.

ROOT HAIRS AS COLLECTORS OF RAW MATERIAL

THE root hairs, closely applied to the soil particles, are the
chief absorptive organs of the plant. They occur only
on young roots, generally on restricted areas just behind the
tips. Older parts of the root, over which the impermeable
corky layer is forming or has formed, have lost their root
hairs.

The particles of a normal soil are surrounded by a thin
film of water which holds many substances in solution. Root
hairs make intimate contact with the soil particles, often
becoming moulded to them. Each cell, with its root hair, is
closely comparable with the collodion bag as a device for
absorption, with two important differences. In the bag the
collodion wall acts as the semi-permeable membrane ; in
the cell the wall affords support to the lining of cytoplasm
inside, and contributes the elastic part of the combination,
but it is not a semi-permeable membrane. The lining of
cytoplasm is the semi-permeable membrane, and—the second

important difference—it is alive, and can only act as a semi-permeable membrane as long as it is alive. If roots are killed by heat or by poisons, there may be no visible difference between their cells and those of living roots, but experiment shows that the root is no longer an efficient absorbing mechanism.

The soil water of fertile soils is not so strong a solution as is the fluid in the vacuoles of the cells of roots growing in the soil. Consequently, water and other substances pass from the weak solution outside to the stronger solution inside. Everything goes in in solution, for the roots cannot take in solid material. As the cells absorb water they swell and the cell wall is stretched. The power of the cells to continue to absorb is determined by the balance set up between the tendency of material to pass into the cell because of the stronger cell sap inside, and the resistance offered to stretching by the walls of the cell. If this balance is exactly reached, absorption will cease, but it is probable that this never happens. The process by which a plant takes in food through its roots is known as *Osmosis*.

The entry of water into the root hairs and superficial cells of the root is only the beginning of the story ; we must still consider how the material is distributed to the rest of the plant. Inside the young root there are many thin-walled cells which, except that they bear no hairs, are very like the superficial cells, and have the same power of taking in watery solutions. Now, the cells on the outside of the root are closest to the source of supply, and it is therefore a fair assumption that, of all the cells of the root, they are the most likely to be nearest to the condition of balance where the pressure of the contracting walls opposes most resistance to the entry of more water. The cells next inside them will not be quite so close to this condition, and they will have a somewhat greater demand for water ; this they will satisfy as far as they can by taking water from the superficial cells, and with the water, other substances also. Cells still further within the root will be still less satisfied, and so will take water from those just outside them, and, as we pass deeper and deeper into the root we find cells whose demands for water are less and less easily met. The effect of all this will be that water will be always passing inwards from the better supplied to the worse supplied cells ; consequently, even the cells on the outside of the root will never quite reach a stage where they retain their full water content, and will therefore continue to take it from the soil.

In this way we may picture the passage of material from the soil into and through the thin-walled living cells of the root, but we presently come to a point, deep in the root, where there is a transfer from the living cells to the dead vessels of the wood, by means of which the water passes into the general body of the plant ; at present, we have no satisfactory explanation of the manner in which this is done.

HOW WATER RISES FROM ROOTS TO LEAVES

WE do know something, however, of the ascent of water from the roots to the stems and leaves. We have already seen that dyes travel upwards in the wood, showing this to be the path followed by watery solutions in the plant, but before we can deal with this matter we have once more to leave the plant for a time.

Paradoxical as it may appear, a thread of water, suitably supported, can take and can transmit a pull much in the same way as a wire can do so. This may be shown in the following way. A glass tube about five feet long is provided with an open, expanded end. This is loosely packed with wet plaster of Paris, which, as it sets, swells and fills the expansion. The tube is then filled with water containing no air in solution, and set vertically with its lower end dipping into mercury. Water evaporates from the plaster plug ; it is replaced by water from the tube below, and mercury rises into the tube to occupy the space vacated by the evaporated water.

As evaporation continues the mercury rises higher and higher. At first, this rise has no special significance, for it could be due to the weight of the air pressing up the mercury, as it does in a mercury barometer. In time, however, if the apparatus has been well prepared, it is found that the column of mercury rises until it stands much higher than the column in a barometer placed by the side of the apparatus. Since the column in the barometer is supported by the weight of the air, and since at any given time the column in the barometer shows the maximum effect that the weight of the air can exert, it follows that the extra length of the mercury column in our apparatus is being supported by something other than the weight of the air.

It is a fair conclusion that the mercury is being pulled up

by the thread of water above it, and that this in its turn is supported by the numerous fine threads of water in the plaster plug, these ending at the upper surface of the plaster where evaporation is in progress. Calculation and experiment have shown that threads of water may be sufficiently strong to take pulls greater than those necessary to lift water from soil level to the tops of the highest trees. In a broad way, the plant may be directly compared with the simple apparatus we have just considered.

THE PLANT S WAY OF MAKING UP LOSSES

IT is easy to show that plants are always losing water vapour from their exposed surfaces, and it is equally easy to show that water is always rising from below to replace losses. The leaves and young branches of the plant provide an evaporating surface comparable with, and no doubt much more efficient than, the surface of the plaster plug, and the system of conducting vessels inside the plant forms an elaborate counterpart to the upright glass tube. It seems highly probable that, in essentials, the water rises in the plant in the same kind of way that it rises in the glass tube.

It follows that the plant has a water supply system by which losses are automatically replaced, provided always that there is sufficient water in the soil to allow the stock in the plant to be maintained, and provided also that the plant can take in that water as fast as it loses water from its leaves. The mechanism is not perfect. Any garden, in the middle of a hot day, will show some plants that look limp ; they are flagging because they are losing water faster than they are taking it in. The same plants may, however, be stiff and fresh looking in the late evening or the early morning, even if they have not been watered in the meantime.

In the heat of the day plants often lose water faster than they take it in, their soft cells shrink, and the leaves and young stems flag ; expenditure exceeds income. With cooler conditions, expenditure decreases, income and expenditure balance, and the plant receives and retains enough water to keep it fresh and rigid. Sometimes, income exceeds expenditure by evaporation, and water which is in excess of requirements may then pass out of the plant in liquid form ; this accounts for much of the dew on grass in the early morning ; the water has not come from the air but has been exuded from the tips of the leaves.

The relation between income and expenditure of water is of vital importance to the plant. Growth is impossible unless the young growing parts are fully charged with water ; a plant flagging from insufficiency of water is not growing. If a plant is wilted for several hours a day in hot weather the loss of growing time may be serious—so serious indeed that it has been found worth while to provide artificial shading for some crops in the tropics. The shaded plants gain many hours of growth and the improvement in the crop more than pays for the expense of providing the shade.

WHEN THE PLANT MUST CHOOSE BETWEEN FOOD AND WATER

PLANTS lose water chiefly through their stomata. These may close when the water supply is scanty, and so exert an automatic check on loss, but they do not act very accurately, and since stomata tend to remain open in bright light they may cease to act as checks on the loss of water from the plant at the very time when a check is most needed. Further, the stomata are essential to two other important activities of the plant, and for these purposes they must remain open. The manufacture of food, at any rate in its preliminary stages, can only go on in the light, and the plant uses carbon dioxide taken in from the air through the stomata. If, therefore, the stomata are closed in the daytime the intake of carbon dioxide must be hindered, and this must limit the making of food.

On the whole, the average plant does not seem well equipped for controlling its water supplies. It must have plentiful supplies of water for all its many activities, and it must obtain carbon dioxide, and also oxygen from the air for the manufacture and utilisation of its food. The gases from the atmosphere enter the plant through the stomata which must be open if the gases are to pass in ; but which, if they are open, may allow too *much* water to pass. Somehow, therefore, the plant has to strike a balance between these two processes. It is well known that many plants have structural devices which limit the loss of water, and the widespread occurrence of such devices indicates how acute the water problem must be.

The loss of water from the plant is not a mere matter of evaporation. If one leaf on a twig is killed by chloroform, and then the whole twig is cut and put to dry in the air, the killed leaf loses water more quickly than the others. Evidently living material, even when it is dying from drought, can impose some check on straightforward evaporation. There is good reason to conclude that the loss of water from the plant is chiefly responsible for the maintenance of the stream of water that passes through the plant. If plants lost water only by evaporation, there could hardly be a water current through a plant submerged in water, as a submerged plant could not evaporate water into the water around it. By means of dyes it can be shown that there *is* a stream of water passing through plants growing submerged in water, and this suggests that the plants are losing water by some means other than evaporation, and that probably land plants also have the same means at their disposal. Probably both excretion and evaporation are concerned, and indeed evaporation must be concerned, since dead plants left standing in soil continue to take water from the soil and give it off into the air. In those plants the usual mechanism for the collection of water has been destroyed, and it appears that the dead cell walls act as a sort of wick, lifting water from the soil to regions where evaporation is possible.

Plants do not lose water to the air so rapidly as water evaporates from an open surface. In one experiment, exposed water evaporated at the rate of about three pints from each square yard in twenty-four hours. At the same time, and under the same conditions, an equal area of beech leaves lost about a quarter of a pint of water. This does not seem much, but it appears that beech trees covering the ground fairly densely may transfer in a day nearly a quarter of a million gallons of water to the air from an acre of ground.

THE GREEN PIGMENT ON WHICH ALL LIFE DEPENDS

THE nutrition of plants has to be treated from two points of view ; we have to see how the plant makes its food and how it utilises it afterwards. Since the making of the food depends upon chlorophyll we may well begin with this mixture, a mixture which is perhaps the most important group of substances on the face of the earth. All living creatures depend on the products of its activity for food, and modern industrial civilisation, based on the combustion of organic remains of past ages, could not exist had not green plants produced the material that the furnaces burn.

If nettle leaves are chopped up and treated with acetone

and water, a deep-green solution is obtained ; this solution contains a mixture of the four pigments known to be present in chlorophyll. When a drop of this solution is placed on white blotting-paper, the liquid spreads, and there is a thin yellow edge surrounding a green centre. This is a rough demonstration that the solution contains a mixture of substances. There are in fact four pigments in crude chlorophyll, two green and two yellow ; of the latter, one, carotene, is familiar, as it gives the colour to carrots. All four pigments are extremely complicated substances ; the green ones, which are much more so, are made up of carbon, hydrogen, oxygen, nitrogen and a little magnesium, the yellow ones of carbon and hydrogen only (and, in some, oxygen as well). Land plants contain rather under one per cent of their weight of the mixture.

PLANTS THAT NEED AN IRON TONIC

MUCH is known of the chemistry of chlorophyll, but we are still ignorant of the way in which it works in the plant. It contains no iron, but iron is used by the plant as it builds up its chlorophyll. Some plants are hindered from taking in iron from soils that contain much lime. Incautious liming of the soil in gardens may be shown subsequently by the development of yellow streaks and spots in the leaves of the plants, and, in calcareous districts, such yellow markings are often seen in the leaves of the wild plants. They indicate a deficiency of chlorophyll in the leaves, no doubt because the abundant lime in the soil has upset the intake of iron by the plant.

Most plants are unable to develop chlorophyll except in good light, and if seeds are allowed to germinate in unbroken darkness, they give rise to sickly yellow plants with little or no chlorophyll ; these plants seldom survive for long, for even if they are put in the light and then form chlorophyll, they are usually so weak that they fall easy victims to enemies which are unable to attack fully healthy plants.

Chlorophyll may disappear from plants if they are darkened ; the yellowing of grass which has been accidentally covered up is a familiar example of this. Recovery to a normal green condition depends on the length of time that the plant has been deprived of light. If recovery is possible, it seems that weak light is more favourable than strong light. When a plant is in the light, it is forming chlorophyll, and at the same time it is losing chlorophyll, since light breaks the pigments up. The stronger the light, the more rapid is the break-up, and, when a plant is in a weakened condition it may not be able to form chlorophyll quickly enough to compensate effectively for losses in strong light.

During those parts of the year when growth is in active progress there is some kind of regulation of the events going on in the cells, so that, with normal conditions, the green cells remain green and always contain about the same amount of chlorophyll. In autumn, however, changes occur in plants which lose their leaves at that season. The chlorophyll is broken up, giving brown substances which are in part responsible for the colour changes seen in autumn ; they are not, however, entirely responsible, since other brightly coloured substances owing their origin to disorganisation in the cells of the leaves, also make their appearance.

THE UNEXPLAINED MYSTERY OF A PLANT'S FOOD

CARBON dioxide enters leaves by means of the stomata, and finds its way into the spaces between the cells of the leaves. The walls of these cells are wet, and the carbon dioxide dissolves in the moisture, passes in solution through the walls and enters the cells. Once there, in some fashion which still awaits complete explanation, the cell brings about union between water and carbon dioxide, with the liberation of oxygen. The oxygen passes into solution, diffuses as gas into the spaces within the leaf, and escapes from these through the stomata, into the open air. As a result of the union between the carbon dioxide and the water, sugars are formed in the cells of the leaf, and these sugars form the starting-point for further food-making operations.

There is no doubt that some of the early stages in these operations are carried out by means of energy from the sun which is arrested by the chlorophyll and used for bringing about chemical changes. Many suggestions have been made to explain the changes which go on, but the experimental investigation is very difficult, and the results are not clear enough to allow of dogmatic conclusions. It is well demonstrated that green plants can only utilise water and carbon dioxide for food manufacture if they are supplied with light —not necessarily, however, with bright sunlight—and it follows that the energy from the sun lies at the bottom of all the changes which lead to the building up of food from simple beginnings.

As sugar accumulates in the cells, at times when that substance is being formed, it necessarily follows that the concentration of dissolved material in the cell sap must rise. Continued increase of this kind might well upset the general relationships of the cells, since, the more concentrated the cell sap, the more vigorously does water enter from without. We find that, as sugar is made in the green cells, much of it is converted into starch ; this, being insoluble in water, appears as small solid granules within the cells, and so long as it remains in this form it plays no part in the activities of the cell. Some of the sugar is used by the cell which makes it, and some of it diffuses out of the cell and passes to other parts of the plant, supplying cells which possess no chlorophyll and cannot manufacture for themselves.

During times when the green cells are exposed to light, the rate at which sugar is being made greatly exceeds the rate at which it is being used up, and it is easy to show during the daytime that starch accumulates rapidly in the green cells of the plant. As the light becomes weaker, the manufacture of sugar, and therefore of starch, falls off, and presently a point is reached when the cell is using sugar, or losing sugar by diffusion, faster than it is making it. Then the starch is converted back into sugar, and, as this is used or passes elsewhere, more starch is converted. In some plants all the starch accumulated during the daytime may be turned back into sugar and used or transported to some other part of the plant during the night ; in others two or three days of complete darkness are necessary to ensure that all the starch in the leaves has undergone the change.

There is some doubt about the part played by chlorophyll in relation to the formation by the plant of food materials containing nitrogen, and other of the more complicated substances of the plant. It seems well established that few of these substances are formed at the expense of light energy, and it may be that none are. It is quite possible that the green plant uses light energy only for the formation of sugar, and that all the other changes which occur in the cells derive their energy from the subsequent breakdown of the sugar.

TINY SUGAR FACTORIES IN THE LEAVES

THE sugar-starch relation just mentioned plays an important part in the opening and closing of the stomata. A simple form of stoma consists of a couple of sausage-shaped cells—guard cells—lying side by side in the epidermis of the leaf, and firmly united with the neighbouring epidermal cells ; the two guard cells are not, however, joined to one another except at the ends, so that there is an opening between them. They contain chlorophyll and so are able to manufacture sugar. In the light, they do so actively, and as the concentration of sugar within them rises, they take up water actively from neighbouring cells. As a result the guard cells swell, and owing to the manner in which they are joined to neighbouring cells they curve as they swell and the pore between them opens. In darkness manufacture ceases, sugar is used or lost from the guard cells, their water content falls, and, as they shrink, they straighten out and the pore is closed.

It has been mentioned several times that the plant makes use of energy from the sun in its manufacturing processes, and it has been implied that solar energy is also used up in the liberation of water from the plant. We may try to construct a kind of balance-sheet as an indication of the way in which the plant uses this energy. The figures given below were obtained from experiments with the common annual sunflower, and they do not suggest that, as a machine for using energy, the plant is specially efficient.

Arbitrary value of solar energy	100
Proportion used in food-making	0·66
Proportion used during loss of water vapour ..	48·4
Proportion transmitted, reflected or otherwise lost	50·94

That is, the plant uses for constructive purposes less than 1 per cent of the solar energy falling on it. The large amount used in connection with the elimination of water suggests the efficiency of this process in cooling the plant. As a rough measure of the rate at which the plant builds up material we may note that it has been calculated that, in a long summer's day, a leaf forms about as much starch as would be equal in weight to a piece of tissue paper of the same size as the leaf.

HOW FOOD IS USED TO GIVE THE PLANT ENERGY

THE many chemical changes which go on in the plant need a supply of energy for their accomplishment. A great deal of this energy is obtained by the breakdown of the food materials already formed by the plant. It appears probable for instance that many of the more complicated food substances are formed with the aid of energy liberated when the sugar present in the plant is broken down by means of oxygen, with the formation of water and carbon dioxide. Everyone knows that sugar burns readily and gives out a good deal of heat as it does so. In the same way the plant is able to break down sugar and liberate energy from it, but the process is not exactly comparable with burning, since it goes on more slowly and more gradually; yet the results are the same in the end.

We thus have the curious position that the plant takes in water and carbon dioxide and brings them together to form sugar, liberating oxygen in the process, and also that it takes in oxygen, and uses it to break down the sugars (and other substances) and liberate water and carbon dioxide. This second process, the breakdown of complicated substances to simple ones, with the liberation of energy, is common to all living creatures, whether plant or animal, and it is important to realise that the process goes on inside the cells of the creature. Moreover, it goes on all the time, so long as the cells are alive, and so contrasts with the more simple of the manufacturing processes of the green plant, which only proceed in the light.

QUICK-BREATHING PLANTS WHICH GROW WARM

THIS utilisation of material, with the assistance of oxygen, is called respiration ; it appears that the commonest substances used in the process are sugars, and, when this is so, the plant gives out approximately as much carbon dioxide as it takes in oxygen. Fats can also be used, and they are commonly used by young plants, since many seeds contain stores of fatty substances ; these need more oxygen for their breakdown, so that a plant using fats in respiration takes in more oxygen and yields less carbon dioxide. For short periods green plants are able to carry on respiration without an external source of oxygen, since they can take oxygen from some of the material present and use it to attack further material, but they cannot live indefinitely without supplies of free oxygen.

So far as we know, the green plants utilise only complicated substances for proposes of respiration, but it is worth notice that some of the bacteria of the soil, bacteria which play an important part in the breakdown of organic material and its reconversion into the simple forms utilisable by higher plants, are able to oxidise very simple substances such as ammonia, and to gain in this way sufficient energy for their needs.

In general, respiration goes on rather slowly in plants, and the energy liberated, probably mostly in the form of heat, is not set free fast enough to raise the body temperature of the plant to any appreciable extent ; in this respect we have a sharp contrast with the warm-blooded animals, in which the rapid rate of respiration keeps up the body heat to the necessary level. Sometimes, however, plants may respire fast enough to produce temperature effects ; germinating seeds are usually a trifle warmer than their surroundings, and in some plants which develop their flowers very quickly, the rapid utilisation of food materials at that time may result in the liberation of considerable quantities of heat. Of course, any heat that can be detected by means of a thermometer placed in the neighbourhood of the plant is heat lost to the plant, but the fact that it can be shown that heat is escaping indicates that respiration is proceeding with special vigour.

We may obtain a good deal of heat energy from sugar by burning it, but we can only do this by first raising the temperature of the sugar to a point where combustion begins. In the plant, sugar is utilised by oxidation, but the plant does not start the process by the application of a high temperature. It seems that the plants possess a number of very curious substances—enzymes—which have a remarkable power of causing chemical change in other substances, at ordinary temperatures, and without much loss of the enzymes themselves, and there is little doubt that the utilisation of food materials in respiration, at the low temperatures alone possible in the plant body, is brought about by these enzymes. These powerful substances are sometimes of industrial importance ; for example, the conversion of sugar into alcohol by yeast, a process which is a modified kind of respiration, depends upon the enzymes of the yeast plant.

ENERGY BUILT UP BY RESPIRATION

IT appears then that respiration is a process by means of which plants and animals break down the complicated substances which serve as food, and that the process ends with the formation of carbon dioxide and water, and the liberation of energy. There can be no doubt that in the living cells in which the process is carried out the breakdown of the food goes on in a number of successive stages, each yielding simpler products and some free energy. Respiration is carried out by all living things, and goes on at all times, furnishing the creature with a continuous supply of energy.

In green plants in the light, it is not easy to show that respiration is in progress, as it is masked by the more vigorous process of food manufacture going on at the same time. It has, however, been shown that green plants respire at the same time that they make up food, and the realisation that these opposing processes are going on in the same cell at the same time serves to emphasise the very complex nature of the proceedings of living creatures. Complete breakdown of the food materials to the simple substances from which they were made is only possible when the plants are abundantly supplied with oxygen ; if the supply of oxygen is restricted the process may continue in a modified form, but this yields less energy, it may result in the formation of substances which ultimately poison the organism, and it can only be carried on successfully by a few specialised fungi and bacteria.

WHAT DOES A PLANT DO WHEN IT GROWS?

UP to this point we have considered some of the processes which go on in plants, and for convenience they have been considered separately. Some attempt must now be made to take the plant as a whole. One of the most striking features of plants is the fact that they grow. This usually means that they increase in size, protecting their real living substance inside walls of cellulose and other substances probably composed largely of carbohydrate waste from the various processes going on in the plant. As most plants are unable to move about, and therefore have to obtain their supplies from a restricted field, it is hardly surprising that the actively growing parts of the plant lie either at the tips of the roots and branches, or disposed in a layer as close to the air as possible, just within the protective coating which covers the surface and does much to check excessive loss of water.

Mere increase in size and weight does not constitute growth ; a piece of dead dry wood will absorb water and increase both in weight and size, but it returns on drying to its former state. On the other hand, when a plant grows, it undergoes a permanent change, and this change cannot be reversed. Once a seed has germinated, it cannot be put back into the resting condition ; cells within it have divided, and chemical changes have gone on ; changes of this sort accompany all true growth. For a short time roots may actually decrease in diameter as they grow, but this is a somewhat unusual phenomenon.

It will be remembered that the unit of plant construction, and the unit of plant activity, is the cell. The growth of the cell starts with the division of its nucleus into two nuclei and the organisation of a cell around each of the two. In general, cells which are able to divide are distinguished by the possession of rich and dense cytoplasm, and by the small development of their vacuoles or sap-containing spaces ; it is only when the cell is approaching maturity that a large single central vacuole becomes prominent. Some cells undergo very considerable changes in size and form before they are fully mature, and, once mature, they have generally lost the power to divide any more, and become incorporated in some part of the plant which is fully organised.

FINDING OUT HOW FAST A PLANT GROWS

THERE are various methods of measuring the rate at which a plant grows. The elongation of stems and of roots can be directly measured, and it has been shown that the rate at which a whole plant is growing can be very satisfactorily determined by periodical measurements of the total area of the leaves on the plant. In stems and roots the whole of the organ does not elongate, but growth is localised in well-defined regions a little behind the tips, and, as the whole organ increases in length, the portion that is actually elongating keeps at an approximately constant distance behind the tip. In roots the elongating region lies between the area covered by root hairs and the tip ; it is obvious that root hairs could not make and keep contact with soil particles if they were attached to a portion of the root which was increasing in length. In stems, the elongating region corresponds approximately to the portion bearing partly developed leaves.

In the whole plant, so long as it is not preparing to flower, measurements of leaf area show that the rate of growth increases in the same way as money increases when it is put out at compound interest, that is, that the rate of growth is proportional to the amount of plant material already present. When, however, the plant is preparing to flower, this relation ceases to hold, since the reproductive processes divert the energy and material of the plant to uses other than ordinary growth in size.

INFLUENCES WHICH CHANGE THE BEHAVIOUR OF PLANTS

ALTHOUGH plants are mostly sedentary organisms, anchored to the soil by their roots, yet many of them are capable of limited movements, which, in the higher plants, usually depend on changes in the direction of growth. It is well known for example that if plants are set in a window and left undisturbed, their branches tend to grow towards the light, and, it may be shown in some plants, that if their roots are exposed to one-sided illumination, they tend to grow away from the light. Similarly, if plants with erect stems and downwardly pointing roots are set on their sides, one soon finds that the ends of the young stems begin to grow upwards, and the ends of the young roots downwards. These changes in direction occur in the parts of the organs that are still elongating, and are caused by one side of the organ growing faster than the other. Old organs which have got beyond the stage when they can elongate are generally unable to adjust themselves in this way.

When plants show a change in behaviour which can be related to some change in the conditions surrounding them, they are said to react to a stimulus. For instance, if a plant is placed on its side its position is changed in relation to gravity ; if a plant which has been growing in a well-lit situation is put into a place where light comes to it from one side only, the direction of the light falling on the plant is altered. These changes provide the stimuli, but it by no means follows that the stimulus provides the energy used up in the subsequent reaction by the plant. Indeed, the stimuli which influence the behaviour of plants have been compared with the trigger of a gun : the trigger starts the explosion, but the violence of the discharge depends on the amount of explosive present ; a stimulus calls forth a change in the behaviour of the plant, but the nature and extent of the change depends on the plant itself.

The chief stimuli which provoke response in plants are connected with light and with gravity ; contact with solid objects is an important stimulus to climbing plants, and variations in the humidity of the soil may provoke response in roots. If a plant is placed on its side it does not at once begin to curve ; it has to be left for half an hour or so before the change in the direction of gravity begins to affect it. Consequently, if we support a plant in a horizontal position on a vertical turntable which rotates slowly and thus neutralises the one-sided effect we find that the stem and root continue to grow straight on ; similarly, if a plant is rotated on itself slowly in a vertical position in light falling from one side only there is no response. Such experiments indicate clearly that gravity—or light—have some part in the behaviour of the plant when it is displaced and left so for some time.

Measurements show that a stem elongates faster in darkness than in light. When, therefore, we place a stem so that light falls on it on one side only, it is not surprising that the tip of the stem is brought towards the light, since the badly-lit side elongates faster than the well-lit side, and so must turn the tip to the light. In a horizontal stem the lower side elongates faster than the upper side, and so the tip is re-erected. The advantage of this to the plant is obvious, but it must not be concluded that the movement is consciously purposeful ; of that we have no evidence whatever.

Movements of these kinds can only occur when the conditions surrounding the plant are favourable to growth, and of these conditions, a suitable temperature is the most potent ; response is always slow in cold weather. It has already been pointed out that the plant has to be exposed to the changed conditions for a definite time if response is to follow. If, for example, an erect stem is placed in one-sided light for 20–40 minutes, and then, while still vertical, is rotated about its own long axis in complete darkness, it nevertheless proceeds to develop the characteristic curvatures, indicating clearly that response does not depend on the continued presence of the appropriate stimulus.

There is reason to think that stimuli are perceived by the tips of growing organs, and that in some way these tips then transmit something to the regions of elongation beneath them, where the reaction becomes apparent. If the tips are cut off from roots, and the roots are then placed on their sides, very little curvature occurs, though the region of elongation remains active. After some two days, however, curvatures may begin to appear, and it may now be shown that the end of the stump has regained some measure of sensitiveness.

If, however, roots are placed on their side for a time, and the tips are then cut off and replaced in position with a little gelatine between them and the stumps, curvature follows in an almost normal way; presumably something diffuses through the gelatine from the tips and the usual growth changes follow.

Many and diverse experiments of this sort suggest strongly that the responses of plants are connected with the production of some special substance inside the plant, and that this affects growth. We know little as yet of these substances, and of the manner in which they affect the behaviour of the plant, but it seems probable that they are akin to certain substances which are already known to have noteworthy physiological effects, and to substances which are believed to cause cancer in animals.

A PLANT THAT COLLAPSES AT A TOUCH

IN addition to these localised movements, many plants show movements of a more general kind. Of such plants, the best known is probably the Sensitive Plant. This is a small plant distantly related to peas and beans. It has feathery leaves which collapse suddenly if the plant is shaken or exposed to the vapour of ammonia or other potent fluids. If the small leaflets at the end of a part of the leaf are gently touched they close together, and then successive pairs farther and farther away from the end do so in turn; this looks as though a stimulus is transmitted along the leaf. With a rougher touch the stimulus travels more quickly, and the whole leaf may collapse. In warm weather the leaf regains its stiffness in about half an hour. Although the exact mechanism remains obscure, it seems probable that the collapse of the leaves is due to the temporary loss of water from the cells, as a result of stimulation.

The opening and closing of flowers is usually due to growth at the bases of the floral leaves. The flowers of tulips and crocuses, for example, open in warmth and close in the cold. When the flowers open there is sudden growth at the base of the floral leaves, and as they increase in length they necessarily separate; when they close the growth occurs at the base of the other sides of the leaves, causing them to shut together.

WHERE TO READ FURTHER ABOUT PLANT LIFE

A N attempt has been made in this survey to indicate some of the many points of interest in the structure and general working of the plants. The list of books which follows will furnish material for further reading ; it covers only a corner of the vast field which lies open. To anyone who wishes to study plants, one last word is offered—do not confine your study to reading, but go to the plants themselves.

A few books, all readily accessible, may be recommended to the reader who desires to pursue his botanical studies further. Much information may be gathered from *Life of Plants* by Sir Frederick Keeble (Clarendon Press), *An Introduction to the Study of Plants* by Professor F. E. Fritsch and Professor E. J. Salisbury (G. Bell & Sons), from *The Study of Plants* by Dr. T. W. Woodhead (Clarendon Press), and from *The Botany of the Living Plant* by Professor F. O. Bower (Macmillan). These books assume very little botanical knowledge on the part of the reader, and lead him by pleasant paths to a sound introductory knowledge of the subject.

Details of the structure of plants may be sought in *Structural Botany* by the late Dr. D. H. Scott (A. & C. Black, 2 vols.), in *An Introduction to the Structure and Reproduction of Plants* by Professors Fritsch and Salisbury (G. Bell & Sons), and in Strasburger's *Text-Book of Botany*, translated by Professor W. H. Lang (Macmillan). This book also contains many physiological details, and a simpler presentation of plant physiology will be found in *An Introduction to Plant Physiology* by Dr. W. O. James (Clarendon Press).

The interesting problem of the movement of water in plants is thoroughly treated by Professor H. H. Dixon in his *Transpiration and the Ascent of Sap in Plants* (Macmillan). Finally, and of very great interest, *The Biology of the Flowering Plants* by Dr. Macgregor Skene (Sidgwick & Jackson), and Kerner and Oliver's monumental *Natural History of Plants* (Blackie & Son) will yield a wonderful store of facts on the general lives of the plants and the relations between the plants and their surroundings.

THE FAMILIES OF PLANTS

by HAROLD BASTIN

THAT plants fall naturally into groups of similar kinds is a fairly obvious fact. We all know quite well what we mean when we speak of a " tree," and do not for one moment suppose it to be the same thing as a fern or a sea-weed. Moreover, if we are interested in such matters, we soon learn to distinguish in some detail between the kinds, or " species," of trees as such, so that we talk of oaks, beeches, elms, poplars, pines, and so forth. Also, we go on to trace numberless resemblances and differences between the various species ; as, for example, that the oak casts its leaves at the approach of winter, while the pine does not ; or, that the fruit of the oak is a nut-like acorn, while that of the pine is a scaly cone. In other words, we find by observation that plants may be arranged for purposes of study into larger or smaller groups of similar kinds—the members of one such group, despite more or less evident divergencies among themselves, being liker to one another than to the kinds which we place in other groups. Thus we arrive at the notion of family relationship among plants.

This is really the root idea in the theory of evolution. If all the existing species of plants have " evolved," as Charles Darwin suggested that they have, by a process of natural selection from a few primitive types—perhaps even from *one* original, then we should expect to discover some evidence of this by comparing the structural peculiarities of one plant with those of others, and by noting the changes which take place as an individual plant grows from its seed to maturity. Geology, too, will be likely to furnish clues to what has taken place ; and may perhaps show conclusively, by producing fossils, that plants which according to our theory *ought* to have existed at some period of life's history did actually exist, but have since become extinct. These, in short, were the kinds of investigation, unremittingly pursued over a long period of years and in many directions, which led Darwin to publish (1859) his famous book, *On The Origin of Species*.

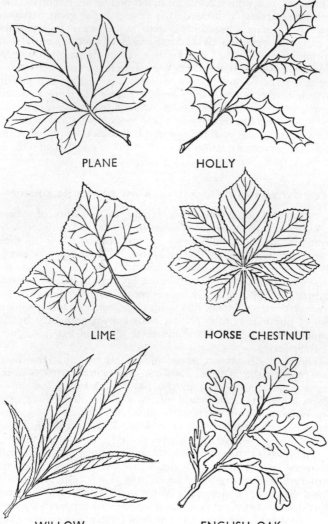

PLANE   HOLLY

LIME   HORSE CHESTNUT

WILLOW   ENGLISH OAK

IDENTIFYING A TREE BY ITS LEAVES

The shape, size and colour of the leaves are ready clues

Prior to this, the classification of plants by botanists had been more or less artificial. It is true that the great Swedish botanist, Linnaeus, based his system on the " natural " affinities of plants as revealed by a comparison of their essential—or reproductive—organs. But because (to quote his own words) Linnaeus believed that " there are just as many species as in the beginning the Infinite Being created," he had no conception that the resemblances which he noted were not merely coincidental, but were indications of descent from a common ancestry. The later view was made possible by the work of Darwin, and it has enabled modern botanists to realise that the ideal aim of classification is to plot out a huge pedigree, or " family tree," of plant life.

EVERY WEED HAS ITS RELATIVES : SOME SURPRISING KINSHIPS

NOWADAYS, therefore, this family relationship of plants is given practical expression in books and museums by arranging the various species in groups according to their true kinship, as far as this is known. " Kinship " is not at all the same thing as mere superficial similarity. Because two people happen to resemble one another in height, weight, features and character, it by no means follows that they are near relatives. To make this point clear, consider for a moment two of our native wild plants, both known popularly by the name " Pennywort," in reference to the coin-like roundness of their leaves.

The Wall Pennywort grows in dry, sunny situations, more especially in the West of England, where it often roots in the scanty soil accumulated in the fissures of rocks and stonework. Expert examination of its specific characters, more especially those of its flowers, indicates that its nearest relatives are the Stonecrops and House-leeks, in which family —or " order "—it is accordingly placed.

The Marsh Pennywort, which creeps among moss and grass in marshes and bogs, has almost identical leaves. But the structure and arrangement of its tiny flowers (they require a close search to be detected) bring to light the surprising fact that this modest plant is really a member of the *Umbelliferæ*— the clan which comprises the stately Hemlocks and the Hogweeds, to say nothing of numerous species useful to man, of which the Carrot, the Celery, and the Caraway are three examples

THE CLUES TO A PLANT'S IDENTITY

A BRIEF survey of the more important families of plants is all that can be given here ; but if the reader bears in mind this underlying fact of real relationship, as distinct from mere " appearances " (which are proverbially deceptive), he will not fail to grasp the principle from which the modern systematic botanist takes his cue. The relative complexity of structure in the plant-body, and the character of the reproductive organs—these are the points to which attention must chiefly be directed.

Starting, then, with a general survey, we find that living plants may be separated into five main groups or divisions, viz.:

(1) Plants known collectively as " Algæ," many of them minute and single-celled, but comprising also the larger " seaweeds ; " fungi of all sorts, including the growths called " moulds." (Thallophyta.)

(2) Liverworts and mosses. (Bryophyta.)

(3) Club-mosses, horse-tails and ferns. (Pteridophyta.)

(4) Coniferous trees and their allies. (Gymnospermæ.)

(5) Plants which in general bear conspicuous " flowers," i.e. groups of " male " and " female " reproductive organs, often surrounded by a whorl or whorls of gaily coloured petals, and perhaps associated with nectar-secreting glands. (Angiospermæ.)

The scientific names of these divisions are given in brackets, so that the reader may ignore or memorise them at discretion. Their chief importance consists in the fact that they are portmanteau words which compress into small compass information concerning some outstanding characteristic common to members of the particular group. Thus, the " Thallophyta " are so called because the individual plant, when many-celled, is what botanists term a " thallus," that is, a simple vegetative body without clearly distinguishable organs, such as stems and leaves.

THE ROOT-STOCK OF PLANT PEDIGREE

IT must be admitted, however, that this first division of the vegetable kingdom is a somewhat mixed assemblage. It includes, for example, the organisms generally spoken of as " bacteria " and " slime-fungi," concerning whose true status so much doubt exists that competent authorities still question whether they are really plants at all, or even lowly

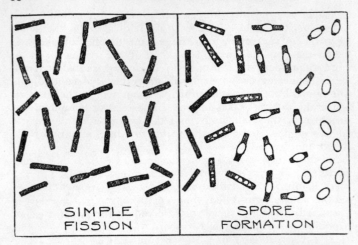

SIMPLE FISSION

SPORE FORMATION

THE TWO WAYS IN WHICH BACTERIA MULTIPLY

In favourable circumstances, bacteria reproduce simply by splitting in two. When this is impracticable, however, they sometimes multiply by shedding spores which have developed within the parent organism.

animals, but perhaps only " living things." Be this as it may they undoubtedly differ widely in many respects from all other known plants.

The bacteria are microscopically small, single-celled creatures which, in favourable circumstances, increase rapidly by splitting or " fission." Some live in the soil, where they often play an important part in preparing food-material for the higher plants. They convert, for instance, nitrogenous substances into forms which can be readily assimilated by green vegetation. Certain flowering plants, notably those of the pea-and-bean family, have entered into a kind of partnership with those species of soil-frequenting bacteria which are especially serviceable to them in this respect, and not only tolerate thriving colonies of these minute purveyors (" nitrogen-fixers," as they are called) in close association with their roots, but may fail to flourish in their absence.

Other bacteria live in the tissues of higher organisms, both plants and animals, sometimes harmlessly—or even helpfully —as in the case of those which normally inhabit the food-canal of the healthy human body; but often injuriously, since specific forms of bacteria are known to be the active agents in many infectious diseases, including cholera, diphtheria and typhoid.

In unfavourable circumstances, when their usual mode of reproduction by fission becomes impracticable, bacteria adopt the method of spore-formation. A " spore " is the technical name for a single cell capable of giving rise without any sexual process to a new individual. Spores lie dormant for a longer or shorter period until the conditions essential for active life again present themselves.

MASSES OF SLIME THAT CREEP FOR FOOD

THIS simple method of propagation also characterises the Slime-fungi—the spore-containing capsules, or " sporangia," of one species, commonly found among the refuse of tanneries, being the so-called " flowers of tan." The capsules of other species occur on dead twigs and decaying leaves in woods, and are rather attractive objects when viewed through a pocket lens. Not so the Slime-fungus in its active state, for it has much in common with certain lowly animals. Generally speaking, it is an almost formless mass of slimy protoplasm, devoid of definite cell-structure or special tissues ; but there are numerous small cavities, or " vacuoles," in the living jelly, some of which contain water or gas, others food-material in process of digestion.

Perhaps the most curious point about this organism is that it travels by a spontaneous movement, and thus brings itself into contact with the food-substances on which it lives. To quote Wells and Huxley, " It will turn aside from its course to flow over an attractive lump of food. In most cases only dead and decaying things are taken into its shapeless interior to be digested, but there are species which feed on living vegetable prey—on fungi, for example."

THE CAUSE OF "CLUB-ROOT"

THE extremely infectious disease called by farmers and gardeners " club-root " or " finger-and-toe "—it attacks plants of the cabbage family—is caused by a minute slime-fungus which is of microscopic size. Some innocuous kinds of slime fungi, however, grow to be conspicuous masses, such as those which may be found in the cavities of rotting logs, or on heaps of decaying matter in damp surroundings.

PLANTS WITHOUT SEEDS

TURNING, now, to living things which are unquestionably "plants" in the strict sense of the word, we find first two large groups of relatively simple kinds called "Algæ" and "Fungi." The former group includes all the marine seaweeds, a host of their freshwater relatives, and very numerous single-celled plants. Some of the latter, called Diatoms, are enclosed in minute flinty shells, exquisitely sculptured, and consisting of two parts, or valves. But a greater number lack these protective coverings, and dwell together in colonies of innumerable individuals spread out in close contact as greenish or yellowish films on the surfaces of rocks, tree-trunks or undisturbed soil.

The large, many-celled Algæ appear to owe their origin to an extension of this communal mode of life. For we may suppose that the individual cells, instead of separating completely after fission, tended more and more to retain physical contact with one another, thus forming threads or thin plates of cells whose needs and normal habitat were identical. By an extension of this process such aggregates of cells would be likely to increase in size as time went on, and to arrive at some simple specialisation, or division of labour, among the various groups of cells forming the mass. Thus, although seaweeds cannot be said to possess truly functional roots, stems or leaves, many of them seem to have taken the first step or two along the road which leads to the development of such organs.

All Algæ are self-supporting. That is to say, their substance contains chlorophyll, which enables them—like most of the higher plants—to build up food for their own use from materials present in their surroundings.[1] Algæ are grouped by botanists into four classes, more or less according to their typical colouring, that is, (1) blue-green, (2) green, (3) brown, and (4) red.

In members of the first group, many of which are inconspicuous, green chlorophyll is replaced by blue-green. The individual cells often occur in colonies, or loosely united as filaments, which in their turn may be matted or interwoven. One simple kind forms patches of scum on the moist window-panes of hot-houses ; while another, somewhat more complex,

---

[1] For an account of how this is done, see pp. 51–55.

is apt to appear suddenly as gelatinous masses on footpaths after rain. Before the rain it lay dormant, and quite invisible to the naked eye, among the particles of the surface soil.

The majority of the green Algæ are also unicellular or small, but include a few large kinds, of which the Sea Lettuces are probably the most familiar. These share with some of the red seaweeds the name of " Laver." In some districts, Laver is esteemed a table delicacy, more especially as a sauce to be eaten with roast mutton. But it is a fact that most strangers who have been induced to sample this alleged dainty regard the taste for it as an acquired one !

HOW SEAWEEDS PROTECT THEMSELVES FROM THE LIGHT

MOST of the large seaweeds which we see growing on rocks or washed up on the shore after a storm belong to the brown and red classes. Their visible colouring seems to serve as a filter which stops out certain light-rays likely to injure the green colouring matter—in much the same way as a photographer protects his sensitised plates, or a druggist his delicate chemicals, by means of deeply tinted glass. This is a legitimate inference because, if we soak these seaweeds in warm fresh water, their red or brown pigment is found to " run," and eventually dissolves out completely, leaving the plant-body " leaf green " in colour.

Algæ most commonly propagate themselves either by simple fission, or by the production of spores—from which, as we have seen, the new generation arises by direct growth when the spore-walls split open. But in many instances we find that a system has been developed which may quite properly be called " sexual," even when—as often happens—the two kinds of organs concerned occur on one and the same individual plant. Briefly, the products of these special organs, which we may call " male " and " female " respectively, are minute unicellular bodies, differing in constitution and function. " Fertilisation " is said to take place when a pair of these —one of each kind—comes into contact and unites to form what is known as an ovum, or fertilised egg-cell, from which in due course a new individual of the particular species takes its origin. This type of propagation is in vogue among the brown " wrack " weeds which often thickly drape the tidal rocks of our coasts. It is not difficult to locate the reproductive organs, which should be looked for at the tips of the branching fronds during the summer and autumn months ; but the actual process can only be watched through a high-power microscope.

HOW FUNGI FORAGE FOR THEIR RATIONS

SEXUAL methods of propagation are also found among the fungi, including some of the simple types called " moulds ; " but practically all the larger kinds—known popularly as Mushrooms, Toadstools and Puffballs—rely wholly upon the production of spores, which they often scatter abroad in prodigious numbers. Indeed, a mushroom or a toadstool *is* the special spore-producing outgrowth of a vegetative plant-body which consists merely of branching threads, or " hyphæ," and whose life is passed burrowing in earth, decaying wood, or some other substance from which it can obtain food.

Fungi differ chiefly from their relatives the algæ in being destitute of chlorophyll. Hence, they cannot make food-materials for themselves,[1] but must needs forage for their rations. Many species subsist on decaying organic matter of all sorts, including the humus of the soil ; but not a few have become actively parasitic—that is, they attack the living tissues of other plants, and even of animals.

Among the parasitic fungi is the curious " Caterpillar Fungus," whose red, club-shaped " toadstool " not infrequently springs up in garden beds during the autumn. Careful examination of the soil beneath invariably brings to light the mortal remains of some grub or pupa which the fungus has done to death !

From the economic standpoint this particular species may be counted as beneficial, since it destroys numerous insects which we call " pests." But many fungi work incalculable injury to man's interests by destroying forest trees, crops of many kinds, and even (in the case of " dry rot ") the timber used in the construction of houses.

TWO PLANTS IN PARTNERSHIP: THE LICHEN'S ODD LIFE-STORY

BEFORE leaving this Thallophyte division of plants, some mention must be made of the group called " Lichens." These are usually very moss-like in appearance, but in point of fact are composite organisms, made up of the matted strands of a fungus among which colonies of single-celled algæ are imprisoned. Exactly how this strange combination originated is one of Nature's secrets. It is fairly certain,

[1] See pages 51–55.

however, that both parties derive benefits from the union, for scientists have discovered that the algæ share with the fungus the food products which—thanks to their chlorophyll —they are able to fabricate from the raw chemical constituents of their surroundings, while the fungus, for its part, collects and conserves the moisture (containing dissolved mineral salts) without which the algæ could not carry on their work. By these means lichens are able to flourish in situations— for instance, the sun-baked surfaces of granite rocks—where neither of the partners could possibly thrive independently.

In the matter of propagation, the fungus element seems always to play the leading part. The methods vary ; but in many instances minute spore-like bodies are produced which may be seen under the microscope to consist of several algæ wrapped round with a strand of detached fungus thread. When these are carried by the wind to suitable situations, growth commences, and in process of time new lichen plants are formed.

THE CASE OF THE CORD MOSS

BRYOPHYTA—otherwise the Liverworts and Mosses—are simple in structure, though less " all-of-a-piece " than the Algæ and Fungi ; for we can often distinguish parts which resemble superficially the leaves, roots and branches of the higher plants. Their most important characteristic, however, is that their life-history always proceeds through two distinct, alternating stages, each culminating in the formation of reproductive cells, either spores or ova, as the case may be.

Suppose, for example, we start with the minute spores of the Common Cord Moss which often forms large patches on walls and rocks, as well as on open ground, especially where forest or heath fires have occurred. In propitious circumstances these spores germinate, and develop eventually into little green plants bearing numerous tiny leaflets arranged spirally round a short stem fixed to the soil at its base by root-like filaments. After a period of vegetative growth, sexual organs appear at the tip of the shoot, and may be either " male " or " female," since the two kinds are produced by separate plants.

Of the egg-cells born by a " female " plant, one at least is likely to be fertilised by a " male " or sperm-cell, which— when a film of moisture covers the moss colony and the surrounding soil—swims through this to its objective from a neighbouring " male " plant. Now this fertilised egg-cell does not develop directly, as we might expect, into a new moss-plant, but growing upward becomes a spore-capsule of complex structure attached by a long stalk to its parent, from which it draws its nourishment. It is from the spores so produced—not from the fertilised egg-cells as such—that new moss-plants subsequently grow.

The sexual and spore-bearing organs vary a good deal in appearance among the different species of Liverworts and Mosses, but the same cycle of alternating generations can always be traced. We may express it in the following short formula :

Spores ⟶ " male " and " female " green plants ⟶ fertilised egg-cells ⟶ non-green spore-developing bodies which are short-lived, being normally parasitic upon their parents ⟶ spores ; and so on through successive cycles.

Certain Liverworts, including a species common in gardens and greenhouses, supplement this method by separating off from their substance minute bodies called " gemmæ." These are matured in tiny bird's-nest-like cups with frilled edges sunk in the frond or " thallus " of the parent plant. When ripe, they are washed out by rain, and soon grow into new individuals.

THE LIFE-STORY OF A FERN

IF, as seems probable, Liverworts and Mosses were evolved from Algæ which in the remote past took to living in fairly dry situations, this is almost certainly true of the Ferns and their near relations, the Horse-tails and Club-mosses. These three types, while differing considerably among themselves in appearance and habits, agree sufficiently in essentials to be classed together as a third main division of plant life—the Pteridophytes. In particular, the egg-cell, after fertilisation, develops into something quite different from the spore-bearing generation of a Moss ; for it gives rise to a conspicuous plant-body, having leafy fronds or shoots which, as they contain chlorophyll, are capable of self-maintenance. This point will be made clear if we consider for a moment the life-story of a common Fern, such as the Hart's-tongue or the Bracken.

The word " ferns," as popularly used, refers simply to the familiar spore-bearing plants, which have fronds, roots and stems. Being entirely self-supporting, they may continue to flourish for many years ; whereas the corresponding stage in

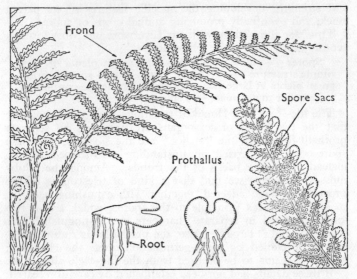

Frond

Spore Sacs

Prothallus

Root

THE LIFE-CYCLE OF A TRUE FERN

*The spores which grow in sacs on the underside of the fern
frond may each develop into a small green prothallus, bearing
egg-cells on its reverse side. A fertilised egg-cell gives rise to
a young fern which will eventually again produce spores ; the
prothallus itself disappears.*

a Moss's life-cycle is nourished by its parent, and quickly
withers away after its crop of spores has been matured and
scattered. The Fern plant, on the contrary, continues to
produce spores each year, as long as it lives, in little cases
which appear as brown groups or clusters on the reverse sides
of the fronds. When the spores fall on damp spots and germinate, they grow into small, green, plate-like bodies, usually
heart-shaped in outline, known as " prothalli," on the underside of which the sexual organs develop.

The process of fertilisation, similar to that already described
in the case of the Moss, appears to be somewhat uncertain
in operation ; for although numerous egg-cells are produced
by a prothallus, the latter rarely gives rise to more than one
young Fern. This is at first a delicate little thing with a tiny
leaf and an embryo root ; but it gradually increases in size

and strength, developing the specific features of its parent stock, and eventually producing annual crops of spores.

Thus, for comparison with our Liverwort and Moss formula set out above, we get the following :

Spores ⟶ insignificant bi-sexual green plants of very simple structure ⟶ fertilised egg-cells ⟶ spore-bearing green plants of large size and complex structure continuing to grow for many years ⟶ spores.

The life-story of a Horsetail resembles that of a Fern, save that the two kinds of sex-organs are produced by separate prothalli (of which the " males " are the smaller), while the spore-cases are carried on upstanding club-shaped shoots, instead of on the backs of the fronds. Among the Club-mosses, however, we find that a kind of telescoping of the process has been effected, together with a pushing back (so to say) of the sex principle to the spores, which are of two kinds, matured in separate chambers and distinguishable as " small " and " large." Also, the prothallus is rudimentary, and is developed by spore-germination *inside* the chamber ; so that it seems to be omitted from the life-cycle altogether.

If these details had not been established by careful research, we might have jumped to the conclusion that the Club-moss propagates itself by means of seeds, like the higher plants. In point of fact, it comes very near to doing this. But technically speaking a " seed " is a complex body, not set free from the parent organism until the fertilised egg-cell from which it takes its origin has undergone considerable development, resulting in the formation of an embryo, or baby plant. In the case of the Club-moss this development has not yet taken place when the apparent " seed " is cast adrift.

SEED-BEARING PLANTS

THE true seed-bearing plants are all comprised in the two divisions Gymnospermæ and Angiospermæ, to which we must now direct our attention. Together, these two groups are often referred to as " Flowering Plants." In botanical language, a " flower " is a special kind of aerial shoot serving ultimately for the production of seeds. The part of the stem on which the flower is borne is known as the " receptacle," while the various parts of the flower itself are regarded as modified leaves. In such a flower as a buttercup, the " male " and " female " organs are called " stamens " and " carpels '

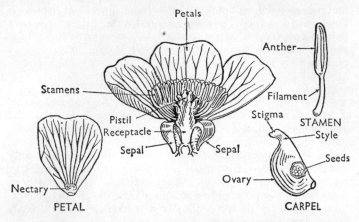

Petals

Anther

Stamens

Filament

Pistil

STAMEN

Stigma

Receptacle

Style

Sepal

Sepal

Seeds

Nectary

Ovary

PETAL

CARPEL

THE PARTS OF A " PERFECT " FLOWER

A buttercup flower is here cut open to show how its parts are arranged. A buttercup is called a " perfect " flower because it has both stamens and carpels (male and female organs) and can therefore fertilise itself.

respectively. A carpel may be thought of as a leaf folded upon itself and joined at the edges, thus forming a chamber or vessel enclosing the egg-cell, or egg-cells, as the case may be. Its upper part, which is frequently a sticky knob, is the " stigma " to which pollen-grains adhere, and from which, after germinating, they grow downwards as " pollen-tubes " into the egg-chamber to fertilise its contents. The grouped carpels of a single flower, are often spoken of as its " pistil." Each of the male organs, or stamens, consists typically of two parts : (1) a stalk or filament which bears aloft, (2) paired pollen-sacs, or " anthers."

Outside these two groups of " essential organs " there is commonly an arrangement of " petals ", often gaily coloured and attractive to insects which render an important service as pollen-conveyers when they fly from one blossom to another. Together, the petals constitute the " corolla," within which, in many kinds of flowers, may be found honey-secreting glands, or " nectaries," whose presence makes the visits of insects " worth while," even when they can make no use of the pollen itself as food. Finally, the outermost whorl of floral leaves, called " sepals," serve as the " calyx," whose normal function is to protect all the other members of the shoot while they are still folded together and in process of development as a " bud."

" CONES " THAT ARE REALLY " FLOWERS "

IN flowering plants an alternation of spore-bearing and sexual generations can still be traced, but only by means of the microscope ; for the whole process is disguised, so to speak, under the apparently straightforward methods of pollination and seed-production. For our present purpose we need only note that the vegetative, leaf-bearing body of a flowering plant represents the spore-producing generation, of which the Fern as such was our outstanding example. It is the sexual genera-tion, typified by the prothallus from which the Fern took its origin, that has disappeared from view.

Not all flowers have the elaborate structure described above. Indeed, the name " Gymnospermæ " refers to the fact that in members of this division the seeds are " naked : " i.e. the seed-producing leaf, or carpel, is not folded together to form a chamber or " pod," but bears the essential organs openly on its concave inner face. The young cones of Pines and Larches are really collections of such simple flowers ; and if we tear apart some of the overlapping scales, we shall see the carpels with their immature seeds or " ovules." Pollen, which is produced in great abundance in the anthers of small stamens arranged in dense clusters on neighbouring shoots, is blown by the wind in dry weather into the crevices between the cone-scales, and in this way fertilisation is effected.

Even in the great Angiosperm division, which—coniferous trees apart—comprises nearly all the conspicuous plants of our countryside, the flower is often very simple. Take, for instance, the Goat Willow—widely known as " Palm." Here, the female flower consists of a single carpel mounted on a tiny bract-like leaf in association with a little nectary or " honey-pot ; " the male flower is just a pair of stamens, also with a honey-pot for the delectation of insect visitors. The two kinds of flowers are massed together in groups— often called " catkins," and are borne on separate trees, so that " self-pollination " is out of the question. But bees are attracted by the scent of the nectar, and keep up a constant traffic from one tree to another, with the result that the female Goat Willows never fail to mature large crops of fluffy seeds.

THE BARGAIN BETWEEN INSECT AND FLOWER

MANY trees and plants whose flowers are inconspicuous and lack nectar—e.g. the Hazel, the Oak and the Stinging Nettle—must rely upon the wind to secure the transfer of pollen from the anthers of their stamens to the stigmas of their carpels. But in the case of showy and sweet-scented flowers we may conclude that insects of one sort or another act as the emissaries of Cupid. Insect-fertilised flowers produce less pollen than those which rely upon the wind as their carrying agent, while the individual grains, instead of being dry and dust-like, are usually adhesive, so that they attach themselves readily to an insect's proboscis, or to the hairs of its body and legs. The arrangement of a given flower's parts will naturally be found to correspond with the structure and habits of the particular kinds of insect whose visits are specially catered for. Hence, we find a great variety of floral mechanisms, all directed to this one end of pollination, with its sequel, the production of seeds.

Botanists recognise two chief subdivisions of Angiosperm plants, in one of which the embryo starts with a single seed-leaf, while in the other it has two. The first subdivision includes the grasses, cereals, rushes, lilies, irises, orchids, and so forth—plants which in general have radiating or parallel leaf-veins, and the parts of whose flowers are nearly always arranged in threes. In the other subdivision, which, excepting the cone-bearers, comprises practically all the trees, shrubs and herbs of the whole world, the leaves are net-veined, while the floral parts are commonly grouped either in fours or fives.

A few examples will help us to grasp how closely the fertility of a flower is bound up with its structure and mechanism. We should bear in mind that in each instance " cross-pollination "—i.e. the transfer of pollen from one bloom to another—is the chief end in view : " self-pollination," when the pistil of a flower is dusted with the product of its own anthers, usually eventuates only as a last resort. Suppose we take as our types the following : Perennial Rye Grass, Yellow Iris, Purple Orchis, Wild Arum, Dog Rose, Bird's-foot Trefoil, Primrose, Foxglove, Dead Nettle, Hogweed and Daisy.

THE INDEPENDENCE OF THE "TINKER-TAILOR" GRASS

OF this varied selection, only the Rye Grass can dispense with the service of insects if cross-pollination is to be achieved. It is a common, wayside species, and may be recognised by its flattened " spikelets," from eight to twenty of which are carried by each main stem. Children call it " Tinker-Tailor Grass." Each spikelet contains eight or ten simple flowers, which are completely hidden from view until the time of blossoming, which is usually on a warm, sunny day.

There are three stamens with large anthers which dangle freely from the spikelet on delicate filaments. The pistil, which stands in the centre of the flower, consists of a pear-shaped ovary, bearing a pair of delicate, feathery stigmas at its upper end, while at its base there are two small processes known as " lodicules." The latter, by swelling up when the time for blossoming arrives, force apart the chaffy bracts which envelop the flower, and thus allow the stamens and stigmas to expand. These details can easily be made out by using a pocket-lens.

The dry, powdery pollen which escapes from the anthers is caught up by the passing breeze and carried hither and thither. Much of it is wasted ; but some reaches the plume-like stigmas of other Rye Grass flowers, thus effecting their cross-pollination and enabling them to set good seed.

SWEET GIFTS WITH A PURPOSE: THE IRIS AND THE HUMBLE-BEE

NOW compare these floral arrangements, common to most grasses, with those of the Yellow Iris or Flag, which depends mainly on humble-bees as its pollen-carriers. Two sets of petal-like leaves can be distinguished, the three outer ones being large and down-curved, the three inner narrow and erect. All six are joined together at their bases to form a short tubular region whose inner surface secretes nectar. If an actual flower is examined, the Iris is seen to offer three separate lines of approach to its store of sweetness, to which the bee gains access by forcing its head and shoulders into a kind of tunnel, roofed over by a pair of essential organs. In doing this, the insect's back comes into contact first with the stigma, then with the anthers of the stamen. Assuming that it has come from a nearby Iris, it will cross-pollinate the one which now engages its attention ; and from this, in its turn, pollen is likely to be carried by the industrious insect to the next flower on its visiting list.

If you watch insects, especially bees, at work in a garden on a sunny morning, you will notice that they have formed the habit of flying rapidly from one bloom to another of the same kind. A humble-bee, for example, which has been busy with the snapdragons does not break off suddenly to pay calls on the delphiniums. Colour seems to be their chief guide. This is fortunate from the standpoint of the flowers, whose egg-cells need to be fertilised by pollen matured in the anthers of their own species. Alien pollen has no power to set in motion the delicately adjusted machinery which results in seed-production.

If the adaptation of the Iris to the requirements of its bee-visitors is remarkable, that of the Early Purple Orchis is even more so. Here, the various parts of the flower are so much modified and twisted as to be hardly recognisable at first glance. Of the six petal-like leaves, no less than five are grouped together to form a kind of hood over the essential organs, while the sixth is expanded below into a sort of lip, or "labellum," which serves as an alighting place for insects. This labellum also extends backwards as a hollow spur, within which the nectar is secreted and stored. When we discover that the stigmatic lobes, connected with the ovary, are located just inside the opening of this spur, we realise that the bee cannot help touching them when it comes to the flower to gather honey.

To make assurance doubly sure, the Orchis also dispenses its pollen in a highly novel and ingenious manner. We may say that it has reduced its stamens to one, while the pollen is made up into two convenient masses, connected by tapering stalks with round, sticky discs. The latter lie loosely in a cup-shaped container, called the "rostellum," placed just in front of, and a little above, the stigmatic lobes. You will grasp these details most readily if you open your mouth before a mirror and examine the entrance to your own throat. The tonsils on either side represent the stigmatic lobes of the flower, while the pendent uvula in the middle line takes the place of the rostellum and its pollen masses.

When a bee alights upon the labellum, and inserts its pro-boscis into the throat of the flower in search of nectar, its head comes into contact with the rostellum, and it flies away with the sticky discs of the pollinia adhering to its forehead, like a pair of horns. As the bee travels through the air, the discs contract unequally in drying, with the result that the pollinia bend forward and at the same time diverge slightly from one another. Thus, when their carrier arrives at another orchid the pollen-masses are in exactly the right position to strike against its stigmatic lobes, and so to effect cross-pollination.

THE CUCKOO-PINT'S TRAP FOR UNWARY VISITORS

THE Wild Arum, known to country-bred children as " Lords-and-Ladies " or " Cuckoo-pint," introduces us to a kind of bloom, or inflorescence, which is also a trap. Superficially, it consists of a central club-like " spadix " enveloped by a large, leaf-like bract, or " spathe." If we tear open the spathe, we disclose the " lords-and-ladies " clustered round the lower part of the spadix. These are really the Arum's simple flowers. Checking them off from above downwards, we find (1) abortive, hair-like flowers not directly connected with reproduction, (2) four-lobed anthers, or male flowers, and (3) female or seed-producing flowers, each with a single pistil.

Insects, especially tiny midges, are attracted by the purple club of the spadix and its carrion-like odour. They creep down into the chambered part of the spathe, where the flowers are—the hair-like ones allowing them to creep in, but preventing their return. The female flowers mature first, and are thus ready to receive any pollen that the midges bring with them from another Arum. Later, the anthers of the male flowers mature, and scatter their pollen over the prisoners. In the end, the abortive hair-like flowers shrivel up, thus allowing the captives to make good their escape ; but not before they have been pressed into the service of the plant as carriers of its pollen to other blooms of the species.

In the Dog Rose we have a fairly simple flower of the five-petal type, not unlike the buttercup in its general arrangement. Inside the circle of stamens there is a swollen rim which looks like a nectary, though it secretes little if any nectar. The flower, however, is visited by many insects—chiefly bees, beetles and flies—which come to collect or feed on the pollen. The bees, of course, carry their spoils home to their hives or nests, whereas the flies and beetles eat it on the spot. The stamens and stigmas mature at the same time, so that either self- or cross-pollination may result from these activities.

Since, however, the centre of the flower, with its group of closely set stigmas, is the most convenient alighting place, an insect dusted with pollen brought from another rose is likely to effect cross-pollination at its first arrival.

HOW THE PEAS AND BEANS PUMP OUT THE POLLEN

IN flowers of the great pea-and-bean family, the five-petal arrangement—exemplified in its simplest form by the Dog Rose and the Buttercup—is not obvious, at first glance. The largest of the petals is called the " standard," and stands erect as a kind of background. Below, and on each side of this, are two smaller petals known as the " wings," between which is the " keel." The latter is composed of the two remaining petals, united to form a tapering, bag-like structure, with a small opening at its tip. This general description will be found to apply to the flowers of the Sweet Pea, the Broom, the Bird's-foot Trefoil, and many allied plants.

The essential organs are completely enclosed by the keel, which serves also as an alighting place for bees. Also, the ripe pollen is discharged by the anthers into the keel, and kept there in reserve, until a bee comes to probe for nectar through openings at the keel's base. When this happens, the insect's weight forces the keel downwards in such a way that the stamens within literally pump out some of the pollen from the tip, thus applying it to the underside of the insect's body. The stigma (which in this instance is receptive only when it is rubbed) is also forced out, and will thus receive any pollen which the bee may have brought from another flower.

The Primrose illustrates a method by which self-pollination, if not entirely eliminated, is rendered unlikely. If a number of Primrose plants are examined, it will be found that the flowers are not always quite alike. There are two forms, in one of which—known popularly as " thrum-eyed "—the pistil has a short style or stalk connecting it with the ovary, while the stamens are situated at the mouth of the corolla tube. In the other form, called " pin-eyed," the style is long, and its globular stigma almost fills the entrance of the tube, while the anthers are low down—being on about the same level as the stigma in the corresponding " thrum-eyed " flower.

Long-tongued flies, and occasionally bees, visit Primroses in search of their nectar, which is secreted low down at the base of the tube. When an insect probes a long-styled flower, its proboscis is dusted with pollen at a point which, if it

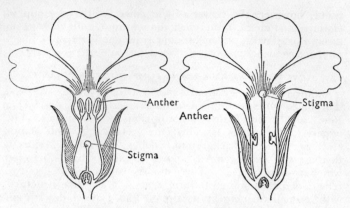

" THRUM-EYED " AND " PIN-EYED "

A diagrammatic section showing that the " thrum-eyed "
primrose (left) has a short style while the anthers can be seen
at the mouth of the corolla tube, whereas in the " pin-eyed "
primrose (right), the anthers are low down in the corolla tube
and the long style supports the stigma which almost fills the
entrance to it.

subsequently visits a short-styled flower, is brought into
contact with its stigma ; and *vice versa*. As the contrivance
is not absolutely fool-proof, Primroses are sometimes self-
fertilised. But experiment has shown that the best production
of seed results from cross-pollination ; and this can only be
secured by a transfer of pollen from one type of flower to the
other by the method that has been described.

FOXGLOVE AND DEAD NETTLE RECEIVE THE HUMBLE-BEE

THE Foxglove and the White Dead Nettle, while differing
in many respects, both have their five petals completely
united to form a tubular corolla. In the former, this is
bell-shaped, inclined downwards, and has a projecting lower
lip for the convenience of humble-bees, which are its chief
visitors. The essential organs are pressed against the roof
of the tube within, so that while they do not hamper the
entrance of the insect, they are certain to rub against its hairy
back when it is probing for nectar at the far end. As the
anthers mature before the stigma, there is a good chance
that cross-pollination will be effected. Should this fail to

occur, however, the flower's own pollen is generally applied to its stigma at the time when the wilting corolla falls to the ground. Pollination by one means or another is thus practically certain ; which explains the fact that almost every flower of the Foxglove's long spike manages to set abundant seed, even in localities where humble-bees are scarce.

In the case of the White Dead Nettle—also a humble-bee flower—the tubular corolla stands erect, and, besides a lip, is furnished with a hood for the protection of the essential organs. When the bee alights on the lip, and thrusts its head and shoulders into the tube to reach the nectar, its back rubs first against the stigma, which thus receives any pollen brought from a neighbouring flower. A fraction of a second later it takes up a fresh supply of pollen from the anthers, which will be carried to the next flower visited. Since the White Dead Nettle's stigma is receptive at the same time that the pollen is being shed, self-pollination may readily occur through the agency of insects. But because the flowers are frequently visited, and the bees pass rapidly from one to another, there is at least an even chance that cross-pollination will be effected.

In the case of the Salvia, the Dead Nettle's near relative, the risk of self-pollination is negligible. The stamens are hinged, and the visiting bee forces them to bend down until the anthers come into contact with its back. This happens when the flower first opens. In older flowers that have matured and shed their pollen, the style of the pistil lengthens and bends down, so that the stigma grazes the bee's back at the exact spot touched by the anthers of a younger flower.

TINY FLOWERS WHICH COMBINE TO ATTRACT

MANY plants produce small, or even diminutive, flowers which are nevertheless conspicuous because they are massed together in large numbers. The Hog-weed, or Cow-parsnip, is an example. Its individual flower consists of five minute sepals, alternating with which are five petals differing in size—especially in the outermost flowers of the group, or "umbel," where one petal of each is much larger than the other four. The pistil consists of two united carpels, while the five stamens shed their pollen before the stigmas are ripe. Each flower is furnished with a nectar-secreting disc, easily accessible to the short-tongued insects, such as flies and beetles, which are frequent visitors to the umbels of the Hogweed and its relatives.

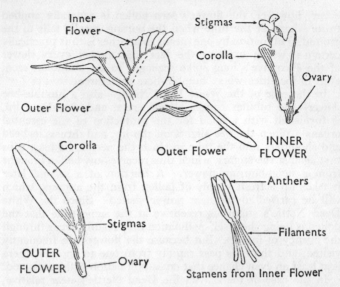

Inner Flower

Stigmas

Corolla

Ovary

Outer Flower

Corolla

Outer Flower

INNER FLOWER

Anthers

Stigmas

Filaments

OUTER FLOWER

Ovary

Stamens from Inner Flower

MANY FLOWERS IN ONE: A COMBINATION TO ATTRACT

A composite flower of the Daisy type cut open to show how the inner and outer flowers are arranged. Each tiny inner floret is a perfect flower with a tubular corolla, often more than half filled with nectar.

The great Daisy family introduces us to another type of co-operative arrangement. Here, the inflorescence—called a " capitulum "—consists of very numerous small florets so closely associated that the appearance of a single bloom is produced. The common Daisy is a familiar example. Each of the tiny disc-florets is a perfect flower, with a tubular corolla which is often more than half filled with nectar. Also, the five anthers are united by their edges to form a tube, within which the pollen is shed, and from which it is gradually pushed out by the developing pistil, whose action resembles that of the piston of a syringe. Eventually, the stigma-lobes—rising clear of the pollen produced by their own flower—gape apart, thus exposing their receptive inner surfaces for pollination by insects coming from other blooms. But as the disc-florets open in succeeding ranks from outside inwards, cross-pollination of two degrees is possible : viz. (1) between two florets of the same capitulum, and (2) between florets of distinct Daisies.

The outer—or " ray "—florets are very irregular in shape, the corolla consisting of a narrow tube below, which expands above into a white, pink-tipped strap. These florets have pistils, but no stamens. If pollen is brought to them, they can set seed ; but probably their most important function is to render the capitulum as a whole conspicuous, and more attractive to insects, which seem to have a *flair* for symmetry and contrast.

COLLECTING SPECIMENS

THESE few examples of floral mechanism and arrangement touch only the fringe of a vast and fascinating subject of inquiry. For general reading, couched in pleasant, non-technical language, a little book, *British Wild Flowers Considered in Relation to Insects*, written by the late Lord Avebury, would be hard to beat. Although it was first published in the early eighties of last century, the information supplied is still sufficiently reliable. A second-hand copy may often be found very cheaply. With this and an inexpensive modern textbook as his guides, the amateur may hope to prosecute his studies of plant life to some purpose. Three good text-books are *Botany for Beginners* by Ernest Evans (MacMillan), *The Study of Plants*, by T. W. Woodhead (Clarendon Press) and *A Text-Book of Botany* by Amy F. M. Johnson (Allman). At the same time, he will be well advised to set about forming a collection of dried plants, which not only gives zest to a country ramble, but serves to fix facts in the memory almost automatically. Ask any botanist, and he will tell you that he has learnt more from the plants that he has gathered and dissected with his own hands than from all the floras that he has ever read!

On every excursion a note-book should be carried and used. As for collecting apparatus, the more important items include a good-sized metal box, or vasculum, fitted with a strap for carrying ; a pair of scissors, a knife, a trowel, a pocket lens, and perhaps a few pill-boxes and corked tubes. A small pair of secateurs will also be found useful at times. Specimens packed carefully in the vasculum will keep fresh for some hours, pending attention. Take typical examples of each species, with leaves, flowers, fruits, and a portion of the root wherever this is practicable ; in the case of the larger plants —trees, shrubs and so forth—cuttings selected to show the more important features must suffice. Twigs, hard fruits and the like may be dried by exposure to the sun, then labelled, and stored in boxes for reference.

To prepare herbaceous plants for the cabinet, first arrange them carefully between several thicknesses of blotting-paper sandwiched between two pieces of smooth board. Strap these firmly together, and increase the pressure gradually every other day for some weeks until the specimens are quite dry. They can then be mounted in folders of stout paper by means of good gum or fish-glue. Finally, each sheet should be docketed with the name of the plant, and such particulars relating to habitat, times of flowering, etc., as may be deemed desirable. Whatever method of storing is adopted, the specimens should be grouped in accordance with their natural affinities ; otherwise confusion will soon result.

Flowers pressed in the above way usually lose most of their colour. An alternative method is to place the freshly gathered sprays between layers of cotton-wool lightly bound together with a book-strap between sheets of perforated zinc or wire-gauze. The necessary outfit may be obtained from dealers in natural history apparatus. If the process of drying is not hurried, the specimens retain much of their fresh beauty. But, not being pressed flat, they must be stored in shallow boxes or drawers, and thus take up much space. The same objection applies to specimens dried in a tray of silver sand poured gradually round the sprays while they are fresh. The results are excellent ; but a really large collection preserved in this manner would call for a special building in which to house it!

STRUGGLE AND SURVIVAL IN THE WORLD OF PLANTS

by GEOFFREY TANDY, B.A.(Oxon.), of the
British Museum (Natural History)

THIS section must begin with a warning or two. One of the most surprising characteristics of man, considered as an animal species, is his capacity for moralising. The words " society " and " social " have an immediate association in the minds of most of us with the words " good," " bad " and " responsibility." It must be made clear, therefore, that when we set out to investigate the social relation of species to species, we are concerned simply with elucidation and our use of words derived from human affairs must not be taken to imply the usually associated moral judgments. This may sound easy enough, but a simple test will indicate probable difficulties : use the word " parasite " of any organism or consider the female spider's habit of devouring her mate and see if you do not feel some moral indignation.

Nevertheless, so long as we remember the danger of pushing comparisons too far, we may, with profit, apply some of the words and ideas derived from a social organism which we know pretty well, namely, our own species, to those which we know less well—the millions of species of plants. Such a method is almost certain to lead into some errors but no other course is really practicable. Even if it were, we may take it as next to impossible for any ordinary person to divest himself of all the preconceptions set up in the whole course of his conscious life. We must, therefore, begin with some fairly simple facts which everybody is likely to know, and use them to get notions which will broaden the scope of our inquiry.

SEPARATING THE INSEPARABLE : A FEAT OF THE HUMAN MIND

A REMARKABLE human ability is that of considering separately things which are never so in our experience. This is a useful trick—indeed for some scientific purposes a necessary one—but we must be careful how we make use of it. When an engineer discusses the attributes of a weightless beam it is not because he has any idea of using such a dangerous structure, supposing he could lay hands on one. It means little more than an intention to consider his problem apart from weight.   Similarly, when an experimental biologist keeps his plants at a temperature constant within one-hundredth of a degree centigrade, he does not imagine he is reproducing natural conditions. He wants to be able to say no more than : " Whatever else causes the changes in my plant, it is not variation in temperature."

So in this consideration of social relations : we may think of the behaviour of a particular species as if no others were concerned, but we must never quite forget that it is a mental feat to do so. Any gardener will tell us that an absolutely pure growth of a single species of plant is a practical impossibility. He knows that he is engaged in a continual fight against the intruders which he calls weeds. Even the elaborate pure-culture methods of the bacteriologist cannot exclude unwanted organisms all of the time.

In the broad sense it is true to say that no portion of space which is capable of supporting living organisms remains unoccupied for long. So much is this true that places which seem fantastically improbable from our own standpoint support a living population of some kind : the thin water-film on the surface of a strong acid like sulphuric ; the intestines of animals ; the arctic ice ; the sandy deserts of Arabia ; all these places, and many others quite as strange, provide conditions in which some living things can carry on their life-processes.

It is not very surprising, therefore, that naturalists have not yet given up hope of finding new species of plants and animals, but, on the contrary, are painfully aware that they are ignorant of the mere existence of enormous numbers of inhabitants of this earth, let alone of anything about their methods of getting a living. It is obvious that of those parts of the world which man has subdued to his purposes we know more concerning the composition and behaviour of the other organisms inhabiting them than we know of the places where he is still a total stranger or very occasional visitor. As land animals we certainly know more of the land than we know of the depths of the sea or the heights of the atmosphere and stratosphere.

WHY PLANTS ARE GIVEN NATIONAL NAMES

WE are accustomed to speak of British plants and of American, Chinese and African plants. When we speak of British plants, we mean plants that are natives of the

British Isles, as opposed to cultivated plants. Of course, nobody supposes that plants are in the least concerned with political boundaries, and actually nearly all British plants are also found on the Continent. Nevertheless it is true that many species are found in America only, others in Africa only and so on. Any detailed treatment of the vast and interesting subject of plant geography is impossible within the limits of our space but we may make a few suggestive comparisons.

How is it that the British Isles are largely inhabited by human beings with relatively pale skins and not by kangaroos ? One important reason is that the seas present an almost insuperable barrier to the kangaroo and not to men. We do not need to say that the kangaroo could not effect a successful colonisation, though that is probably true. All that concerns us at present is that the kangaroo lives in Australia and nowhere else because he cannot leave the continent without man's assistance ; he is neither a good swimmer nor a boatbuilder. Other organisms are incapable of successful migration because they are poor climbers or are incapable of taking to the air.

This leaves out of account the still more important inquiry whether a migrant can live in the country of its adoption. In human terms, having secured a passage to America, can a man find a place to live and the means of living in it ?

In the plant world the migration of active adult individuals is by no means common, but movements of plants about the surface of the earth do occur in one way and another and some of these we must consider.

It is usual for plants to spend the whole of their lives in one place, but there are interesting exceptions to this. Among them are the rose of Jericho and the so-called " resurrection plant " of the florists. Both of these plants, though they are widely separated in any system of classification by relationship, have a very similar trick. Both of them are able, in a dry period, to curl up into a ball, in which condition they can be blown about by the wind with the chance of being carried to a more favourable locality. It is, however, far more common for plants to have organs of reproduction specialised for the production of units by which their offspring are enabled to occupy new territory. Chief among these units produced by plants living on the land, is the seed. The seed is a very complicated biological mechanism and may very properly be called the triumph of the land plant. It is one of the most important means by which land areas are colonised and occupied by plant-life.

It should be observed that seeds should not be confused with spores but, from the point of view which we wish to take at the moment, the distinction does not matter. The aspect of the matter which concerns us is, that a portion of a plant capable of being detached from the parent is also capable of facing the world on its own account. Since a grain of wheat is a kind of seed familiar to most of us and the adventures of the seed are fairly familiar in the parable of the Sower, it may well serve as an illustration for us now.

THE FACTORS WHICH INFLUENCE THE GROWTH OF A SEED

A LARGE number of factors, some more important than others, will determine whether or not our seed is going to grow up into an adult plant and produce seeds of its own account. We shall not try to consider all these factors, but we can quickly see how they may be divided into two groups. The first group will include those which are associated with the place—the kind of ground upon which the seed falls : the second, those associated with the climate of that place. Thus the ground may be granite rock or limestone, sand or clay ; but the successful development of our seed will depend on the presence of sufficient sunshine and moisture. It is conceivable that any one of these kinds of ground may afford sufficient harbourage for the seed to germinate, that is, to begin its growth ; but, as is noticed in the parable, the soil may not be enough for the plant to grow to maturity and produce seed of its own.

Again we may apply to the gardener ; he knows that some kinds of plants will grow in any kind of soil, while others are very unaccommodating. The matter is complicated still further when we remember that the population of any tract of ground is rarely, if ever, of one species, but is usually of many. What is more there is, for every species, a combination of soil and climate factors in which it flourishes best and it is reasonable to expect that in any one place, at any one time, the combination of conditions will not be equally favourable for all the species which we may find occupying the territory.

Just as the occupations of particular sorts of men give a distinctive character to the territory they inhabit, so it is with plants. We are all more or less aware of the highly competitive nature of our own largest groups—the great cities—and, in a general way, where men can get most, there they congregate thickest and there we shall find nearly every sort and kind of trade—except those concerned with the primary production of food. For our own communities we have names, as hamlet, village, town, and so on. The biologists have a highly developed system of names for the aggregations of species in the formation of which man has had no hand. Some of these are : socion, sociation, consociation, association, federation, formation. These terms are not likely to assist our present inquiry so they will be avoided ; but they are exceedingly useful when the inquiry is sufficiently detailed. We need not push ours beyond the point at which we can see that a great deal still remains to be done.

It is necessary to make it quite clear that we do not even know what are all our units of vegetation, and it is, therefore, not surprising that we have, as yet, no precise system for naming them. After all, we have had reasonably precise records of every *individual* human being in Great Britain for over one hundred years—such a record as we can never hope to have for the plant population—and still the record is not as complete as we could wish. Add to this that the units of our human population can answer questions themselves and the problem assumes daunting dimensions.

TAKING A PLANT CENSUS

IN earlier days botanists were principally occupied with the compilation of a record of species and the building of that record into a system which might exhibit the relationship of species to species, genus to genus and so on. Without that work it would be impossible to consider what the effect of species upon species in a natural population may be. Nevertheless, there is *in principle* nothing more difficult about discovering the composition of a population of species than there is in taking a census of the population of the British Isles. The latter job is a big one because of the number of persons involved, and the diversity of occupations makes classification troublesome at times, but it is, after all, only a matter of finding out who is in a particular place and what he does when there. The questions of how he came there and how he continues are comparatively simple extensions of the inquiry. The fundamentals do not demand any more elaborate apparatus than a pencil and notebook. We can investigate a population of species in nature by equally simple methods.

Unfortunately there is the difficulty mentioned earlier : you can ask a man his name, age and occupation ; a plant is unable to tell you and so you must know how to find them out for yourself. For the British Isles we know the composition of the plant population by species tolerably well : in other words, the discovery of a very distinct species of flowering plant hitherto unknown to botanists would be a noteworthy event. The catalogues of British plants are, at any rate, as complete as for any country, and the identification of the majority of species is not really very difficult. Given a piece of ground occupied by plants, it is within the capabilities of any person who is interested enough to take the trouble, to find out what species are there and what kind of job they are doing. This is work well worth doing, especially if carried on for the same territory all the year round and supplemented by abundant photographs. The extensions of the inquiry— how the species came to be where they are and what conditions make it possible for them to stay there, or force them to give way to other species—are not so easy and are better left alone for the moment.

LIFE IN AN OAKWOOD: A STORY OF INTERFERING NEIGHBOURS

FOLLOWING our principle of proceeding from the familiar to the less familiar, let us consider the state of things we may expect to find in an English woodland. Nobody would expect to go to what is called an oakwood and find nothing but oak trees. The oaks are merely the largest and most conspicuous occupants of the ground. One oakwood differs from another in greater or less degree, according as it is on the sandstone soils of the Midlands or the clay soils of Surrey. For purposes of illustration one place is pretty well as good as another, so let us see if we can get any enlightenment out of an oakwood on the Wealden clay in Surrey. We shall not expect to find anything like real oak-forest often ; that is to say, a close canopy formed by the intermingling of the crowns of the trees over a large area. What we shall probably find is a relatively small number of mature oak trees to the acre— say between ten and twenty. The rest of the population will consist of various species of shrubs, herbs, climbers and a host of humbler plants which very few people ever notice.

Much will depend, however, on the time of year at which our visit takes place and here we may stop to consider what are the changes in the general conditions for plants which account, in part, for the difference in aspect in May from that at Christmas-time. In May we shall see large numbers of plants active and about their business of maturing seed and storing food : in December we shall have to look hard to find any signs of life among the plant population. The reason for this is not far to seek. It is because of the lack of a sufficient energy supply, due to the low sun and the very short day. This is, perhaps, a rather cumbrous way of coming at the extremely familiar procession of the seasons, which nobody living in the British Isles, or in any similar high latitude, can have failed to notice. It is this very familiarity which allows us to pass over many fundamental facts without once thinking of their implications. If, instead of Spring and Summer, we think of the Period of Growth and, instead of Autumn and Winter, of the Period of Endurance, we may avoid some of the dangers of familiarity.

WHEN A PLANT MUST LIVE ON ITS SAVINGS

IF a plant has not accumulated sufficient reserves of energy-producing materials during the Period of Growth its chance of tiding over the Period of Endurance until a renewal of supplies becomes possible is very small. In some plants (the annuals) the reserves are concentrated in the seeds : the rest manage by consuming themselves, much as a hibernating bear is fat when he goes to sleep and thin when he wakes up in the Spring. Since light is the ultimate source of energy for plants (and, indeed, for nearly all life on this earth) those plants in our oakwood which are nearest the sun will have least interference with their energy supply. On the other hand, the smaller plants will have to put up with very considerable interference with this supply, due to overshadowing by their tall neighbours. So it happens that many of the herbs which manage to live in an oakwood are those which can take advantage of a short period of growth and flowering before their light supplies are seriously cut down by the leaf-growth of the larger plants. For instance, the bluebell and the primrose, common inhabitants of our Wealden oakwoods, are plants which are able to make a quick start by using last year's stores to produce leaves and flowers before the bracken overtops them.

There is, of course, no suggestion that the plants *know* that the bracken is going to overtop them : it is reasonable to think though, that plants without the ability to store food-reserves or the capacity to exist on meagre supplies of light would not survive in such company. Furthermore, if the tall plants take the light they do something else at the same time ; they screen the ground against evaporation and so give rise to a set of conditions suitable for plants which demand little light and much moisture. Such plants as the wood-sorrel, some ferns and many mosses come into this class.

We have so far tried to avoid professional technical terms, but there is no reason why we should do so if our understanding can be enlarged by a consideration of some of them. The branch of biology which deals with the dependence of species upon places, climates and other species, is called *ecology*. When we wish to discuss the intricate business relationships of man with man, town with country, people with people, we talk *economics*. Both words have a common root in the Greek word *oikos* which means house, but in both departments the inquiry goes far beyond mere domestic relations. Any population of living organisms may be thought of as strictly limited in size by the available resources of food and energy. These will include light, water and so on.

If there is any important change in these ruling factors the population must change too, either in numbers or in the species composing it. Consider, for instance, the city of Old Sarum which subsisted for centuries when liability to attack made its population relatively small and its strategic strength important. When the liability to attack became less the population grew beyond the capacity of the available water to support it and the restrictions of the military site became a nuisance to the civilians and the churchmen. As a consequence the city of New Sarum was founded in the well-watered meadows to the south.

PROBLEMS THAT HARASS BOTH MAN AND PLANTS

OWING to the increased productivity brought about by the Industrial Revolution the human population of England and Wales about doubled itself in the fifty years between 1811 and 1861, whereas it took something like two hundred years to accomplish the doubling from the beginning of the seventeenth century onwards. It is important to notice that the increase became possible not by the doubling of the native food-supply, but by the exchange of large quantities of manufactured goods for foodstuffs produced overseas. It is not suggested that anything exactly like this happens with a population of plant-species. There is no attempt to push plants into an anthropomorphic scheme, but rather to push man into a biological one—to show that his fundamental problems are not peculiar to him, but to all living things.

When, in our oakwood, for any reason, the population of tall trees over a given area becomes reduced, there is a consequent reduction of cover to the soil and this means increased light for the smaller plants and increased evaporation of water as well. The result will be that the moisture-loving, shade-enduring species will be penalised and their places taken by plants which can stand more light and are well-equipped to conserve their water-supplies.

The reduction of cover may bring other changes in its train. For instance, the more open character of the plant population will give free access to the larger animals so that the chances of survival of mechanically weak and unprotected plants will be reduced when the growth becomes very open. The tough, thorny plants will still survive and the ground-flora will consist of close-growing herbs. This change from one type of vegetation to another is commonly spoken of as degeneration, but again it is necessary to remind ourselves that no moral reproach is implied. It really means little more than that the change of conditions will cause some species to die out from that territory and allow others to get the upper hand.

THE PLANT'S EQUIPMENT FOR GETTING A LIVING

IT has become customary of late years to pay a great deal of attention to what is called " vocational testing." Much has been written on this subject and we do not need to consider it in detail. It may be summarised by saying that psychologists and sociologists have devised a large number of experiments by which the suitability of any boy or girl for any particular occupation may be assessed. It is possible to classify human beings in respect of their equipment in manipulative skill, resistance to fatigue, toleration of repetition, inventive capacity and so on. It is found, for instance, that people employed in the manufacture of photographic emulsions which are handled in red light are much less subject to depression than those handling the emulsions in green light. It is therefore good business to see that the workers of the green light section are naturally cheerful, leaving the more exhilarating red light to their less cheerful associates.

Qualifications can be considered under a number of headings. Obviously the first of these is anatomical, or we may say, comparing it with our machines, constructional. In other words, has an organism the necessary parts to do a particular job ? We can decide at once that a child born blind will not make a publisher's proof-reader, but not everybody with the power of sight can do that job. In other words, having got the machine with the necessary parts, will it work ?

THE WATER BUDGET: HOW A PLANT BALANCES INCOME AND EXPENSES

IT has already been made reasonably apparent[1] that for all organisms living on the land there is a water problem. An organism living in an atmosphere which is not saturated with water is liable to lose water into the atmosphere by evaporation and we may remind ourselves yet again that the living substance of all living organisms—the protoplasm —contains more than 98 per cent water, and on the maintenance of this the continuance of the life-processes depends. It is therefore easy to see that a plant subject to a dry atmosphere must be capable of conserving its water-content or it will die. On the other hand, all land-plants maintain a stream of water from the soil into the atmosphere and thus accumulate the necessary supplies of mineral salts. What the plant has to do, therefore, is to balance the income from the soil with the expenditure into the atmosphere, or, since the study of international economics is so popular, to make water-imports slightly exceed water-exports.

Plants living in a dry soil and a dry atmosphere, that is to say, having a very poor water income and the possibilities of a heavy water expenditure must keep a tight hand on that expenditure or die. For the plant living in a very damp situation, in an almost water-saturated atmosphere, the problem is the other way about ; how to pass a sufficient

[1] See pp. 43–51.

amount of water through the plant body to leave behind the required amount of mineral salts. We cannot consider all the various devices by which these problems are solved, but we may realise that, in a broad way, plants of damp situations have large leaves, that is, good evaporating surfaces, and plants of very dry situations have very small leaves or none at all. As a comparison we may consider that an income which will enable one to live very comfortably in a remote country village will probably be less adequate in a country town, and inadequate in a great city ; much depends on the company one keeps.

It is a commonplace to remark that the climate of the British Isles is not a climate of extremes and we shall not expect to find any extreme examples of water income and expenditure. As one of the chief factors in bringing about a high water-expenditure is the sun, we shall be justified in expecting to find our most extravagant examples in the tropical parts of the world. We have neither tropical rain-forests where there is very heavy expenditure of water, nor desert plants which live in conditions conducing to heavy expenditure but, in fact, adapt themselves to a ridiculously small water-income. Nevertheless, it is easy to find in the British Isles plant populations which, for one reason or another, have to make do on very scanty water supplies. Coarse, sandy soils, though they may receive fairly abundant rainfall, are incapable of retaining very much moisture, and so the plants found on them are those which are able to exercise rigid control over water-expenditure. Well-known examples of this kind of thing are the pine-heaths which we often know as commons ; they probably would not be common land if they were good for anything else.

HOW THE SCOTS PINE STARTS A NEW COLONY

THE simplest type of heath country is likely to be pretty well known to most people. It is what would commonly be called open country ; that is, there are few or no trees. The coarse sandy ground has a dense covering of low-growing tough, shrubby plants, all well equipped to live on very low water-imports. In the extreme condition we shall find very few species of plants at all, though there may be complete cover to the soil by the common ling. When this is so, success-ful competition by other species is so difficult as to be next to impossible. Nevertheless, it is no uncommon thing to find practically pure growths of the Scots pine under almost identical conditions of soil and climate, and the possible stages leading to this are of interest.

The fossil record suggests that the Scots pine was once a common tree in southern England, but two hundred years ago it was rather scarce. Clement Reid writing on the origin of the British flora says : " *Pinus sylvestris* seems to have been abundant throughout Britain during part of the Neolithic Period, for its cones are abundant at the base of peat-mosses and in ' submerged forests.' It afterwards disappeared from the south of England and only recently has been reintroduced." The seed of the pine is light and winged, and consequently any territory down-wind from an established group of seed-producing trees is certain to get well seeded.

The plants of the heath country provide very good protection for the pine seedlings and once they are started they can compete very successfully with other species. They are fast-growing and if there is no serious interference, such as a heath fire, they will thrive so as to form a real pine-forest. The shade created by the leaf-canopy is so great that there is little or no light at the forest-base and consequently no extensive ground-flora. Add to the absence of light the fact that the needle-like leaves of the pine are less subject to decay than those of broad-leaved trees such as oak and beech, and it will not be very surprising that the pine tends to get the territory all to itself.

WHAT WOULD HAPPEN IF NOTHING DECAYED

THIS leaves out of account a very important group of organisms—fungi ; but, as they receive special treatment elsewhere,[1] the omission is not so serious as otherwise it would be. It is exceedingly rash to assume that any group of organisms is unimportant : the fungi are such important agents in the economy of the living world that they must be given separate consideration. Nevertheless we should observe, in passing, that the large-scale debris of forest life—leaves, dead wood and so forth—are reduced and become again available for the use of plants by the agency of fungi, bacteria and other organisms lumped together as destroying. Imagine what would happen if nothing decayed ; if the dead tree and the dead elephant lay without change where they fell !

[1] See p. 156.

PLANTS THAT MUST COPE WITH A WATER SHORTAGE

THE Scots pine, though capable of producing successful forest on poor, ill-watered soils in a climate where the sun-supply is very meagre, lives in comparative luxury compared with some other species. The available light seems to suffice and is very rarely too much. Where there is superabundance of sun and the most meagre water-supply imaginable, plants are in poor case indeed. We cannot find the extreme of these conditions in the British Isles. If we want to see what plants can do in such circumstances we shall have to go abroad. Yet we should remind ourselves that the problem remains the same in essentials : how to get and keep enough water to carry on the life-processes and at the same time to evaporate enough at the exposed surfaces to keep the plant-body cool and leave behind enough mineral salts. It should be reasonably apparent that the greater bulk of plant-life on this earth does not find itself in the most favourable conditions all of the time. The actual amount of land areas upon which plant-life is quite impossible is probably much smaller than most of us imagine. In other words, an absolute desert in which there is no life whatever is a very rare thing.

The next thing to it, in which the living organisms are just, and only just, above the level of subsistence, is pretty common. A glance at a map of the world will show enormous areas marked " desert " in nearly every large land-mass. Most of these deserts, however, have enough of the essential supplies to support some kind of plant-life. When the water-supply fails completely for a long time that is an end of the matter as far as the plants are concerned. They are accustomed to suspend operations until there is sufficient improvement in conditions to make possible a small amount of constructive or reconstructive work, but if the improvement is too long delayed, even the resources of the seed become exhausted, and when the improved conditions do come there is nothing left alive to take advantage of them.

The conditions of desert life have been considerably investigated at the Desert Laboratory of the Carnegie Institution of Washington at Tucson in the State of Arizona. Conditions are not pleasant enough to make such studies really popular, even among scientific workers. On the other hand there is great fascination in finding out as exactly as possible how plants and animals manage to survive such rigorous conditions. One of the first things to try to know accurately is the annual rainfall. For this purpose a special rain-gauge had to be invented. Obviously in such arid conditions any rain that does fall is very quickly evaporated unless means are devised to prevent it. This is achieved by allowing the rain-water to be delivered into a collecting vessel under a layer of heavy oil. Other meteorological data are collected in much about the ordinary way, and so we have a fairly good knowledge of the climatic factors.

The plants of this region are of two main types ; those which are equipped with water-storing tissues and those without any notable storage but with such modifications of the plant-body as reduce the evaporation to a minimum. Chief among the water-storers are the cacti—familiar to many people because their bizarre forms have caused them to be objects of cultivation, though the really magnificent members of the family are too large and slow-growing to be common pets. It may be noted in passing that the two thousand or more known species of the cactus family are, with one possible exception, natives of the American continent, and they are to be found chiefly in the arid regions of the tropical belt.

The giant cactus of Arizona and Texas is a superb example of what plants can do even in the most extreme conditions of heat and drought. In about two hundred years it can grow to a height of thirty-five feet with a diameter of about two feet. The whole plant-body has a thick waterproof covering, and the only communication through it to the dry, water-hungry atmosphere outside is by means of the stomata (or breathing pores) which are sunk in deep, longitudinal furrows. Water is stored in the bulk of the inner tissues, and breach of the water-controlling outer tissues by animals is prevented by a plentiful equipment of spines.

HOW PLANTS SURVIVE IN SPITE OF DIFFICULTIES

HITHERTO we have been concerned with actual shortage of water. Now we may pass on to consider what we may call virtual shortage ; a state, let us say, when there is plenty of water about, but the plants are for some reason unable to make use of it. It has been explained elsewhere [1] that the passage of water into a plant-cell depends on the difference between the amount of dissolved substances in the cell-sap

[1] See p. 47.

and that of the fluid outside the cell. When the available water has a large quantity of substances dissolved in it, the passage of water from the roots of a plant through the plant-body to the atmosphere is difficult from the start. We might very properly say, on seeing a tropical mangrove swamp for the first time, that we had never seen anything wetter in our lives. We might, therefore, be justifiably astonished, not to say incredulous, if we were told by a plant-physiologist that the soil was " physiologically dry ". Yet this is a very good way of expressing what we know of such places.

So it is that the plants of mangrove swamps are those which have the means of rigid control of such water as the roots can take in. The same rigid control will be necessary if any plant is to have its roots in highly saline water and the rest of its body in the atmosphere. The trees of the mangrove swamp do this by having thick, leathery, well-waterproofed leaves. In spite of these restrictions some species are able to colonise coral reefs ten miles off-shore and maintain themselves as a dense forest of magnificent sixty-foot trees. The probable course of such a colonisation is well worth considering.

THE MANGROVE SEED'S FUTURE DEPENDS ON THE TIDE

IT is not easy to give a comprehensive description of what is meant by mangrove swamp. The term is probably associated in the minds of many people with the steamy, muddy estuaries of tropical rivers ; indeed mangrove swamps are very commonly found in such places. The only soil they have is subject to regular inundation by tidal water, which may vary in salt content from that of the open sea to being only brackish. There are tidal-lands in the British Isles which are no less interesting, but they are, perhaps, rather less easy to describe and have fewer obviously novel features.

Let us begin, as before, by considering the seed, and let us remind ourselves that a seed is a very young plant in a state of arrested development. All seeds have some more or less efficient protection against mechanical damage and drying up and are therefore able to withstand a certain amount of transportation and so establish the species at some distance from the parent plant. It is a very notable fact that if we find plants on any seashore we shall find many of them have seeds which are capable of floating unimpaired in the sea for long distances. The important plants of the mangrove swamp are able to do this and more also. Unfortunately it is not possible to see mangroves nearer than the United States and then only in the far south. The most impressive swamps are found in the tropical regions of the Indian and Pacific oceans, but there, interestingly enough, nearly all the species are different from, though related to, those of the Atlantic.

An interesting species for us to consider is the Red Mangrove. We may properly do so because it forms practically pure forest without human interference. Besides the evaporation control by the leaves it has several other features which make it remarkably fitted for the situations in which we find it. The seed germinates before it leaves the parent plant and the young plant continues its growth until it may be eighteen inches long. When it falls from the tree it will have two chances, depending on the state of the tide. Owing to its swollen, pointed lower end, if it falls at low-water it will plant itself in the shade of its parent. Falling at high-water will give the seedling a chance of being carried away by the receding tide.

When it goes aground it will, owing to its length and its power of floating upright, be able to occupy territory not available to its associates. It is, in fact, the length of the young plant which decides the level in relation to the tide at which it can and does grow : the longer the seedling, the lower the level at which it can colonise. As there are a number of species each with seedlings of different lengths it is not difficult to see that they should occupy separate zones from just below low-water mark upwards. On the low wooded coral islands of the coast of Queensland we can find an extremely interesting arrangement of the plants due to these facts.

THE FOREST THAT GROWS OUT AT SEA

ALL coral reefs provide a great deal of limestone in one form or another. These dead results of the activities of living organisms accumulate on the beaches in the coral seas and range in size from a boulder, five or six feet across, down to the finest sand. One of the very common kinds of this debris is a sort of shingle consisting of sticks of coral limestone up to an inch in diameter and maybe a foot or so long, but usually less. When a coral reef grows to the level of low-water this debris begins to accumulate behind the reef ; that is, away from the prevailing wind. The finer material is carried farthest, but eventually a wall or rampart of coral shingle is formed on the surface of the reef.

ROOTS OF RED MANGROVE

The roots of the red mangrove grow downwards from a height
of several feet at an angle of about 45 degrees from the trunk.
They often interlace to form a dense, impenetrable entanglement.

In the shelter of this wall the young plants of the red mangrove, carried out in the first instance by flood-water from the
mainland rivers, are able to establish themselves and produce
an almost impenetrable forest miles out at sea. On the rampart itself, the white mangrove is found. The seeds of this
species also germinate on the tree, but, owing to their small
size, have no chance of occupying any territory below low-
water mark. The species is, therefore, restricted to a narrow
strip of shingle at and just below high-water mark. Other
species with intermediate lengths of seedlings occupy intermediate levels.

Nevertheless, this amphibious plant population is no more
fixed and stable than any other. The system, like so many
others, contains the seeds of its own decay. The red mangrove has a very successful arrangement of buttress or stilt
roots by which it is enabled to withstand water movements
in a soil of soft mud. When the forest is established these
roots, which commonly grow out from the trunk of the tree

at an angle of 45 degrees from a height of several feet downwards, form a densely interlacing entanglement over the whole area. This provides a means whereby the level is gradually raised by the accumulation of entrapped material, thus giving opportunity to species of higher levels to establish themselves. At the same time the shingle is driving in from the windward side, thus killing off the mangrove swamp at its fringes. As the ground rises, low-level species give way to higher-level species and new areas of dry land arise from the sea.

If we go on to examine the ground as it goes downwards into deeper water, we shall soon find that plants without the seed-habit become increasingly common and plants with it increasingly rare. However, there are flowering plants which grow and form extensive meadows under twelve feet of seawater. The eel grass or grass-wrack, common on the shores of the British Isles, and indeed of the temperate Atlantic generally, is a seed-plant growing in the sea. In the tropics under-sea meadows of sea-grasses are the grazing grounds of turtles and other marine animals. Yet the seed-habit, so common on the dry land, is very much the exception in the sea. It is obviously true to say that for plants living *in* the sea there is no water problem. It is only when a living organism is exposed to the atmosphere that the danger of drying up becomes a serious menace to its continued existence. By means of the seed-habit the young plant survives the period between dependence on its parent for water supplies and getting them for itself.

The plant populations of the sea have to face just the same sort of competition for every available square inch of ground as we see happens on the land. It is one thing to get there first and get started : quite another to hold the territory against the better-equipped species which may come along later. Broadly speaking, the more favourable the locality the greater the number of species we shall find occupying it : the worse the place, the fewer the species. For instance, if we examine the vegetation of a breakwater, at Lyme Regis say, we shall find the space between the tide-marks occupied by brown seaweeds, leathery plants well-equipped to withstand the daily exposure to sun and air to which the tidal movements subject them. Looking closely, we shall find that there are only four or five species of larger plants, each of them occupying a horizontal strip or zone, pretty clearly defined

AN UNDER-SEA MEADOW

A composite picture showing the grasses and various kinds of seaweeds which form extensive meadows at the bottom of the sea, peopled by turtles, sea-anemones and the myriad kinds of fish.

in relation to the level of the tides. Once we get below the level of low-water the number of species becomes greater, and any zoning there may be is much less obvious.

Investigation of the social relations of under-water plants is obviously a much more difficult matter than that concerning land-plants. Something can be done under favourable conditions by means of diving gear of a simple sort, but most of our knowledge has been gained by means of dredging, grabbing or trawling. All of these methods have very serious limitations ; grabbing gets too little material from too small an area ; dredging and trawling cover a larger area and get more material, but then material from different levels will be mixed indiscriminately. Nevertheless we do know that plants in the sea are sorted out by their particular requirements in quality and quantity of light. Here it may be remarked that the four great groups of spore-bearing plants in the sea (*Algæ*)[1]—commonly referred to as blue-greens, greens, browns and reds—have different capabilities in respect of light ; their colours are the expressions of that fact.

The details need not concern us ; all we need to realise is that the quality and the quantity of light available at different depths in the sea differ likewise. We are fairly safe in saying that brown plants need red light and are, therefore, not plants of deep water. The same is usually true of the green plants. In temperate seas they are comparatively insignificant and restricted to comparatively shallow water. In tropical seas, however, they are important elements in the population, and have been taken from water more than 300 feet deep—in fact the greatest depth record is held by a green plant. In northern waters the deep water is occupied by the red plants which are capable of using green and blue light.

THE SEA-PLANT'S STRUGGLE TO STAY IN ONE PLACE

PLANTS of the sea have one great problem to solve : having found a suitable place, to stay there ; a plant needs to be attached to a rock and to allow the water to flow over it. A drifting plant just moving with the current is, for all practical purposes, in stagnant water and soon uses up the food supplies in its immediate neighbourhood. It is easy enough to hold on in quiet water, but an exposed coast is an impossible locality for plants without a strong and efficient holdfast system. We find that the finest and largest plants in the sea are at a level where light and atmospheric gases are plentiful. The associated disadvantage is wave action, which will tear weak plants from their moorings and break up those which are not flexible enough to stand the constant washing to and fro. An alternative equipment is that of growing close to the sea-bottom, either as a skin on rocks or stones or in moss-like masses on which the surf beats harmlessly. The family of the kelps, which includes the longest plants we know, is represented on the shores of the British Isles by a number of species. They are found within the influence of wave-action at and below low-water mark and are, characteristically, large, slippery, flexible plants with a mass of strong root-like branches by which they are attached to rocks and stones. It is no uncommon thing to find a dense growth of a single species with no other large plants able to compete successfully at that tide-level.

[1] See p. 70.

These and other sea-plants are subject to a further effect of their method of life and that is weighing their moorings. We might perhaps say " take up " instead of using the nautical term, but we should gain nothing in accuracy and lose a graphic metaphor. What commonly happens is that a sea-plant grows until it has acquired sufficient buoyancy to float the rock or stone to which it attached itself in infancy. It is then subject to some of the disadvantages of a drifter. If the currents carry it off-shore it may lose enough buoyancy, by decay or other damage, to sink in deeper water than that in which it has grown. This is not necessarily fatal : there may be enough light in the new habitat for the plant to grow up to the surface again. This is the sort of thing which happens to the giant kelps in the An arctic Ocean. Plants of something like a thousand feet lon ; are reported in those conditions.

It may be ren.arked here that we ought to be very wary of considering a change as advantageous. At first sight we may be tempted to think that there is an advantage in being floated to a place where it is possible to grow very big ; but the increase in size is the price of survival in the deeper water. We do, very readily, think of survival as an advantage in itself, but the notion of advantage gained from our observation of human affairs is apt to be misleading when transferred to other species of living organisms. In any case, the habit of weighing moorings is likely to be occasionally fatal when the currents are on-shore instead of off.

THE OYSTER-THIEF : A PLANT THAT ROBS THE GROWER

A N interesting effect of the habit is furnished by a plant native to the Mediterranean, which has established itself in northern waters. It is one of the relatively few seaweeds which have acquired common names—the oyster-thief The plants grow into an irregular sort of bladder on the shells of the young oysters. The activities of the plant produce a gas bubble inside the bladder which will, if growth proceed long enough, suffice to lift young oysters from their moorings. An off-shore current will carry them into deep water where they are lost to the oyster-grower. Various methods of combating the nuisance have been tried, but nothing but mechanical bursting of the bladders by sweeping the oyster-beds with a brushwood contrivance has proved of much use so far. What we need to know are the conditions which are favourable to the oyster and unfavourable to the plant. Even if we knew them it may be doubted if we could find means to have them in combination. It may reasonably be argued that if general conditions, including the population of species previously in occupation of the territory and their relations one with another, were not highly favourable, no intruding species would have a chance of establishing itself.

If man, as an economist, wishes to eliminate a species unfavourable to his plans, he must turn to and record *all* the species in the vicinity and the limits of their toleration in respect of the master-factors of the environment. He will then be able to see if the species he does not want can be crowded or otherwise driven out. There is nothing very remarkable or mysterious about this : it is the problem which is solved with varying degrees of success by every cultivator, whether of oysters, wheat or cow . Of course, all that we can do, usually, is to destroy the hostile species ; as by hoeing weeds or shooting wolves.

CHANGE : THE BASIS OF ALL LIFE

WHEN man wishes to exploit any part of the earth's surface he is rarely, if ever, presented with absolutely unoccupied territory. He has usually to contend with an established population of one or more species. We have tried to see how such a population is not continuously constant ; that it varies from time to time, though the population of a particular area in May of one year may be almost identical in May of another. In more formal language we may say that the balance is shifting (or dynamic), not fixed (or static). It is deplorably easy to forget this—the outstanding feature of all living systems. Nobody is more prone to the error than the professional scientist : it is something of which he must continually remind himself. We may take the practice of photography for comparison.

Everybody who has ever taken a snapshot of his friends knows how often the likeness is disappointing. Yet why should we expect that an expression captured in one-twenty-fifth of a second will record a faithful and satisfactory impression of somebody of whom our observation must extend to thousands of times that amount ? We may note in confirmation that nobody ever says that a cinematograph picture is " not a bit like you." Our observations of a living population are equivalent to a sort of snapshot or " still " picture of a continuous process of which we can, at best, see or hope to see, fragments only. It is a fairly common trick in the bag of the nature-cinematographer to take a film of a growing plant with an interval of some minutes between each picture. When the film is projected at the normal rate the plant appears to grow and move about at a most astonishing speed. It is one way of seeing a process which is too slow for our perception in time ; we manage to contract or condense the time-dimensions of the operation. We extend that dimension by a similar process when we take a slow-motion picture of a fast-moving object. We " give ourselves time " to see a series of movements which happen too fast for our senses.

HOW A FILM OF GROWING LIFE COULD BE MADE

IF we could (and it is by no means impossible ; only rather tedious and difficult) get a moving-picture record of our Wealden oakwood, making our exposures at hourly intervals throughout the year, we could contract a year to less than ten minutes. This would condense the happenings of a long summer's day to about one second and day and night would flash on and off our screen with rather unpleasant rapidity. We should, therefore, choose a more " open " or large scale so that we had a day of fifteen to twenty seconds. Comparison with large- and small-scale maps, which enable us to see a town, a county or a continent entire, will elucidate the point further.

Pictures of this kind could not give us complete understanding of the annual succession, but they would be a great enlargement of our understanding of the shifting balance. We could also use the trick to see the stages by which such a succession is established on entirely unoccupied territory. In this matter, however, we can get enlightenment by less elaborate and costly methods. By providing territory which has been artificially cleared of all living things we can study the stages by which it is populated. This would seem to be a very easy thing to do but in practice a great many difficulties arise. To start with, an area devoid of all life is a matter requiring no little thought and care to obtain. The sea is a favourable place to conduct such experiments, but that will tell us little or nothing about the process on land. It may assist us to establish some general principles, but it cannot answer all our questions. So much depends on the question which we wish to answer by means of experiments on living organisms.

Our question must be asked with great care and we must try to be certain that we do not ask one thing and mean another. If all we are able to do by way of experiment is to remove in April all large plants from an area of meadow-land one yard square and observe the subsequent events, we must not assume that the answers we shall get will be equally true for an area twenty yards square cleared in May.

HOW THE SOIL SUPPORTS THE PLANT

NEARLY everybody will readily accept the statement that to grow a flowering plant we must have soil of some sort. We have talked about soil often enough, but we have, as yet, given it no sort of detailed consideration. Our use of the word implies a capability to support plant-life of some sort. We should not consider a quantity of powdered glass as soil worthy of the name ; yet it would deserve it quite as much as a quantity of pure quartz sand with no admixture of any kind. We should need to add a great many other things before the word soil could be properly used to describe it. If we added a quantity of decaying animal and vegetable matter we should be on the way to having a soil. Until we do that our sand may be regarded as a very stable system, little liable to change of any kind : when we have done it we have, so to speak, inaugurated a dynamic system in which changes will be taking place constantly. By means of the destructive activities of the organisms living within the soil, the constructive activities of those with only their roots in it are rendered possible.

The destructive effects of climate in reducing large masses of rock by the action of rain, wind, frost and so on, are exceedingly important, but need not detain us long. We must allow ourselves to begin at the point where the activities of living organisms are necessary to make a disintegrated rock-mass into a medium in which the roots of land-plants can thrive. Here it may be well to stress an important difference between plants living in the sea and those with their roots in the earth and the rest of their bodies in the atmosphere. The lower end of a seaweed is an attachment organ ; its function is to hold on and not to gather supplies. For the land-plant the earth is practically the sole source of raw materials and so the roots must perform a double function : maintaining the plant in position and collecting water with the necessary supplies of dissolved salts and gases. To make the point in a slightly different way : the food-factories of the land-plant (the leaves) are at a distance from the sources of supply and so need and, since they continue to survive, have a system of transportation both to and from those factories. In the sea, the food-factories are surrounded by their essential supplies and so the transportation is one way—away from the factories.

When there is any demand for supplies by the plant on the place of attachment, we may expect to find that the place will be altered by the activities of the plant. This is one of the ways to the formation of a real soil, capable of supporting a flora of flowering plants. A landscape of rocks does not, at first sight, seem a very good situation for the growth of plants. The faces of the rocks themselves, when unsheltered from the sun, will be very hot and subject to great evaporation. In addition most rocks will hold very little moisture. The equipment necessary for survival in such a situation will include : water—low requirements ; ability to conserve such water as is available ; toleration of great amounts of light and heat ; low habit of growth so that a strong root-system is not necessary.

This equipment is not common among flowering plants ; so uncommon in fact that the colonists of bare rock-faces are nearly always algæ and lichens, which form no more than a skin or crust on the surface. The activities of these plants, coupled with those of the climate, provide material which accumulates in the crevices as soil. Such soil provides har-bourage and supplies for the hardier sorts of flowering-plants having a stout root-system and a cushion habit of growth. These will lead the way to an accumulation of soil over the rocks themselves and thence to a plant-covering of grassy turf.

LIFE IN THE OAKWOOD : A DRAMA IN THREE ACTS

IF we apply our cinematograph idea to such a story we shall be able to make some interesting comparisons with oak-woods, seashores and even deserts. Our film-record for a year's life of an oakwood would probably do as well for one year as for another. Our first act would show the activities of the spring-flowering plants—bluebells, primroses and the like—and their suppression by the bracken and the leaf-canopy of the trees. Then we should see the principal units of the population working at full pressure : adding to their stature, producing flowers and maturing fruit. We might even see the oaks produce a second crop of leaves to replace those devoured by the leaf-rolling caterpillars of the oak-moth. Towards the end of the act the leaves would begin to fall from the trees. The colder nights of autumn would prepare the plants for the third act—the Period of Endurance. The second act ends with everything closed down and sealed up against the cold, sun-starved winter months. In essentials the drama is the same year after year : the spring outburst may be a little early or a little late ; the Period of Growth may be shortened a little or lengthened a little ; but the actors and the parts they play are very much the same.

Our film-record beginning on unoccupied territory would show some important differences. The pioneer species would appear, hold the ground and carry on their lives for a season or two and then disappear for good. Their places would be taken by others for which they had prepared the soil. The colonisation of new territory by our own species is a very similar story. In the early days, there is need for men skilled in overcoming the opposition of other inhabitants. If a permanent settlement begins to take shape, the soldier and the hunter must be assisted by the cultivator, the builder, the smith and the host of other craftsmen who go to make up a stable human society. It is a commonplace of recent human history that mere strength and fierceness have been little rewarded. Highly civilised society puts a premium on intelligence : brawn gives place to brains. This is only to say that the qualities required for successful acquisition are not always those necessary for continued occupation. So it is with one species in competition with others for the resources of any place on the earth's surface which is capable of supporting life.

TRYING TO LABEL THE PLANTS BY OCCUPATION

WE do not always find it easy to classify the occupations of human beings : it is still less easy to do a similar job for all the plants known to us. The old joke about the man who gave as reason for his unemployment that he was a coronation-programme-seller embodies a principle that is not infrequently to be seen in operation in the plant-world. The chances of continuous occupation of any place at all may be few and far between for a very highly specialised organism. Our own species does not show anything like such great variation in equipment as do the various species of plants. We do not have men twenty feet high as window-cleaners nor six inches high as needle-makers. Yet the range of size alone, in the plant kingdom, is very much greater than that. It is not surprising, therefore, that there is considerable difference of opinion among scientists concerning the best system for expressing our knowledge of the types of equipment possessed by living organisms and the uses made of them.

WHY THE BOTANIST CANNOT BE CONTENT WITH EVERYDAY WORDS

THE term "life-form" has been in common use among scientists to include such words as refer to the large-scale appearance or habit of a plant. Many of these words are in everyday use and are perfectly familiar : as tree, shrub, herb. These are very useful terms, but they are inadequate to deal with even our present knowledge. The simple words green or red may suffice for the traffic-policeman and the seaman : they will be inadequate for the haberdasher and the dye-manufacturer. As the latter practitioners need to distinguish a great number of shades of green, so the practitioner in the knowledge of plants needs to distinguish a large number of different kinds of woody or other plants. This approach to classification is a very old one—older than the attempt to classify according to relationship by descent. The early botanists used what we may call life-forms as the basis of their classifications. Nowadays most botanists would agree that *Prunus Cerasus* and *Fragaria chiloensis* belong to the same family (Rosaceæ); yet the first is the cherry, which can be a substantial tree, and the second is the strawberry, which is a lowly herb.

In order to understand some of the attempts which have been made and some of the difficulties of the subject it will be necessary to present an outline of one or two important systems of classifying life-forms. A simple one for land-plants is that of F. E. Clements :

I.	1. ANNUALS.		9. CARPET-HERBS.
II.	2. BIENNIALS.		10. SUCCULENTS.
III.	HERBACEOUS	IV.	WOODY
	PERENNIALS.		PERENNIALS.
	3. SOD-GRASSES.		11. HALF-SHRUBS.
	4. BUNCH-GRASSES.		12. BUSHES.
	5. BUSH-HERBS.		13. SUCCULENTS.
	6. CUSHION-HERBS.		14. SHRUBS.
	7. MAT-HERBS.		15. TREES.
	8. ROSETTE-HERBS.		

It should not be difficult for anyone to place any given land-plant in its appropriate class in this system. For many purposes it is adequate but the further the analysis is taken, the more elaborate becomes the system. Warming's great work on the life-forms of plants takes account of seventeen great groups, of which seven are water-plants. The following account of the ten groups of land-plants is here given in as simple a form as possible :

ATMOPHYTES do not grow in soil but make use of atmospheric water by absorption over the whole of their exposed surfaces.

OMBROPHYTES also grow without soil but absorb water by means of roots or similar organs or have means of storage.

CHYLOPHYTES are the plants capable of living among rocks or in similar places not porous enough to hold more than very scanty water-supplies.

HALOPHYTES grow on salt soil where the water though plentiful is poorly available.

AGROPHYTES are the herbs of ordinary well-watered soils with broad, not grass-like leaves.

POIOIDS are the grasses and similar plants having long, narrow leaves.

XYLOIDS include all plants with definitely woody stems.

KLINOPHYTES are the climbing and other plants which are unable to get into the light without support.

SAPROPHYTES are plants deriving their essential supplies from dead organisms.

PARASITES get their supplies from living organisms.

Each of these large groups is divisible into a large number of smaller units ; for instance, the Agrophytes can be considered under some thirty or more minor divisions. It is not suggested that any non-professional person will find it necessary or desirable to pursue the analysis into such minute detail, but it is no bad thing to realize, if possible, that the complexity is presented to us by the organisms themselves. It is not a mere piece of learned perversity on the part of scientists.

Whether we use the high-sounding names or not, we must not, if we wish to understand the lives of plants, fail to recognise the units for which the words are, after all, a short means of reference only. We can agree that it is an affectation to speak of tonsorial artist when we mean barber or hairdresser, but that should not lead us to suppose that there are no such people as those dealing almost exclusively with the hairy growths on the human head. When there is a simple term it is best to use it, but when the only simple word is inadequate or, worse still, is definitely misleading, it is time to get hold of another. It is doubtless a great mistake to fail to see the wood for the trees ; but that must not blind us to the fact that a wood is composed of trees and a great many other things beside, or it would not be a wood at all. Purely professional terminology has been kept out of this account as much as possible, but it ought to be apparent that increase of understanding means increase of words if we are to communicate our knowledge.

WHY WE SHOULD STUDY PLANTS

WHETHER our knowledge of the social relationships of plant species is worth having when we have got it, may be doubted by some. Perhaps it may be felt that study should be restricted to such plants as we can use directly ; or extended at most to those associated with the useful ones. To such objections there are two answers : first, that we never know when any species of living organism is going to have a serious effect on our health, wealth and welfare ; second, that it is well to realise that if anything happened to bring to an end the plant-life of this earth, the whole animal kingdom, including our own species, would inevitably and speedily perish. Of that there is not the least doubt. The inhabitant of the great modern city is apt to forget his dependence and it cannot be otherwise than salutary occasionally to remind ourselves of the extent of the interdependence which underlies our own lives and those of every other species of living organism. These considerations should be enough to convince anybody that such studies, the scope of which we have tried to indicate, are more than a pleasant means of passing the time. If more be needed we may consider the words of A. H. Church :

" So long as the earth goes round the sun, with its axis inclined at a very constant angle with the plane of the ecliptic, seed-time and harvest, cold and heat, summer and winter, day and night, cannot cease in this part of the globe ; the main cycle of the annual succession of plant-life being the response to the astronomical organisation of the solar system. Hence the story repeats in successive years with a precision which at once affords the most mysteriously beautiful feature of the countryside, as it is the most constant factor in determining the main lines of all social organisation. In an age which exploits coal and petrol, it is well to remember that human life is still wholly dependent on living plant-plasma, and likely to remain so indefinitely. The world-supply of coal and petrol is, after all, finite, and the plant remains the simplest and cheapest means of obtaining current supplies of solar energy, as well as being the source of essential food-substances beyond the hope of chemical synthesis."

PLANT LIFE FROM THE
DAWN OF TIME

by W. N. EDWARDS, B.A., of the
British Museum (Natural History)

THE age of the earth, according to the most probable astronomical estimate, is in the neighbourhood of two thousand million years. Geological time, as measured by the evidence from radio-active minerals in the rocks, extends back some fifteen hundred million years, and the first unequivocal fossils are considerably more than five hundred million years old. Man, as such, cannot have been on the globe for more than a few million years—the last few moments of a long pageant. It is essential, when picturing the plant life of the past, to bear in mind this background of Time.

In order to follow the story of fossil plants it is necessary to be familiar with terms like " Devonian " and " Jurassic," but it is well to remember that the divisions of the stratified rocks have been based in the main on the successive faunas of marine animals ; had fossil plants been used for dividing up the geological time-scale, some of the lines would have been drawn in different places. Thus the flora of the Upper Devonian is much more closely allied to that of the succeeding Lower Carboniferous period than to the preceding Middle Devonian, and that of the Upper Jurassic is almost indistinguishable from that of the lowest Cretaceous beds. Moreover, as will be seen later, the three primary divisions of the stratified series, into Palæozoic, Mesozoic, and Cainozoic or Tertiary, do not coincide with the great transformations of plant life.

TELLING THE AGE OF THE EARTH BY PLANTS

THE division of plant history into a number of eras each with its own general type of vegetation is, of course, simply an abstraction based on our present knowledge of the floras of the past. There are no sharp lines between the different eras ; the whole story was really continuous. On the other hand, it is clear that at various periods different groups of plants have been dominant, and with a more detailed study

119

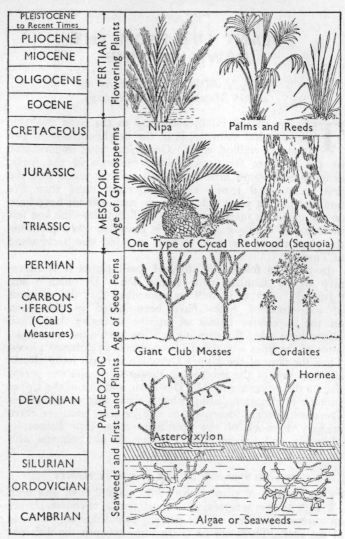

PLEISTOCENE to Recent Times	TERTIARY — Flowering Plants	
PLIOCENE		
MIOCENE		
OLIGOCENE		
EOCENE		

Nipa   Palms and Reeds

One Type of Cycad   Redwood (Sequoia)

Giant Club Mosses   Cordaites

Hornea

Asteroxylon

— Algae or Seaweeds —

THE GEOLOGICAL "AGES" OF PRE-HISTORY

In this table of the geological epochs of the earth, the periods nearest our own time are shown at the top of the page.

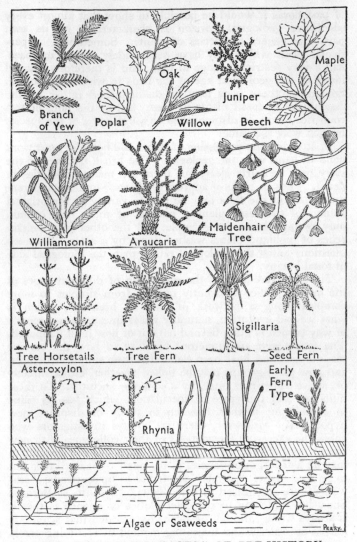

Branch of Yew
Poplar
Oak
Willow
Juniper
Beech
Maple

Williamsonia
Araucaria
Maidenhair Tree

Tree Horsetails
Tree Fern
Sigillaria
Seed Fern

Asteroxylon
Rhynia
Early Fern Type

— Algae or Seaweeds —

THE GEOLOGICAL "AGES" OF PRE-HISTORY

*Some major changes in the earth's vegetation. The plant shown
as a type of Williamsonia is known as "Williamsoniella."*

of past floras it would be possible to show that almost every successive geological horizon is characterised by its own particular genera or species of plants. Sometimes one particular plant which may have been widely spread in space, had a very restricted range in time, and is therefore a useful index of the geological age of the beds in which it is found. Sometimes these beds may be distinguished rather by the assemblage of fossil plants in them, just as the flora of two countries might be distinguished although some of the species in each were the same.

In studying the succession of floras, the botanist must work hand in hand with the geologist. The broad outlines of the story may be fairly clear, but there are many difficulties in detail. Thus in rocks of approximately the same age apparent differences in the flora may be due to variety in the original habitat of the fossil plants ; one set of rocks may contain only swamp plants, for example, and the other may contain relics of highland plants washed down by a river. But such questions touch the geological rather than the biological side of fossil botany.

The observed facts of the succession of different types of life on the globe, apparently ranging from simpler to more complex along a network of lines or branches, which is what we call evolution, naturally raises questions not merely of why (which is quite beyond us) but of how it all happened. The fossils give us numerous hints as to how the various plant organs may have been elaborated from simple structures, and how plant groups may be linked together, either directly or, as we sometimes infer, by a common ancestry. To these hints we add the spice of speculation, which has its value in stimulating further research to verify or disprove new hypotheses. Moreover, there are always investigators who check the excessive speculations of their colleagues with new speculations of their own. Even the " facts " of one generation may be half-forgotten fancies in the next. " Ferns " turn out to be seed-plants, " corals " are found to be seaweeds, " seaweeds " are recognised as land plants. In short, as Bernard Shaw has said, one of the chief glories of science is that it is always wrong, though he might have added that science is indeed an orderly and unceasing method of rectifying errors —its own as well as that of others. Nevertheless those who want dogmatic and immutable certainty must turn away from the halls of science.

The account here given of successive eras of plant life spread over hundreds of millions of years, with suggestions as to the relationship and descent of certain groups, is a mere sketchy outline based on the present state of knowledge. One general conclusion may perhaps be emphasised : progressive change is not a constant inherent feature of living beings. Many a group of plants has reproduced its kind with little change in structure or habit for many million years ; in other groups great changes seem to have taken place comparatively rapidly. "Persistence of type," writes A. C. Seward, "and from time to time the apparently sudden influx of new types, are among the outstanding features of the history of plant evolution."

One of the greatest palæobotanists of our time, Dukinfield H. Scott, once remarked that we know a good deal about extinct plants, but not enough, as yet, to throw much light on the exact course of their evolution. "It is impossible," he wrote on another occasion, "to construct a genealogical tree of the Vegetable Kingdom, but the tree symbol is probably still the best scheme for picturing the course of evolution to our imagination. The symbolic tree must have had very long parallel branches—perhaps something like a Lombardy Poplar."

When we ponder further on the vast sea of our ignorance concerning Lombardy Poplars and other living organisms —although we can watch their development from seed to tree, study their habits, experiment on them, and dissect them in our laboratories—we shall not be surprised that our knowledge of the past history of plants, based on casual assemblages of fragmentary fossils, is so incomplete.

THE SEA CITIZEN THAT INVADED THE LAND

No more is known of the origin of life than of the origin of the world. The probability that life originated in the sea is discussed elsewhere,[1] but the earliest organisms, whether animal or vegetable, cannot have left any traces in the rocks. Indeed, it may be questioned whether the earliest and simplest living beings, which may be envisaged as minute one-celled blobs of protoplasm, could reasonably be classified as either "animal" or "vegetable"—the distinctive characters of these two branches may have taken millions of years to evolve.

[1] See pp. 346–349.

Here, at the very beginning of our story, the present gives the only clue to the past. There still exist microscopic aquatic organisms which might equally well be referred to the animal or the vegetable kingdom, and have often been claimed by both zoologists and botanists; these are probably the little-altered descendants of primeval ancestors which, having found their niche in the scheme of things, have managed to escape extinction. There are indeed numerous examples of both animals and plants which have persisted practically unchanged for very long periods.

THE OLDEST PLANTS OF ALL: SEAWEEDS

THE first recognisable fossil plants, and the only ones that have so far been found throughout the Cambrian, Ordovician, and most of the Silurian periods, are without exception algæ, or seaweeds. Most of the soft and flimsy seaweeds of our coasts do not seem likely subjects for preservation as fossils—they decay far too quickly—but there are certain groups of algæ which secrete a coral-like skeleton of lime. Forms such as these have frequently been preserved in marine deposits of the past, and were in some cases actually responsible for building up extensive limestone masses which may be called algal reefs. The familiar coral reefs of the present day, as well as of the past, are often indeed partly built up by these calcareous algæ.

The forms found in the early Palæozoic are very varied; some of them belong to an extinct family of the red algæ, and some to a group of green algæ with whorled branches. Lime was deposited by the living plant round these branches, producing a cylindrical, club-shaped, or spherical body. By cutting sections of these bodies it is possible in favourable states of preservation to study the structure, often quite complicated, of the plant itself, which is represented by tubes or hollows, or perhaps merely by lines of discoloration in the hard fossil.

These whorled green algæ are found in rocks of almost every age from the Ordovician onwards and several kinds still exist. Each geological formation has its characteristic types, and a general progression of structure within the group can be traced almost throughout the series. In referring to the pre-Cambrian and early Palæozoic times as the age of the seaweeds, the existence of numerous fossil seaweeds in later marine sedimentary rocks must not be overlooked, but after the Silurian period the main interest in fossil botany naturally shifts to the land-plants.

THE SEAWEEDS THAT BUILT ROCKS

IN addition to those algæ which can be related, sometimes distantly, to those of the recent flora, there are others in the far-off Palæozoic which, though recognisable as belonging to the algal class, can only be dubiously fitted into a classification based on living forms. Like many of the fossils, their preservation is imperfect and their reproductive organs are unknown, but they are often very important geologically as rock-builders or because they show the age of the rocks in which they are found.

There are other bodies again about which controversy still rages ; the best known of these are concentrically-banded masses of limestone, for which an algal origin has been claimed, mainly on the ground of their resemblance to certain recent deposits which are supposed to be due to algæ. In these cases there is no question of the deposition of lime in the form of a skeleton round the plant itself ; the precipitation of the bands of lime is a by-product of the plant's physiological activities. But similar banded precipitates may also be produced by purely inorganic means, and convincing proof that these large fossil forms are really due to algæ or (as has also been suggested) bacteria is usually lacking.

We may note in passing that minute organisms like bacteria would naturally be singularly difficult to recognise in the rocks and that their presence in the past can as a rule only be inferred from the results of their activities. The same may be said of another group of lowly organisms, the blue-green algæ, which at the present day undoubtedly play an important part in marine sedimentation. Maurice Black has shown that " in addition to those forms which actively contribute calcium carbonate to the sediment there are other species which function primarily as sediment-binders, without necessarily precipitating any lime themselves." The latter are usually responsible for the characteristic form of the sediments, and in the Bahamas " where such deposits are now accumulating over large areas, structures are being produced which are reminiscent of those formed in some of the great limestone formations of the Lower Palæozoic and Upper Pre-Cambrian." It is therefore quite possible that the rock-forming processes which are going on in West Indian seas at the present day are identical with those of six hundred million years ago, and are due to similar organisms.

PLANTS TAKE TO LAND AND LEARN TO BREATHE IN THE AIR

WE do not know when marine (or at any rate aquatic) plants first invaded the dry land nor how long they took to develop those adaptations which fitted them for life in an aerial instead of a watery medium. We may speculate on the possibility that certain seaweeds of the shore, left dry at every low tide, and already differentiated into an attached or rooted portion and a more or less erect stem, developed a stronger skin, with pores (stomata) for breathing, and a central strand of thick-walled elements which served to strengthen and give rigidity to the stem as well as to conduct water within the plant. Finally, they must have produced air-borne instead of water-borne spores.

The earliest known land-plants fit in extraordinarily well with this simple hypothetical description. A black rock found at Rhynie in Aberdeenshire, which is practically a petrified peat of Middle Devonian age, contains beautifully preserved examples of the oldest-known land-flora, whose minute anatomy can be studied in every detail. In this region of Aberdeenshire there was in Devonian times a peat-bog which underwent periodic inundation, resulting in the formation of peat beds alternating with thin sandy layers. The period was one of declining volcanic activity, and the final petrifaction of the peat was probably due to an influx of water highly charged with silica in solution, from hot springs or geysers. The inundation was probably quite sudden, since in the upper layers the plants are embedded, almost in their position of growth, in a practically pure flinty rock.

The plants have a simple generalised structure : one of them, called *Rhynia*, was rootless and leafless, and consisted of tufts of forked erect stems continued into a creeping underground portion which bore root-hairs. The simple spore-sacs, containing only one kind of spore, were borne at the tips of the branches. There was a solid central conducting strand, which was somewhat more elaborate in another genus, *Asteroxylon* (so called from the star-shaped appearance of the woody strand in transverse section). The stem of *Asteroxylon* was clothed with small veinless leaves, and the spore-sacs were borne on special branches ; both genera had breathing-pores (stomata) similar to those of modern plants.

A DISCOVERY THAT IS EAGERLY ANTICIPATED

THE simple form and primitive anatomy of these plants suggest on the one hand that they are derived from sea-weed-like ancestors, and on the other that they may themselves be members of a group from which various higher types of plants have been evolved. It would be unwise, however, to assume either that these particular early Devonian forms were the direct ancestors of later plants, or that land-plants originated in Devonian times. One of the discoveries to which botanists and geologists eagerly look forward is of *pre*-Devonian land or freshwater deposits in which plant relics have been preserved. Whether or not because the conditions under which the sedimentary rocks were deposited were unfavourable to the preservation of plants, such fossils are at present unknown, except perhaps in the Uppermost Silurian beds which may here be classified with the Devonian.

The Rhynie plants may have had a long history as land-dwellers, and the fortunate accident of their preservation in the Aberdeenshire chert may have taken place in the old age of their race, almost at the moment of extinction. The group to which they belong is unrepresented in fossil floras of later date than the Middle Devonian, and there are no living plants which can definitely be claimed as closely allied to them. In addition to those found in the petrified peat of Rhynie, plants of similar type (so far as can be judged from less well-preserved material) are found in early Devonian rocks of every continent.

REMARKABLE AND PUZZLING EXTINCT PLANTS

INTERESTING and important as the primitive Devonian land-plants are, the co-existence of other types must not be overlooked. Many of these are so imperfectly known that their affinities are still quite uncertain ; some of them are so puzzling that they do not seem to fit into any of the main groups of the vegetable kingdom. Thus there are certain large stem fragments, sometimes three feet in diameter and apparently showing rings of growth, which are found in Upper Silurian and Devonian beds of Europe and America ; they were first called *Prototaxites*, from a supposed relationship to the ancestors of the yew, but this view was soon discarded.

The loosely interwoven tubular tissue of which the fossil is composed is rather like that of some living brown algæ (such as the large Antarctic *Lessonia*), and for long *Prototaxites* was accepted, though rather doubtfully, as a colossal fossil seaweed. When, later on, the supposed seaweed was found definitely associated with land-plants the question of its nature had to be reconsidered, and there was even a suggestion that it might be a fungus. But nothing has yet been found to connect the chunks of petrified " stem " (as they are still presumed to be) with any leaves or other appendages, nor with any reproductive organs, and *Prototaxites* remains, in the words of W. H. Lang, " one of the most remarkable and puzzling extinct plants."

The dominant plants in the age of the early land-floras were lowly types of vascular plants, mostly belonging to groups which are now extinct. However, as D. H. Scott has put it, " that each new type arose much earlier than its full manifestation is obvious, and there is often direct evidence of precursors in an age previous to the transformation of the flora." One of these precursors in the Middle Devonian, discovered long ago by Hugh Miller, author of *The Old Red Sandstone* and *The Testimony of the Rocks*, was a stem with its internal structure preserved which Miller regarded as an undoubted cone-bearing tree. Whether it really belongs to the group of Gymnosperms (which includes the conifers) is uncertain, but the elaboration of its structure indicates a higher type of organisation than the primitive Middle Devonian plants of Rhynie. Looked at from the present, it may well have belonged to an archaic group ; three hundred and fifty million years ago it was perhaps a forerunner of the flora which in Upper Devonian times was to extinguish most of the primitive land-plants and usher in a new era.

The Middle Devonian beds of Germany have yielded a series of plants, including stems anatomically resembling the one found by Hugh Miller, which also suggest that the vegetation was very far advanced and diversified compared with the earlier land-flora. Again, however, there is no definite evidence of seed-plants, but there are leafy and woody plants of various kinds, some with small leaves and some with compound fronds which suggest an approach to the fern type. Some have obscurely pointed stems and whorled leaves, with fructifications in loose spikes or cones ; these may be the forerunners of that group of fern-allies (or *pteridophytes*) which to-day is represented only by the horse-tails.

There is abundant scope for the fossil-collector in exploring the plant-bearing beds of the Old Red Sandstone in Scotland and the Welsh borders ; new discoveries of high botanical importance undoubtedly await the student in these rocks.

THE AGE WHEN COAL WAS A FLOURISHING PLANT GROWTH

THE five main eras of plant life were not of equal duration. The age of seaweeds (from the first beginnings of life to the appearance of land-plants) was perhaps the longest, and the succeeding era the shortest, though these two overlapped, at any rate, in the Silurian epoch. The central era, which is much better known, extends from the Upper Devonian to the end of the Permian. Its close, therefore, coincides with one of the great geological divisions—that between the Palæozoic and the Mesozoic, and it is most characteristically developed in the Carboniferous period. That is to say, it is the age of the great coal forests of the northern hemisphere, with an introductory period covered by the Upper Devonian and Lower Carboniferous and a period of decline in the Permian.

A WORLD WITHOUT FLOWERS

WHAT types of plants were dominant in this important period ? We have called it the age of the seed-ferns—those familiar coal plants with fern-like foliage which are now known to have borne seeds instead of spores—and though these perhaps best typify the era, it was also the age of the tree horse-tails and the giant club-mosses. True ferns were present, though, like the mosses and liverworts, they were never a dominant feature in the flora, and there were other groups of less important fern-allies, such as the slender Sphenophylls.

The higher seed-plants, including forms allied to the conifers which are grouped together as Gymnosperms, were an important element, especially towards the end of the era, but there were no true flowering plants. The spore-producing fern-allies and the fern-like seed-bearing Pteridosperms roughly held the balance between them in the vegetation. The primitive land-plants had disappeared ; the conifers were still unimportant ; the flowering plants had not yet arrived. It was a green world, but the forests may not have been entirely without other colours. The great yellow cones of the giant club-mosses, the feathery, branched pollen-producing organs and the husked seeds of other plants may well have diversified the dense mass of foliage much as flowers do in a forest to-day. But although insects were there—cockroaches and giant dragonflies—the plants seem to have been mainly if not entirely wind-pollinated, and there was no occasion for gay colours and elaborate flowers to attract insect visitors.

PLANT LUXURIANCE TURNS TO MINERAL WEALTH : THE COAL BEDS

FROM the debris of the luxuriant vegetation of this age, coal was produced. Coal may be described as the compact residue of plant remains which have undergone varying degrees of maceration, decomposition and chemical change, resulting in a hard brittle substance rich in carbon. In some cases the plants grew in swamp forests or peat bogs and accumulated on the spot ; in others the vegetable matter drifted into lakes, estuaries, or even out to sea. Some coals are formed of a mixture of many different kinds of plants ; others are mainly the product of a few or of only one kind. Some are built up mainly of wood ; others contain abundant leaves, twigs, bark, cones and spores ; some consist almost entirely of spores. Nearly all coals, even the much-altered anthracites, consisting of almost pure carbon, retain traces of the plant tissues from which they were produced, as can be demonstrated by examining thin sections, or highly polished and etched surfaces, with a microscope. The original vegetable matter is always much compressed and reduced in bulk in the course of conversion into coal ; it has been estimated that a coal seam one foot thick represents some fifteen to twenty feet of plant debris.

Although the familiar coals of this country are all of Carboniferous age, coal deposits are known in various parts of the world in all geological periods from the Upper Devonian to the late Tertiary. The later coals were, of course, derived from different types of plants but were probably formed in similar ways.

PLANTS THAT BECAME STONE INSTEAD OF COAL

IN many coal-fields the seams of coal rest on an under-clay which is full of stumps and ramifying roots evidently belonging to the plants now forming the seam. Clearly in such cases the plants must to a large extent have accumulated on the spot where they grew, though some may also have drifted there through inundations. In some seams stony nodules, called coal-balls, are found ; these do not consist of coal, but are calcareous bodies containing petrified plant remains. They are in short, only partly compressed masses of the same debris as that of which the coal is composed, but petrified by solutions containing carbonate of lime before the rest of the deposit was converted into coal.

Under certain conditions the solutions started centres of concretionary action, and sometimes a number of such concretions grew or were cemented into one solid block, rarely as much as five feet long and four feet thick. It is fortunate for mankind in general that most of the plant accumulations were not thus petrified, but were turned into a combustible mineral ; it is, however, fortunate for the botanist that some relics of the ancient vegetation were almost perfectly preserved for his inspection.

Our knowledge of the anatomy of Coal Measure plants is very largely derived from these coal-balls. Thin sections ground down on glass until they are translucent can be examined under the microscope, and reveal the structure of the tissues almost as if they were sections of living plants. This is because in the course of petrifaction mineral matter has been laid down along the cell-walls and in the cell-cavities, completely preserving a skeleton, as it were, of the tissues. The cell-contents have disappeared or been replaced by mineral, except in certain rare cases ; resins, for example, are sometimes preserved in petrified woods. In many coal-balls much of the vegetation had decayed before petrifaction, but in others the preservation is astonishingly perfect. An ingenious method of making microscope preparations from coal-balls depends on the fact that the organic matter of the cell-walls is not mineralised. By etching a polished surface with hydrochloric acid the mineral matter is removed, and the thin layer of plant tissues which remains upstanding is then embedded in a solution of cellulose or gelatine. This dries to a thin film which can be readily peeled off.

Petrified plants of all geological ages can thus be prepared by one method or another for microscopical study. The commonest petrifying agents are silica (as in the case of the Rhynie plants mentioned above) and carbonate of lime (as in the coal-balls). In very few geological horizons, however, were the conditions favourable for the preservation of plants on such a scale as in the coal measures, and in most deposits one only meets with isolated examples of petrified wood and cones. Sedimentary deposits from estuaries and lakes often contain abundant *impressions* of plant remains, especially of leaves, and much of our knowledge of fossil plants must be derived from these. They supplement what can be learnt from petrified fossils, but since both types are usually fragmentary the task of piecing together the evidence in order to get an idea of the plant as a whole is a long and difficult one. Even in the coal measures, which have such an abundant flora, and which have been intensively studied for a hundred years, we scarcely know one single species of plant completely in all its parts. Anyone, therefore, who lives near a coal-mine may add materially to our knowledge by carefully collecting and studying the plant impressions to be found in the shales of the tip-heaps.

HOW THE PLANTS DEVELOPED THEIR ORGANS

BEFORE proceeding to give an outline of the main groups of extinct plants which composed the Upper Palæozoic flora, it may be useful to sketch briefly some of the lines along which the higher land-plants became differentiated, with regard to the types of structure that they show in their various organs. From the simplest unicellular plants one passes to multicellular forms with an undifferentiated plant-body known as a *thallus*. The seaweeds are typical thallus-plants ; except in the highest forms they show little differentiation into root, stem, or leaves, and have practically no internal conducting system. The simplest land-plants, having escaped from the watery medium, must develop a root system for attachment and for water absorption ; a conducting system ; strengthening tissues, since they are no longer held up by the surrounding water ; and breathing pores.

Some of the early Devonian plant fossils have not got very far in the differentiation either of organs or of tissues. The underground portion of *Rhynia*, for example, has the same structure as the aerial stem, and differs only in bearing root-hairs, while *Asteroxylon* has not even got these. In later Palæozoic times, however, we find numerous types of highly elaborate root-systems, often differing so much structurally from the stems they bore that they have been mistaken for independent plants until found in connection.

THE LAND-PLANT'S GREATEST LEGACY: THE STEM SYSTEM

WE have already remarked that the central strand of the primitive land-plant served the double purpose of support and water-conduction, and this dual function has been retained throughout the whole subsequent history of every group of the higher plants. Increase in size, however, together with branching and the development of leaves each supplied with its own strand led to complex developments in the conducting system, which followed different lines in the various groups of plants. The primitive strand (or stele) of *Rhynia*, consisting of a solid cylinder of wood surrounded by a sheath of bast (phloem), became more complicated in *Asteroxylon*, which itself may be regarded as a basic form from which the type of stele found in the club-mosses and their allies may have been derived. Along some lines of development, the woody projections of the stele may branch in a complicated manner ; along others, a central pith may develop in the wood, and the cylinder thus formed may be broken up in various ways by branches and leaf traces.

With growth in size, a simple woody strand becomes insufficient, and new wood must be formed, either in small patches, or in layers all round the stele. When this *secondary wood* continues to be formed from a growing layer, the herbaceous plant becomes a tree. So far as the primary wood of the stem is concerned, two main types of growth have been observed : an older type, the centripetal, developing towards the centre of the stem, and a newer, the centrifugal, developing from within outwards. The latter gradually replaces the former in various groups of plants ; the presence of centripetal wood in the stem is recognised as an archaic character, and is only found among living plants in the cycads, themselves the relics of an ancient group.

One other anatomical character of many Palæozoic plants may be briefly mentioned ; the frequent occurrence of bands of strengthening tissue in the outer part of the stem. This no doubt balanced a certain weakness in the central woody column in cases where the latter was mainly concerned with water-conduction. Plants in those days developed varied mechanisms in order to adapt themselves to the conditions under which they lived, just as do the plants of the present, and there is nothing in the structure of any known fossil plants which even suggests that they lived under conditions which cannot be paralleled at the present day.

THE LEAF MAKES ITS APPEARANCE

AMONG the early land-plants, in addition to the leafless *Rhynia*, there are two different types of leafy appendage— first the little scaly outgrowths which clothed the stems of plants like *Asteroxylon*, and which may have given rise to the small crowded leaves of the kind found in the club-moss group, and secondly, the flattened branch-systems of some other plants which seem as if they were the precursors of the fern type of compound frond.

The green leaf is the special organ concerned with carbon assimilation, which in the simplest plants may be performed by the whole vegetative body, and there is no reason why leaves may not have originated in several different ways. Among living flowering plants, for example, the apparent leaves of the " butcher's broom " are (botanically speaking) flattened stems. Thus even when a part of the plant has been specialised for its particular function, it may also take on other duties.

The variety of leaf-form and venation is almost as great among Coal Measure plants as among flowering plants of to-day. There are the linear or lanceolate whorled leaves of the tree horse-tails or *Calamites*, graceful and feathery ; the conifer-like foliage of the giant club-mosses ; the wedge-shaped and fringed leaves of the Sphenophylls ; the huge strap-like parallel-veined leaves of *Cordaites* ; and among the seed-ferns almost every type of simple and compound frond, including some which might easily be mistaken for the leaves of modern flowering plants, as well as many which at first sight are almost indistinguishable from those of living ferns. As A. C. Seward has said :

> " In the course of ages, similar results have been achieved by many diverse groups of plants; age after age there has been a repetition of unconscious effort towards the same end. Groups which had reached what might be regarded as an advanced state of efficiency became extinct; after a long interval new creations repeated with little or no change in plan the structural design produced by long-forgotten and possibly blindly ending lines of evolution."

THE PLANT SLOWLY EMERGES AS A COMPLEX STRUCTURE

IN the simplest Devonian plants the fertile part was merely a terminal sac containing spores—the differentiation of the axis into sterile and fertile parts seems to have preceded the evolution of more or less specialised organs like roots, stems or leaves. The terminal spore-sacs were sometimes borne singly and sometimes in clusters, and from the latter it is possible to derive the cone, which is simply an aggregation of spore-sacs on a specialised branch, and may be with or without interspersed bracts or leafy structures.

In the fern type the spore-sacs are often borne on ordinary fronds, but here again we must remember that these fronds are themselves probably modified branch systems. The spores were at first all exactly alike, but in various Palæozoic groups of plants one soon finds that two kinds of spores are produced, differing in size. One of these doubtless produced the male cells, and the other the female. Here it is important to bear in mind the " alternation of generations "[1] so characteristic of ferns and their allies as well as of mosses and liverworts. In the latter the " plant " is the sexual generation, and the spore-producing generation is relatively unimportant ; in the ferns, and in all the other fossil land-plants from *Rhynia* onwards, we have to do with the spore-producing generation, nothing being known of the generation which bore the sexual organs.

In the higher plants the sexual generation is much reduced, and is not an independent body. When the number of " female " spores in each sac is reduced to one, and this after fertilisation remains attached to the parent plant and is provided with a covering, we have an approach to the *seed*. The origin of the seed-habit is, however, not yet solved ; it arose independently in different groups of Carboniferous plants, and some Carboniferous seeds were considerably more complex than any seeds of to-day.

We cannot deal in any detail with the innumerable variety of spore-sacs (sometimes borne on special branches, sometimes on ordinary fronds), cones and seeds found in the coal measures and the other deposits of this era, but we must emphasise that all these organs are usually found detached. Moreover, some very seed-like bodies have turned out on

[1] See pp. 74–76.

microscopical examination to have been spore-bearing organs, and vice versa. Every scrap of evidence which will serve to relate one set of organs to another, or to throw light on structural details, is therefore of value, and the amateur collector should keep a sharp look-out for seeds or spore-sacs attached to stems or fronds.

HORSE-TAILS THAT GREW INTO TREES

THE well-known horse-tails of the present day, common in marshes and shallow water, are herbaceous plants which at most grow to a height of about six feet, and are usually smaller. Their relatives in the Carboniferous period were very similarly organised, and probably had quite a similar appearance, but were woody trees often of considerable height. The delicate branches bore whorls of linear leaves and the cones, borne on the ends of slender branches, were sometimes six inches long. Various detached remains of the tree horse-tails or Calamites, particularly what are known as pith-casts, are exceedingly abundant as fossils in the coal measures. The stems were hollow, and became filled with sand or mud when they fell into the swamps, streams, or pools where they grew; when the stem decayed and the sediment hardened a cast of the hollow pith was formed, showing the transverse joints of the original stem.

The cones were more elaborate than in the living horse-tails, and those of the Upper Carboniferous type were rather more highly organised than the Upper Devonian and Lower Carboniferous forms. It would be a mistake to suppose that the living horse-tails are the direct, simplified, and as it were degenerate, descendants of the ancient ones. The two families are closely related, but there is no evidence that the older group is ancestral. There is indeed some evidence that herbaceous horse-tails may also have been in existence in the Coal Measure age, but the specialised giant forms that dominated the swamps of those times seem to have been completely extinguished by the close of the Palæozoic era.

"MOSSES" THAT WERE GIANT TREES

PERHAPS the most abundant of all Coal Measure plant fossils are the remains of the giant club-mosses. The remarks just made about the horse-tails apply to this group also. The living representatives are small herbaceous plants some of which are popularly known as club-mosses, though

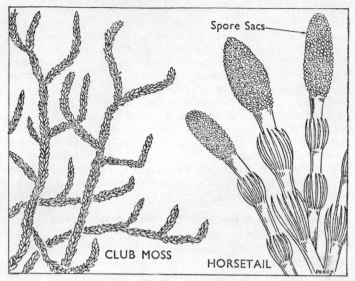

TWO MODEST PLANTS OF ANCIENT LINEAGE
These small herbaceous plants are the relatives living to-day of the Tree Horse-tails and Giant Club Mosses so conspicuous in the landscape of the Carboniferous Period.

in spite of the name they have nothing to do with true mosses. Their allies (but not actual ancestors) in Carboniferous times were often huge trees over a hundred feet in height, capable of increasing in thickness by forming secondary wood ; in many cases their foliage of small densely-crowded leaves was similar to that of the club-mosses. It is well to be familiar with two of the principal genera of these trees, *Lepidodendron* and *Sigillaria*, for fragments of their stems, showing impressions of the crowded leaf-bases, lozenge-shaped in the former and more rectangular or hexagonal in the latter, are exceedingly common in the coal-beds. Still commoner, perhaps, is the fossil called *Stigmaria*, which is now known to be the ramifying underground rootstock of both *Sigillaria* and *Lepidodendron*. The finer rootlets penetrated everywhere in the coal swamps, and the coal-balls described above are always full of them.

The cones of these plants produced two kinds of spores,

and were so prodigal of their pollen, as the smaller spores may be called, that certain deposits of coal are practically made of nothing else ; probably in such cases the pollen drifted into the still waters of a pool and collected at the bottom. The larger spores (also very common in coal, their resistant coats often remaining when the vegetable matter decayed) were sometimes reduced to a single one in each spore-sac. By a further development in which the spore-sac was closely invested by a leafy structure, leaving only a slit for the entrance of the pollen, a seed-like organ was produced. Other types of seed have also been found in this group, showing that seed formation was not confined either to the flowering plants or their ancestors, for the seed-bearing club-mosses belong to an entirely different line of descent which died out long ago.

SLENDER CLIMBERS WITH COMPLICATED CONES

ONE characteristic group of Palæozoic plants must be mentioned briefly : the delicate Sphenophylls. The ribbed and jointed stems bearing whorls of wedge-shaped, sometimes fringed or forked leaves, indicate a relationship with the tree horse-tails. The stems had a solid woody axis, which produced secondary wood, but never reached a very great size, and they were probably trailing or climbing plants. The cones of most members of the group were complex, and do not suggest any close affinity with other groups. One of the Lower Carboniferous forms, known as *Cheirostrobus*, of which only a few specimens have ever been found, at Pettycur in Scotland, is quite the most complex fructification known in any spore-plant, either fossil or recent, with whorls of elaborately segmented scales bearing well-protected spore-sacs. So far as structure is concerned, the group apparently reached its climax early in the seed-fern era ; representatives are still to be found up to the close of the era in rocks of all parts of the world, but after that it died out completely.

The complexity of structure exhibited at such an early stage as the Lower Carboniferous by plants like *Cheirostrobus* is a very striking and interesting phenomenon. It suggests for one thing that such plants must be the result of a very long period of evolution, but in this connection there are two points to be remembered : first that we have very little idea of the *rate* of evolution in living beings ; second, that the apparent suddenness with which groups rose to importance or developed in organisation is often due to an inevitable foreshortening as we look back over geological time. Thus between the Lower Devonian, in which so far as we know only relatively simple plants flourished, and the Lower Carboniferous, with *Cheirostrobus* and other highly specialised types, there was an interval of many million years—a far longer period, probably, than that covered by the whole evolution of man from anthropoid apes. Whether or not *Cheirostrobus* was the result of comparatively rapid evolution from some earlier type of jointed spore-bearing plant, one lesson seems clear : that extreme complexity and specialisation lead inevitably to extinction.

AN IDENTITY PUZZLE: FERNS THAT BELIED THEIR APPEARANCE

TRUE ferns were not nearly so common in the Coal Measure period as was formerly supposed, but their existence is well-attested by petrified remains of stems and leaves as well as spore-sacs. The fossils fall into two main sections : a group of " early " ferns which first appear in the Upper Devonian, with a fairly simple type of anatomical structure, and a group of tree-ferns which are characteristic of the later part of the era, with a very elaborate stem anatomy. The curious thing about the former is that many of them had most unusual fronds borne in definite rows, which branched repeatedly in planes at right angles to each other, so that they must have looked quite unlike any ferns we know at present, while the really fern-like fronds of the Carboniferous period were many of them not ferns at all. These early ferns seem to be another extinct specialised stock, though they show points of contact with certain later families of ferns, and especially with the family to which the Royal Fern belongs.

The Early Ferns may also be related to the tree-ferns of the later Palæozoic, and although the latter, too, are extinct, it is commonly believed that they are allied to certain living tropical ferns of the family Marattiaceæ. Their petrified stems are particularly common in certain Permian Beds of Saxony, and have long been familiar, when cut and polished, as decorative objects under the name of " starling-stones." They obtained the name because of the mottled appearance of the thick mass of felted roots which grew round the stem. More is known about the stems than about the foliage and reproductive organs of most of these ferns ; with the fertile fronds bearing spore-sacs, it is difficult to know whether or not they are really true ferns or whether they are the pollen-bearing organs of plants such as those we are about to describe.

STRANGE KINDS OF PLANTS THAT HAVE LEFT NO DESCENDANTS

THERE is now not the slightest doubt that the majority of the commonest fern-like fronds of the Coal Measures did not belong to the ferns at all, but were seed-plants of an entirely extinct group. In several cases the seeds have actually been found borne on the fronds, sometimes on a naked part, but sometimes on fronds with normal leaflets. There was nothing in the nature of a specialised flower.

In appearance many of the seed-ferns must have resembled the tree-ferns of the present day. In the structure of the stem as well as of the reproductive organs they show an amazing variety, and in spite of the superficial resemblance it does not seem that these plants were at all closely related to any known ferns, either fossil or recent. Moreover, the earliest-known forms of the ferns and of the seed-ferns found in Upper Devonian rocks are not in the least alike. Both groups may have had a common origin, but if so it must have been in an earlier era. The seed-ferns may be related to the gymnosperms, especially the cycads, for there are similarities in the anatomical characters of the stem as well as in the structure of the seed.

In the fertilisation of the seed-ferns we have an interesting example of the dependence of highly-developed land-plants on water at one stage of their life-history. Fertilisation in the ferns and other spore-plants, and also in the cycads, still takes place by the liberation of an active male cell which requires the presence of water in order to swim to the female organ. The higher seed-plants of to-day have got beyond this dependence on water, and the male cell is passive, but the seeds of the Carboniferous seed-ferns resemble those of cycads in having a pollen-chamber into which when it was filled with water the male cells were no doubt liberated. In some of these fossil seeds pollen-grains have actually been found in the pollen-chamber.

Palæozoic seeds also differed from those of modern flowering plants in another important respect : they did not contain an embryo. Some of them were quite small—only a few millimetres in length—but a few were as large as a duck's egg, with a very thick coat. The question of whether the higher seed-plants are all descended from a single stock is still undecided. Many botanists, however, are inclined to see in the network of forms grouped together as the seed-ferns the starting-point of the several lines of gymnosperms, and also of the flowering plants of to-day. This problem will be referred to again below.

TREES THAT WERE TRIUMPHS OF ENGINEERING

THE last important group of Upper Palæozoic plants is exemplified by the tall trees known as *Cordaites*. Their lofty branched stems bore large, strap-shaped leaves, sometimes as much as a metre in length. The complicated internal structure of the leaves, with strands of thick fibres to act as girders, show that they were mechanically well adapted to withstand bending and tearing strains. On this point D. H. Scott writes :—

" It is interesting to note that the construction of the leaves of this extinct race of gymnosperms was, from an engineering point of view, on the same lines as that of the similar leaves of certain Monocotyledons at the present day. Thus, when the conditions were identical, the adaptations of Palæozoic plants were the same as those of plants of similar habit now living."

The structure of the wood much resembles that of the monkey-puzzle conifers of the present day. The pith was very large (and thus was more like the cycads than the conifers) and was divided by a series of transverse diaphragms. Casts of the pith (comparable with those of the horse-tails mentioned above) are among the commonest fossils of the Coal Measures. The fructifications were of an elaborate structure, rather like catkins in form, and the seeds, like those of the Pteridosperms and the living cycads and the Maidenhair-tree, were provided with a pollen-chamber. The Cordaiteans were certainly an advanced and highly-developed race and they afford evidence of relationship with all the chief groups of gymnosperms.

The flora in the early part of this era, that is to say, in the Upper Devonian and Lower Carboniferous, was somewhat different from that of the Coal Measures and the Permian, which also may be classed together in a general way. Although most of the same plant groups are represented throughout the era, some of them, such as the *Cordaites* trees just mentioned, and also *Sigillaria*, attained their main development later, while towards the end there is an increase in the conifers and cycads. Many genera are especially characteristic of the earlier period, and one of the most abundant of these, supposed to be a seed-fern, has suggested the name *Archæopteris* flora. Where marine beds occur in the Lower Carboniferous, reefs of calcareous algæ abound, but in this sketch we can deal only with the land vegetation of these and later times.

The interesting thing about this *Archæopteris* flora is that it was world-wide in distribution, like the preceding early land-flora, representatives of it having been found from Spitsbergen to South America and Australia. When we come to the Coal Measures, however, we find that the profuse and varied flora which provided our most important coal deposits was almost confined to the northern hemisphere. Even in the north more than one floral province can be distinguished, and there are many plants in the coal-beds of China which are not found in those of Europe and North America.

AN ICE AGE IN THE SOUTH

IN the southern hemisphere the vegetation was not nearly as varied, largely because the climatic conditions were less favourable. Vast areas in the south were in the grip of an Ice Age while luxuriant vegetation flourished in the north. The southern flora had no true Calamites or tree horse-tails, few giant club-mosses and few of the common seed-ferns so familiar in our coal-beds. The most abundant plant fossils are certain tongue-shaped leaves with netted veins, called *Glossopteris* (" tongue fern "), of which there are numerous varieties. Hence the name *Glossopteris* flora, which has been applied to the whole assemblage of Upper Carboniferous and Permian plants of South America, South Africa, India and Australia. It has been surmised that these areas, with their very uniform flora, were formerly more or less united into one great continent, to which the name Gondwanaland has been given.

In spite of its name, it is now regarded as certain that *Glossopteris* was not a fern at all. It may have been a seed-fern, or it may have belonged to some gymnospermous group, but the conditions of preservation have not left us anything comparable with the coal-balls of Europe and America, and we really know little of the internal structure or of the reproductive organs of *Glossopteris* and its allies. Gymnosperms were certainly well represented in the flora, and some of them seem to have belonged to the same group as *Cordaites*. The Sphenophylls were represented, and the horsetails were of more herbaceous types than the Calamites, though still unlike those of to-day.

THE SOUTH POLE PLANTS THAT SCOTT DISCOVERED

THE northern and southern floras did not occupy entirely distinct territories. There was an admixture of the two in Central Africa down to Southern Rhodesia, while in Sumatra and Malay a northern flora has been found unaccompanied by *Glossopteris*. In south-eastern Asia *Glossopteris* itself lasted on into the next era, and thence perhaps spread northwards and westwards in the early Mesozoic. But in general, the very distinctive *Glossopteris* flora belongs to the southern region known as Gondwanaland, which, in this era, included Antarctica. One of the most important discoveries of Scott's last expedition to the south polar regions was of strata containing *Glossopteris* and other fossil plants at Buckley Island on the Beardmore Glacier, within three hundred miles of the South Pole. Evidently the climate of the Antarctic must then have been considerably warmer than at present.

We have already mentioned that the earlier *Archæopteris* flora flourished in Arctic regions, and many later plant-bearing deposits are known within the Arctic and Antarctic circles, so that we may be justified in regarding the present extreme frigidity of these regions as being, geologically speaking, abnormal. It would be out of place, however, to enter into a full discussion here of the questions connected with changes of climate and of the distribution of land and sea in past ages. It is necessary to mention these changes because of their influence on the distribution and evolution of plants.

The coming of an ice age in the southern hemisphere was evidently connected with the extinction of the *Archæopteris* flora and the rise of *Glossopteris*; in the northern hemisphere, the gradual disappearance of the seed-fern flora of the coal swamps was largely due to increasing desiccation. At the close of the Permian period and in part of the succeeding Triassic period desert conditions prevailed over large tracts. The break in the succession of floras seems, of course, more complete when we study only a limited area; or when conditions happen to be unfavourable for the preservation of fossils, but the change in the vegetation was undoubtedly very great in the northern hemisphere.

A WORLD WITHOUT GRASS

AT the end of the Palæozoic Age the great tree club-mosses and tree horse-tails had died out completely; the little Sphenophylls that trailed over them disappeared too; the older types of gymnosperms, such as *Cordaites*, were replaced by conifers and others which were only beginning to creep in at the close of the Palæozoic. The familiar seed-ferns had all gone, and the general appearance of the vegetation must have been completely different. Nevertheless it was also unlike that of to-day, for there were still none of the higher flowering plants. It is strange, for example, to think of a world without grasslands, but so far we know of no fossil plants which can have carpeted the ground in quite the same way as do the grasses of this latest era in which we live.

The plants which gave character to the vegetation in this era, which we have therefore called the age of gymnosperms, belonged to three groups of seed-plants, the conifers, the maidenhair-trees, and the cycads—or better, the cycadophytes. The living cycads are rare and few in number; they are mainly tropical, and have no popular name—some of them have been called sago-palms, but they have nothing to do with the real palms and the sago they produce is of no account. The fossil cycadophytes had very similar, stiff, sometimes palm-like foliage, but their reproductive organs differed considerably.

The age in which these groups were dominant is roughly the Mesozoic era of the geologists, but it ended, so far as the plant life is concerned, about the middle of the Cretaceous period—that is, rather earlier than the conventional line between the Mesozoic and the Tertiary. In actual time, it is safe to say that it lasted a hundred million years—probably not so long as the preceding age of seed-ferns.

PLANT LIFE BECOMES COSMOPOLITAN

THE difference between the vegetation of the northern and the southern hemispheres which was so pronounced at the close of the Palæozoic era continued into the Mesozoic. In the south, where the distinction between Palæozoic and Mesozoic—or the age of seed-ferns and the age of gymnosperms—is not so easily drawn, the dominant Triassic plants differed markedly from those of the north. The *Glossopteris* flora, after changing its character very gradually, becomes known as the *Dicroidium* flora, from the name of a very characteristic plant with forked fronds which is common in most parts of the old continent of Gondwanaland.

Into the problems of the possible changed position of continents through crustal drift, or of the former existence of land-bridges across oceans, we cannot enter here, but as a result of migrations and invasions from south to north and vice versa over long periods of time, the vegetation of the whole word seems to have grown much more uniform again in Jurassic times. From Alaska and Siberia to the Antarctic the same kinds of plants were dominant, and the Yorkshire cliffs yield fossils which are indistinguishable from those of China and Japan, or of Graham Land in the far south. This flora lasted on into the early part of the succeeding Cretaceous period.

SOME FAMILIES WHOSE DESCENDANTS SURVIVE TO-DAY

THE horse-tails of the Mesozoic need not detain us long. They continued to form a minor element in the vegetation, but though often much larger than the present-day relics of the class, they all seem to have been herbaceous and not woody forms. Except for some obscure fossils in the Triassic, the giant club-mosses were also herbaceous, and quite comparable with the modern club-mosses. These two great classes had passed their zenith ; the small herbaceous forms had the tenacity to survive right down to the present day, but they were fixed and gave rise to no new types.

The true ferns were very abundant in this era ; the primitive Palæozoic ferns as well as most of the tree-ferns of the Permian had disappeared, and a great many of the Mesozoic fossils can be fitted into families which still exist. It is very interesting to find, however, that some of the most abundant and widespread of these fossils belong to families which have now only a few living representatives, with a very restricted distribution. The tropical ferns *Dipteris* and *Matonia* of Borneo and Malay are the last survivors of families which in Mesozoic times contained various genera with many common species, found in the rocks of almost all parts of the world.

The Royal Ferns, which have had a long history from the Permian to the present day, with a very interesting series of developments in the structure of the stem, were abundant in the Jurassic and Cretaceous, and so were the Gleichenias, now confined to the tropics. Several other families of ferns which were well represented in the Mesozoic have survived to the present day. This does not mean that the species, or even the genera, are the same ; they may have changed considerably, and we do not know the fossil remains completely enough to be able to compare them fully with living forms. Moreover, there are many fossil ferns of this era whose affinities still puzzle us.

PLANTS THAT HAVE CHANGED THEIR HOMES

THE origin of the conifers is still a matter of uncertainty. It is commonly supposed that they were derived from the same stock as *Cordaites*, but, though they certainly existed in the Upper Coal Measures, they only became abundant during the Mesozoic era. All the present-day types are well represented : pines, yews, Araucarias and others. In addition there are forms which seem to combine the characters of more than one group, either in the structure of their wood or of their cones, and numerous others which belong to extinct families. Two instances of changed geographical distribution may be mentioned : the Araucarias (which include the Norfolk Island pine and the Monkey-puzzle) are now confined to the southern hemisphere, but were formerly abundant all over the world ; and the Sequoias, which are known from the latter part of the Mesozoic and were widely spread over the northern hemisphere almost throughout the succeeding Tertiary era, are now reduced to two species (the Mammoth-tree and the Redwood) growing only in a narrow belt of country in California, where they are remarkable for their size and longevity.

The Maidenhair-tree (*Gingko*) is now unknown in the wild state, and probably owes its survival to its cultivation in the gardens of Eastern temples. It is the sole living representative of a group which in the Mesozoic era had an almost world-wide distribution and showed a very considerable range in habit and structure. The leaves, which are more frequent as fossils than the other organs, may be entire or slightly notched and fan-shaped, like those of the cultivated Maidenhair-tree, or long and deeply divided, often with very narrow linear segments. They always have characteristic forking veins, and the microscopic structure of the breathing-pores is always of the same general plan. Like most leaves of gymnosperms, recent and fossil, they were tough and resistant, and are often preserved in Mesozoic rocks in a mummified state, flattened between the layers of sediment, but with the outer cuticle practically unchanged. Such specimens, after being removed from the rock and cleared by appropriate chemical treatment, can be examined microscopically ; the differences in structural detail so revealed, especially of the breathing-pores (stomata), have proved to be valuable guides to affinity. The conifers and the cycadophytes (which we are about to discuss) have also been intensively studied in this way.

THE FLOWER APPEARS AT LAST

IT has been estimated that one-third of the species of Mesozoic plants belonged to the cycadophytes, and even if this includes a number of strange forms whose real affinities are uncertain, we may also say that the group exhibits as wide a range of structure as is to be seen in the seed-ferns of the Palæozoic. Though some of them bore cones, the fructifications of others may rightly be described as flowers.

In the Jurassic rocks of the Yorkshire coast one may often find fossils which look something like a *Magnolia* flower ; they are known locally as Cliff-Roses—one of the very rare instances in which a fossil plant has been given a popular name—and their scientific name is *Williamsonia*. They usually have an outer whorl of large leafy bracts which look like sepals or petals, surrounding either a whorl of stamens or a central seed-bearing cone. In some related forms seeds and stamens are found together in the same flower. The seeds, though surrounded by protective scales, were exposed at their tips and not enclosed in a carpel or seed-case as in the familiar flowering plants of to-day. That is to say that they were of the " gymnosperm " and not the " angiosperm " type. The stamens were sometimes elaborately branched, and not so simple as the stamens of the higher plants.

The flowers of *Williamsonia* were freely exposed on slender branching stems ; another group had short stumpy stems, and the numerous flowers were embedded among the leaf-bases. Many examples of the latter type (known as *Cycadeoidea*) have been found in a petrified state, and their structure and minute anatomy are very fully known. The female cones consisted of seeds borne on long stalks, between which were sterile scales whose ends enlarged beyond the seeds and fitted closely together, leaving a small opening. The whole was surrounded by protective bracts, and in some species the compound stamens were present in the same flower.

The general arrangement of the parts, as in *Williamsonia*, thus resembled that of modern flowering plants. The suggestion has therefore been made that the latter were derived from Mesozoic ancestors like *Cycadeoidea* or *Williamsonia*— more probably the latter, for it was less specialised, and also rather older. But there are wide differences in detail, even in the flowers, and the other organs do not support the idea of a really close relationship. Just as the seed habit appeared in various groups of plants in the Palæozoic era, so the flower type of fructification may have been evolved in groups which do not belong to what we now regard as the " flowering " plants. The analogies between a cycadophyte flower and that of a *Magnolia* (which many regard as one of the more primitive flowering plants) may be only due to parallel development. These Mesozoic cycadophytes are still a great mystery ; early forms belonging to the group are found rarely in the Upper Coal Measures, but we do not know whence they were derived, nor exactly how they are connected with the living cycads.

WHAT HAPPENED TO THE SEED-FERNS?

THE flower (which is essentially a special arrangement of the fertile parts) may then have arisen in more than one group, and it is interesting to inquire further into the history of some of the organs of which it is composed. The stamen of a modern flowering plant is nearly always a simple structure consisting of a single stalked anther, but there are a few cases, such as the Castor-oil plant, in which the stamens are much branched. It is tempting to regard this as a primitive character, recalling the branched pollen-bearing organs of various Mesozoic plants. Other fossil male organs are known in which each stalk bears a tuft or tassel of anthers, and these may have given rise by reduction to the ordinary stamen with one anther. The carpel or closed seed-case is so characteristic of living flowering plants that it has given the name Angiosperm (hidden seeds) to the whole group.

Now in the same Yorkshire beds which yield the cliff-roses some small fossils have been found looking rather like bunches of currants, and on investigation each " currant " proves to be a carpel containing seeds. These fossils, which have been named *Caytonia*, are quite unlike any known flowering plant :

are we then to regard them as an early isolated group of Angiosperms, or is this another case in which a classification based solely on recent plants proves a stumbling-block when we come to consider the fossils? We must not allow our own imperfect terminology to entangle us, and " angiospermy " (the possession of a closed carpel) may well have arisen in Jurassic times in groups now extinct which we cannot really call angiosperms.

None the less, though we do not yet know sufficient about this Jurassic carpel-bearing fossil *Caytonia* to give an answer, we cannot help asking ourselves whether it may not be on the line which led to the modern flowering plants. Whence was *Caytonia* derived ? There are several points, not only in the structure of the carpel and seeds, but in the associated branched stamens with tufts of anthers, which are comparable with some of the seed-ferns of the Palæozoic. Moreover, in the early Mesozoic rocks of South Africa (earlier than those in which *Caytonia* has been found) there are other fossil reproductive organs which, while recalling *Caytonia*, are still more like the older seed-ferns. These organs are associated with leaves known as *Dicroidium*, already referred to above as characteristic of the southern flora in the Triassic period.

The evidence therefore suggests that the one great group of Palæozoic plants which survived in a flourishing condition into the Mesozoic era was the seed-ferns ; that though the changed conditions in the north may have exterminated most of the Coal Measure forms, the somewhat different southern families continued to evolve and later invaded the northern hemisphere ; and that the modern flowering plants may have arisen from early Mesozoic seed-ferns.

THE AGE OF FLOWERING PLANTS

THE final great transformation in the plant-life of the earth—the fourth we have described—introduced the vegetation of to-day. The old Mesozoic flora lasted, as we have seen, well into the Cretaceous period, but when we come to the Upper Cretaceous a complete change is manifest. The cycadophytes have disappeared almost entirely ; the Maidenhair-trees are insignificant in numbers and variety ; there are no strange problematical relics of groups now unknown. Instead there is an abundance of flowering plants belonging to families with which we are familiar at the present day. Palms, reeds, and other Monocotyledons (plants which have only one seed leaf) make their appearance, and there is a profusion of Dicotyledons (plants which have two seed leaves)—walnuts, willows, oaks, laurels, breadfruits, tulip-trees, planes, and maples among others—mainly trees, for their deciduous leaves are rather more likely to be preserved, but with a good sprinkling of herbaceous plants too.

" In fact," as D. H. Scott has said, " if we judge by present evidence, it would not be surprising to find that by about the middle of the Cretaceous period the angiosperms generally were developed very much as they are now so far as the families and even some of the genera are concerned."

For this same general type of flora has persisted throughout the whole of the Tertiary period to the present day, and it may be said that, botanically speaking, we are still living in the Cretaceous epoch.

DARWIN'S "ABOMINABLE MYSTERY": THE TRIUMPH OF FLOWERS

ALTHOUGH we may follow certain definite lines along which individual plant organs may have evolved, we do not yet know any fossil plants which can with certainty be regarded as ancestors of the flowering plants. Nor do we find that the first fossil forms are particularly primitive. So far no undoubted angiosperms have been found earlier than the Cretaceous. A few rare and dubious Jurassic records may be disregarded, and the lowest Cretaceous rocks still contain an abundant cycadophyte flora without a trace of Dicotyledons or Monocotyledons. But in the Lower Greensand rocks of this country (that is, in the later part of the Lower Cretaceous), among numerous fossil woods which are mainly conifers with a sprinkling of cycadophytes, there are several distinct kinds of broad-leaved trees. Leaves and flowers are not known from these rocks, but so far as their stem anatomy is concerned, the Dicotyledons were " already highly differentiated in various directions."

From this time on the flowering plants gained in importance at the expense of the older gymnosperms. Darwin referred to the rapidity with which they developed and overspread the world as " an abominable mystery." In a letter to Hooker, Darwin wrote :

> " Nothing is more extraordinary in the history of the Vegetable Kingdom, as it seems to me, than the *apparently* very sudden or abrupt development of the higher plants. I have sometimes speculated whether there did not exist somewhere during the long ages an extremely isolated continent, perhaps near the South Pole."

As we have seen, the ancient continent of Gondwanaland included the south polar region (either as a continuous continent or as a series of closely grouped island masses), and, moreover, there is some reason for thinking that the stock which gave rise to the flowering plants may have evolved partly in Gondwanaland. But further than that we cannot go. Polar regions have frequently been suggested as the original homes of various groups, but on general grounds the teeming tropics seem more likely to have cradled a new race. The more favourable conditions of tropical or subtropical climates would permit the survival of novelties which under severer circumstances might be destroyed as useless.

THE MYSTERY OF FLOWERS' ANCESTRY

IT is clear that the actual ancestry of the flowering plants, which is still shrouded in mystery, must be sought far back in the Mesozoic era. Their apparently rapid spread is a different matter, and to begin with we must note that in any case it took a few million years at least, which though geologically rapid, is slow compared with the rapidity of man's own evolution and spread. In the case of man, however, we are dealing with a single species, whereas there are now more than a hundred thousand different species of flowering plants. A second point to remember is that we are less likely to find records of rare and restricted plants than of those which are common and widely distributed.

Two different sets of factors may be mentioned as influencing the rise of the modern flora : first, changes in the physical aspect of land and sea due to crustal movement ; and secondly, the interaction of plant and animal life. About the middle of the Cretaceous period there was, as A. C. Seward puts it,

> " a remarkably widespread marine transgression; vast regions which had previously been dry land were flooded

by an invading sea. May we not see in this sinking and flooding a possible influence on the course of evolution in the organic world, an almost world-wide interference with the physical environment which had its repercussion in the altered trend of plant development?"

Great changes such as this must have been accompanied by alterations of climate, and the two together may have been largely responsible for the extermination of the older flora. As the land re-emerged a newer and more vigorous stock peopled it, suggesting that the evolutionary periods, which seem to alternate with periods of quiescence, are stimulated by great physical changes.

The interrelationship of plants and animals is a large subject, but one aspect of it is very important in connection with the rise of the flowering plants. There is little doubt that the mutual adaptation of pollinating insects and honey-bearing flowers was an important factor in the success of both groups. In species the insects now outnumber all the rest of the animal Kingdom, just as the angiosperms form the most numerous group of plants. Insects were already in existence in the Coal Measures, but they do not seem to have become really important until the later Mesozoic. Although, of course, many flowering plants are still wind-pollinated, the marvellous variety and subtle mechanisms of all the most conspicuous flowers of to-day have obviously been evolved for the attraction of insect visitors and the insurance of cross-pollination.

FLORA UNIFORM ALL OVER THE WORLD

THE history of plant life throughout this last " modern era," that is, from the Middle or Upper Cretaceous to the present day, is intimately connected with changes of climate, and with the differentiation of genera and species rather than with the rise of new groups. Some of the old groups, such as the conifers, still retain a measure of importance, but this is definitely the age of flowering plants, and on the whole, in spite of the existence of distinct botanical provinces, it may be called a world-wide flora. Some botanists have claimed that the era of world-wide floras began to pass away after the Cretaceous age, but there is no doubt that if a geologist could look at the fossil relics of to-day's vegetation from a distance of a few million years he would regard it as the most uniform flora that the world has ever seen.

Differences in detail should not blind us to the essential similarity of the vegetation all over the world for the last sixty or seventy million years. The various floral migrations and changes do, of course, make an intensely interesting study. Thus we may refer once more to the presence of abundant fossil plants in Arctic regions where to-day the vegetation is scanty or nil. At the beginning of the Tertiary period the flora of Greenland might be described as warm-temperate, and temperate plants have been found fossilised as far north as Grinnell Land. In southern England, the Eocene flora was distinctly tropical. The London Clay has yielded a very extensive series of well-preserved fossils and seeds, particularly abundant on the foreshore at Sheppey ; these had accumulated in the estuary or in the sea near the mouth of a great river, comparable to the tropical rivers of to-day which bring down quantities of driftwood and various fruits and seeds, depositing them in the mud at their mouths.

The commonest and most characteristic fossil of the London Clay is the fruit of a species of swamp-palm called *Nipa*, which is to-day found only on Indo-Malayan coasts, but several other palms are known, and a whole series of fruits and seeds belonging mainly to tropical families. Most of these have not got common English names, but the general conclusion is that the London Clay flora was mainly of a tropical rain-forest type, allied principally with the living Indo-Malayan flora. In those times a great sea—a sort of extended Mediterranean—stretched from England to further India, and the fossil *Nipa* has been found at various points which were then on the shores of this sea. Subsequent geographical and climatic changes have resulted in this Eocene tropical flora being now confined to the Indo-Malayan region. It will be interesting to follow some of these general changes during the Tertiary epoch.

HOW PLANTS GOT THEIR PRESENT HOMES

THE main factors influencing plant distribution over long periods of time are first climatic change and secondly those movements of the earth's crust which result in mountain building or in extensive alterations in land and sea areas. (Mountain ranges are often more effective barriers to plant migration than arms of the sea.) There are, of course, other minor influences, such as the relation of the plants to a changing animal population. The interaction of all these factors, extinguishing some species, driving others from their original habitats, or leaving tracts of country open for re-colonisation, has gradually led to the establishment of the present floral regions, and to the apparent anomalies of discontinuous distribution.

A combined study of the geology and of the numerous relics of fossil floras enables us to trace in a general way the changes which have taken place throughout the Tertiary period—at any rate in the northern hemisphere, where the fossils have been more adequately studied. In early Tertiary times the flora of what is now the north-temperate and circumpolar region seems to have been fairly uniform in general character, and until after the close of the Miocene the vegetation changed but slowly. The oncoming of the Ice Age drove many plants southwards, and in Europe and western Asia the east-and-west mountain ranges which had meanwhile been uplifted effectively barred their escape to warmer latitudes. In North America and eastern Asia, however, the north-and-south direction of the main ranges made no such barrier ; hence the survival in Central America and the Sino-Malayan region of many Tertiary relics. In warmer post-glacial times some of these exiles were able to spread northwards ; this is especially noticeable in eastern America, but in the western part of that continent the uplift of the Rocky Mountains had so changed the climate by cutting off moisture-bearing winds that the region was no longer suitable for the " Miocene " flora.

PLANTS DRIVEN FROM EUROPE BY THE COLD

IN Europe many of the Tertiary species were extinguished because they had no southward refuge from the cold, nor could there be any later northward re-colonization. Consequently the present European flora is comparatively poor in species ; thus, plants like *Azolla* (a tiny floating water-fern) and *Brasenia* (a water-lily) are now native in every continent except Europe, though both of them were abundant in Oligocene beds of the Isle of Wight, for example. Nevertheless, the present climate of Europe is perfectly favourable to many of the missing forms ; *Azolla*, reintroduced by man after the lapse of ages, flourishes once more in the ponds and streams of southern England, and to look through a nurseryman's catalogue of trees and shrubs is to find a whole group of plants, such as *Gingko*, *Abelia*, *Actinidia*, *Dipelta* and *Koel-*

reuteria and many another, all of which have been introduced into our gardens from eastern Asia, and all of which lived in Europe during the Tertiary period.

WHERE TO READ MORE ABOUT PLANTS OF THE PAST

THOSE who wish to study the methods of estimating the actual lengths of geological periods should read A. Holmes, *The Age of the Earth* (Benn's Sixpenny Series, 1927), which also gives an admirable brief sketch of historical geology. For the general botanical reader D. H. Scott's *Extinct Plants and Problems of Evolution* (Macmillan, 1924) is to be recommended, and the same author's *Studies in Fossil Botany* (A. & C. Black, 2 volumes, 3rd edition, 1920 and 1923) is a classic textbook for more advanced students. *Plant Life Through the Ages*, by A. C. Seward (Cambridge University Press, 2nd edition, 1933) is partly popular and partly suitable for the advanced student. It contains a good bibliography. R. Crookall's *Coal Measure Plants* (Arnold, 1929) is of use for identifying impressions of coal plants, and F. J. North's *Coal, and the Coalfields in Wales* (National Museum of Wales, 2nd edition, 1931) gives a good detailed account of the nature and formation of coal. All these books, except the first, are well illustrated. Specimens of fossil plants may be seen in the geological or botanical galleries of most museums. The fullest series is in the British Museum (Natural History), South Kensington, where an illustrated *Guide to the Fossil Plants* is obtainable.

HALF PLANT, HALF ANIMAL: THE CURIOUS FAMILY OF FUNGI

by E. H. ELLIS, B.Sc.

IN the last hundred years a great new science has grown up—the science of Mycology. Mycology comes from two Greek words μύκης, slime, mould, and hence any kind of fungus, and ὁ λόγος, study. A mycologist then is one who studies moulds and other fungi. This study has acquired such great economic importance that many mycologists are employed by industry and by various governments, and special courses in mycology are given at the universities.

Fungi [1] are a group of parasitic and saprophytic organisms. Their bodies are made up of hyphæ instead of ordinary cells, and they reproduce themselves by spores instead of seeds. A parasite is an organism that lives on other living organisms. There are many degrees of parasitism. Ivy, for example, is not a parasite, for though it clings to other plants by means of short roots, it is rooted in the ground and manufactures food with its leaves. Mistletoe is partially parasitic; it has green leaves, but derives its mineral requirements from the tree on which it grows—the host-plant as it is called. These are not fungi because they have closely-joined cells, a vascular structure or skeleton, and reproduce by seeds.

Instead of the brick-like cells characteristic of the higher plants, the fungus body consists of tubular threads called hyphæ (*hy* rhyming with *fly*). Hyphæ are elongated thread-like cells, matted together in the bulkier forms like the mushroom, the fungi with which most of us are best acquainted. Mushrooms and toadstools are not parasitic but saprophytic. A saprophyte, from the Greek σαπρός, and φυτόν, a plant, is a plant which grows on decaying matter, a scavenger rather than a parasite. The fungi with which the mycologist is mainly concerned are the parasites, small organisms like rusts, mildews and smuts which cause disease in plants.

The Bacteria, popularly called germs, are another group of organisms, which, though mainly saprophytic, often cause disease in man and sometimes in plants. Bacteria are single-celled. Almost all rot and decay is caused by fungi or bacteria.

[1] See pp. 67 and 72.

The bacteria are similar to the fungi in their modes of life and may be studied in similar ways. Their one-celled body may be round, rod-like or spiral in shape. The bacteria are, of course, familiar owing to the part they play in human diseases, though some human diseases, such as ringworm and thrush are caused by fungi. Fungi, on the other hand, more frequently cause disease among plants than do bacteria. It is in these parasitic organisms like rusts, mildews and smuts that the main interest of applied mycology centres.

THE FUNGI'S UNCONVENTIONAL WAY OF LIVING

FUNGI are traditionally considered to be plants, although a trifle unconventional in their behaviour. For many years this opinion was held more by default than for any better reason, because decisive evidence was absent. As research has increased our knowledge of the group, the old ideas have become suspect, but the suspicion does not necessarily commit us to the alternative of declaring fungi to be animals. There is the possibility that fungi are neither plants nor animals in the ordinarily accepted sense of those words, but are some third kind of organism, and it is perhaps rather towards a view of this kind that modern thought is tending. It was thought at one time that fungi show a relationship to the red seaweeds because of certain resemblances in their life-histories. To-day, although these resemblances are generally regarded as being more superficial than real, the affinity of fungi is still thought to be closer to the plant than to the animal world.

Fungi must earn their living either as parasites or saprophytes because they do not possess chlorophyll (green-colouring matter) and so are unable to manufacture their own food. From this point of view alone therefore fungi are not normal plants but, like animals, are dependent on green plants either at first or second hand, for their continued existence. This animal method of nutrition is not the only resemblance between fungi and animals, as there are some astonishing similarities in reproductive methods. On the other hand there are some fundamental differences in methods of construction between plants and animals that emphasise the plant features of fungi.

Plants differ from animals notably in respect of the units of which they are composed. All living organisms are composed essentially of protoplasm, but the protoplasm is in tiny pieces and each piece has a nucleus that exerts control on its surrounding protoplasm. There is a balance between the size of the nucleus and the surrounding piece of protoplasm. In plants each piece is characteristically surrounded by a wall, often of other material, while in animals the cell or protoplast is often naked, though the term " cell " is still applied in spite of the absence of a surrounding wall.

Some of the lowest animals consist of nothing more than a naked piece of protoplasm, but sometimes they develop a thick wall round themselves to make what is called an " encysted " form. A piece of protoplasm enclosed in this way is effectively sheltered from the hazards of adverse surroundings, but the rate at which the process of slow combustion of food can proceed is thereby retarded. The effect of the cell-walls of plants is to enclose the constituent protoplasm so that a plant is almost comparable to a mass of encysted animals.

The animal cell consists of a minute mass of protoplasm in which lies the nucleus, a denser part of the living substance. The protoplasm is bounded by the thinnest of membranes which is part of the protoplasm. There is nothing, therefore, to stop food materials—even solid particles—entering the animal cell. It is very different with the plant cell. As the plant cell grows, it surrounds itself with a solid and often thick wall of cellulose, through which only substances dissolved in water can pass. Therefore all food supplies for the plant must be in solution, that is, must be dissolved in water before they pass into the cell. The hyphæ of fungi, like plants, generally have a solid wall within which the protoplasm is contained and therefore the general construction of a fungus resembles more that of a plant than an animal and the fungus, like the plant, can only get its food supplies in solution.

HOW FUNGI PUZZLED THE ANCIENTS

As might be expected, the ancient Greeks and Romans had some knowledge of fungi, though naturally enough it would be the larger and more striking forms that would at first command attention, and any interest that was taken in the group was from a practical rather than from a scientific point of view. The possibilities of eating some kinds of toadstools, for example, became widely explored because of the passing of the *Lex sumptuaria*, the law that forbade the Romans to eat certain costly foods. Fungi, as products of the earth, were excluded from the operation of these laws and soon became in such great demand, that a measure of their appreciation can be obtained from the epigrammists of the time. From a practical interest also certain kinds found their way into the Chinese catalogue of drugs, though it is doubtful whether they earned this place so much from their curative value as from the air of mystery which surrounded them. Ergot, however, a fungus parasitic on cereals and especially on rye, is still a valued drug in modern medicine that has held an honoured place from a remote past.

At the time of the revival of learning in Europe there was a considerable knowledge of the larger toadstools, though there was still a tendency to endow them with magical properties—almost of the kind possessed by the mushroom that Alice ate when she was adventuring in Wonderland. Gradually the horrific glamour of finding them growing near serpents' holes and such places lapsed. Then followed the invention of the compound microscope, and with it a growing knowledge of household pests, such as mildews, helped to build up a better picture of the whole group. An understanding of the group, however, still eluded them, and it was probably a realisation of the lack of knowledge that led Linnæus to give the whole lot the rather despairing title " Chaos ".

THE BLACK SHEEP AMONG THE PLANT CITIZENS

TO-DAY we recognise fairly clearly what may be called the true fungi and two possibly allied groups, the bacteria and the mycetozoa, which in America are called " slime-moulds." The mycetozoa are perhaps even more exciting than the bacteria, with their dramatic associations with human ills, as even more than fungi are they animals rather than plants. Like fungi they lack chlorophyll. The mycetozoa are found in one of two phases that succeed each other throughout the life-history of each individual. One is a " vegetative " phase ; that is, simply a mass of naked protoplasm showing a streaming motion. The vegetative phase is followed by a " reproductive " phase of spores (reproductive bodies analogous to seeds) that are formed when the protoplasmic mass breaks up and special spore-containers appear. The spores germinate and either form a protoplasmic mass directly, or there is an intermediate stage in which the germinated spores swim about independently until they unite to make the normal jelly-like mass (plasmodium).

Most of these organisms live either on animal excrement or on decaying vegetation and are important accordingly. For, just as the health and growth of a town are limited by the speed at which waste material can be disposed of, so the waste products of life have to be broken down and in this work mycetozoa as well as bacteria and fungi play a part. Occasionally members of this group break the bonds of discipline and become parasitic inside plants in the same way as the malaria-parasite lives inside man. The normal processes of the host are upset and disease is produced. The well-known " club-root " of cabbage plants is a diseased state produced by a member of this group (*Plasmodiophora brassicæ*) living in the root of cabbage.

To say that bacteria are so well-known that they are in everybody's mouth would be merely one way of expressing the ubiquitous distribution of these organisms. They form the " germ " or " microbe " with which we are all familiar. But though they are so richly endowed with opportunity to cause disease, even bacteria have to show a balance-sheet to the world's auditors, with something on the balance side. We find, actually, that bacteria cannot live in the air, and that when present, they are merely there during transit. Their normal environment is soil, water, a plant or an animal body or one of the substances produced from them like food-stuffs or sewage. Their small size precludes us ordinarily from being aware of their presence and so they live their lives unobserved except for their effects. Their minuteness also makes them difficult to study, as while the largest may be of the thickness of a human hair, many are small spheres only one ten-thousandth of a millimetre in diameter, and can only just be seen individually with all the resources of modern scientific equipment. It is not surprising therefore to find that details of their structures are imperfectly known. We are aware, however, that while some are motionless, others possess locomotory organs at one or both ends of a rod-shaped body.

BACTERIA'S COMPOUND INTEREST: CELLS THAT INCREASE HOUR BY HOUR

No cell, either a bacterial organism or any other, can grow in size indefinitely, because physical difficulties of nutrition cause the inner portion of the cell and the actual wall itself

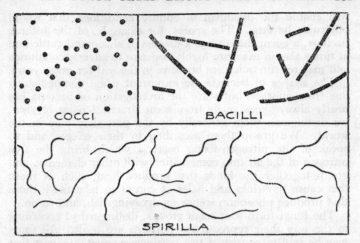

SOME SHAPES BACTERIA ARE KNOWN TO TAKE

Bacteria are so small—some are only one ten-thousandth of a millimetre in diameter—that it is difficult, even with a microscope, to be certain of their structure. The diagram shows three common types of bacteria, all highly magnified.

to increase disproportionately. In bacteria this limit is quickly attained under favourable growth conditions, and then the cell divides into two. It is said that bacteria divide directly without a nuclear division, but other authorities dispute this and it may well be that eventually a normal nuclear division will be demonstrated for these organisms. A division may take place every twenty or thirty minutes.

It can be shown that a mass of bacteria increases in size according to the compound-interest law in the same way as a sum of money increases. Estimates based on cells dividing once an hour show that in two days the descendants of one cell would number 281,500 millions. Lack of food and the accumulation of waste-products prevent this rapid growth, and the cells will then die according to the operation of the same law. If bacterial growth is being held in check by the application of a disinfectant it is thus possible to say how many will die in a certain time.

Occasionally bacteria may produce spores instead of the normal vegetative cell and then the thick wall of the spore

6

will enable the organism to endure conditions that would otherwise be fatal. The spores, for example, of the anthrax bacillus, a germ that causes a disease in sheep and cattle and at times also in man, are highly resistant to adverse conditions and may remain quiescent but alive in the soil for many years.

The shapes of bacteria are important when distinguishing one from another, but since the investigation of bacteria has nearly always been made from some practical point of view, we distinguish them generally by the part they play in the world. We group them according to their effects, and so speak of the nitrogen-fixing bacteria which bring the free nitrogen of the air into combination with other elements; and group together the kinds that produce heat, such as those that cause hay-ricks and bales of cotton to take fire ; those that produce phosphorescence on decaying fish, and so on.

The fungi form four main groups, distinguished according to the way their reproductive portions are built. All fungi may be said to consist of two portions, a vegetative part that is concerned with the absorption and assimilation of food and a reproductive portion containing a number of reproductive units, called spores.

When a spore germinates it pushes out a small tube which grows and becomes a *hypha*. A number of threads of hyphæ may make a felt-like mass that is vegetative and is known in the aggregate as the *mycelium*. All the bizarre shapes of fungi, from the ordinary mushroom shape, to puff-balls, truffles and the mildew that grows on bread and cheese are made up of compacted masses of hyphæ. The vegetative part of the mushroom is the mycelium or spawn that runs underground. The mushroom itself is the part which bears the spores. They are to be found in countless numbers in the ripe mushroom, borne on the radiating gills under the cap. The fact that no matter how the shape of the mushrooms or toadstools may vary, the spores are borne in groups of four, serves to distinguish mushrooms and their allies from other groups of fungi.

For example, although completely unlike in appearance and possessing no massive toadstool-like spore-bearing body, the rusts parasitic on wheat and other cereals also bear their spores in groups of four and are therefore regarded as belonging to the same general alliance as the mushroom.

An alternative arrangement that is characteristic for another of these great groups is that the spores, instead of being on

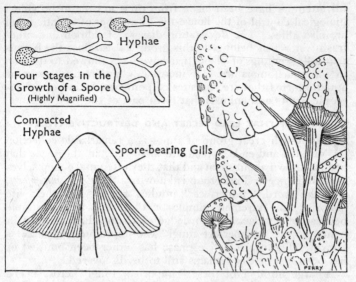

Four Stages in the Growth of a Spore (Highly Magnified)

Hyphae

Compacted Hyphae

Spore-bearing Gills

PERRY

FROM SPORE TO TOADSTOOL

Mushrooms and toadstools, like all fungi, spring from spores too small to be seen with the naked eye. Their whole structure, including their caps, consist of tubular threads known as " hyphæ ", matted together into a felt-like mass.

a free surface, are enclosed at first in small bags that tie the spores together in groups—usually groups of eight. Ultimately the bags burst and the spores are exploded into the air. Here again the range of variation of size and shape is considerable, with more or less massive plants like morels at one end of the scale and microscopic plants like yeasts at the other.

Both of these two groups have a number of transverse walls at intervals in their hyphal threads and this fact serves to distinguish them from the next big group that is usually without transverse walls. This group includes the moulds such as the common one that grows on moist bread. From the cobwebby mass that grows over the surface erect threads arise that cut off spores in special receptacles. Various relatives of this mould are of special interest. There is one, for example, that grows on oil cake and fodder, while another is the well-known " fly-cholera," a disease by means of which unsuccessful attempts have been made from time to time to provide a biological control of the house-fly. A number of aquatic fungi are also allies. The devastating disease of salmon and other fresh-water fish belongs to this group as also does the fungus that kills seedlings of plants that have been allowed to develop in too much moisture. Of increasing importance are some aquatic forms that are parasites of pond-weeds and of microscopic plants and animals that form part of the food of fishes.

FUNGI THAT LEAD SECRET AND DESTRUCTIVE LIVES

THE fourth great group of fungi is a remarkable collection of odds and ends, which are alike only in the facts that little is known about them and that they often make themselves great nuisances. This group is known as the *Fungi imperfecti*, and the word "imperfect" implies rather that their life histories are extremely simple or that they appear simple because of our lack of knowledge of them. For example in many of the "imperfect fungi" no reproductive phase is known. The reproductive phase has either been omitted or has been lost or else remains still to be discovered.

A large number of these "imperfect fungi" cross man's path at various points, and because of the economic importance they have assumed they have been subjected to detailed examination, with the result that some have been shown to be stages in the life-history of "perfect" forms. It is preferable to use the term "perfect" stage rather than to speak of a sexual stage, for, as will be shown later, the problem of sex in fungi is so complex that the subject is even more difficult than it is in human life.

SEX OR NO SEX? THE ELUSIVE SINGLE FUNGUS

SOME interesting problems connected with the power of vegetative reproduction arise in fungi. Notably there is the difficulty of defining the limits of the individual, and a rather arresting one that arises out of this is the development of the capacity for death. Let us consider the first problem. It is a characteristic of the group of *Fungi Imperfecti* that they reproduce themselves by vegetative bodies that can, if necessary, endure a surprising amount of barbarous treatment. Even in the other groups we find that the vegetative method of reproduction is retained throughout as an alternative to the sexual method and operates when the conditions of the environment are suitable. In fact we almost think that the fungus hesitates to indulge in sexual reproduction unless some particularly unpleasant surroundings threaten the extinction of the organism. Note how death and reproduction are at once closely related even if only as alternative possibilities.

If we are examining under a microscope a confused mass of hyphæ and reproductive spores it is difficult to say where any individual fungus begins and ends. Then, when we remember that a number of apparent individuals (if we can determine their limits) can exist together at the same time in a colony, all having originated from one spore, it is obvious that the term individual may take on a new meaning. We have indeed what is known as the problem of the " greater individual." A similar occurrence is found frequently in horticultural practice where garden strains are reproduced vegetatively, for instance, from " cutting " or " slips." All the plants come from one original plant, so that all the plants may be regarded as being part of the original one. The term " individual " may thus be applied to one plant in your own garden or to all the plants in everybody's garden.

When we are thinking of individuals in terms of trees it is sometimes possible to distinguish between the greater individual and the particular individual, but when we are dealing with a mass of microscopic fungus growth the problem becomes well-nigh impossible of solution. We can, however, look at it in this way. The term individual is one that has a fairly definite meaning when we apply it to ourselves, and it is possible to think of a number of fungi in which it would have as definite a meaning. For example, we can think of a spore of a mushroom that has been produced by a kind of sexual process, germinating and producing hyphæ, making up the mass of mushroom " spawn " that the botanists call the mycelium. All the products from the one spore would make up one individual.

THE FUNGI'S EXPERIMENTS IN REPRODUCTION

INDIVIDUALITY is thus some quality that becomes distinguishable only with definite sex, and in its absence we should be attempting to apply a label that cannot properly be applied at all. Our problem then is solved for practical purposes, so far as any solution of so complex a matter is possible. When plants are reproduced vegetatively there is no such thing as an individual, and so death of an organism is not possible until individuals become differentiated as separate entities. We have become so accustomed to the idea of reproduction following sexual fusion that we regard them as cause and effect. But other organisms have other methods, and frequently these two processes are not so intimately related as they are in ourselves, and there may even be an appreciable time interval between the two. In general, it would appear that the more organisms have developed special parts of themselves to serve for special purposes, the more closely are sex and reproduction related.

In fungi almost any part can perform the function of any other part and frequently reproduction is purely vegetative. Almost any odd piece can regenerate an entire organism. Even when organisms are fully developed, however, and are made up of a number of complicated parts such as those of which the human body is made, at the moment of reproduction they concentrate all their possibilities into one cell, as it is only in a one-celled stage that the sexual fusion that precedes reproduction can take place. In fungi something even less clearly marked than this occurs. It seems almost as though, in fungi, sex itself is in an experimental phase, and that various methods are being tried.

FUNGI WITH SIXTY-FOUR SEXES

THE problem of individuality that we have discussed was shown in some respects to be only one aspect of a wider problem of reproduction. It has been insisted that fungi have two methods of reproduction ; one, vegetative, the other requiring some kind of sexual fusion. Now sex and sexual processes are things that defy definition. Normally we expect a sexual process to involve some kind of fusion of two cells that we term male and female. Our confidence in this theory is born of some acquaintance with our own bodies ; it is useless, however, to take a set of ideas devised for ourselves and apply them to organisms like fungi with any hope of an accurate fit. In fungi, reproduction can, as we have seen, exist apart from sex. In as much as these two processes are not virtually one in fungi, we must enquire whether sex itself is less specialised in this group than it later becomes. We are so accustomed to two kinds of animal—male and female —between which fusion occurs, that we think of sex in terms of the reproductive cells of two sexes. But conditions in fungi are so erratic that sixty-four or more kinds may exist. In one of the higher animals, when an egg-cell is ripening, small pieces of its nucleus are thrown away, so that eventually the cell becomes a concentration of protoplasmic material. A male cell on the other hand forms a number of very small cells, each one of which is little more than an active nucleus provided with a tail. The tail is a very necessary part of the organisation, because the male has to undertake an adventurous journey in order that it may reach its nemesis of an egg-cell.

Fusion of eggs and sperms rarely occurs in fungi, though what amounts to the same thing frequently happens ; that is, the fusion of the nucleus of some small body with that of a larger one. Often a portion of a fungus hypha is cut off from the rest and becomes differentiated into what functions as an egg-cell and is therefore called the female part. Then quite commonly from a neighbouring portion a tube grows out and fuses with the female part. Because of this action the small tube that grows out is regarded as the male. The two nuclei fuse, so that we may be watching some kind of sexual process, though it is not the well-marked affair of the " higher " animals.

Variations on this theme occur throughout the fungi. Rarely does the male nucleus have any extensive journey to undertake outside the limits of the fungus wall, while sometimes as in rust-fungi there is a fusion of nuclei between neighbouring cells, that can hardly be regarded as, and which probably is not, sex at all. Acrimonious discussions on this particular point have raged round the nuclei of rust-fungi.

HOW A FUNGUS EARNS ITS LIVING

IN the same way as a certain number of mineral substances and chemical elements are necessary to the life of green plants, so fungi are unable to live without most of the same substances. Analysis shows that phosphorus, potassium and nitrogen are required, but quite tiny quantities of other substances also are necessary for growth. The fact that iron is concerned in the formation of the green colouring matter of flowering plants led to the assumption that no iron is necessary in fungi from which the green-colouring matter (chlorophyll) is absent. But when tests were made, it was found that

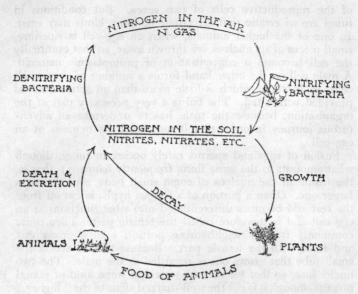

NITROGEN IN THE AIR
N. GAS

DENITRIFYING
BACTERIA

NITRIFYING
BACTERIA

NITROGEN IN THE SOIL
NITRITES, NITRATES, ETC.

DEATH &
EXCRETION

GROWTH

DECAY

ANIMALS

PLANTS

FOOD OF ANIMALS

BACTERIA'S PLACE IN THE " NITROGEN CYCLE "

Certain bacteria which convert nitrogen derived from the atmosphere into soluble substances that can pass into soil, perform a useful service to mankind in thus preparing food-material for the higher plants. The " nitrogen cycle " and the part played in it by what are known as the " nitrifying " bacteria is here shown in diagrammatic form.

small quantities of iron are essential, and that iron could also act as a growth stimulant. The chief food of fungi is provided by the material forming the living or dead bodies of plants and animals.

This property of converting atmospheric nitrogen into soluble substances that can diffuse through a cell-wall is one of the most important of biological processes, and amongst the " nitrogen-fixers," as they are called, particular mention must be made of the nodule organism which occurs in the nodular swellings on the roots of plants of the pea and clover family. When the seed of a clover plant germinates, the root is at once attacked close to the tip by nitrogen-fixing bacteria

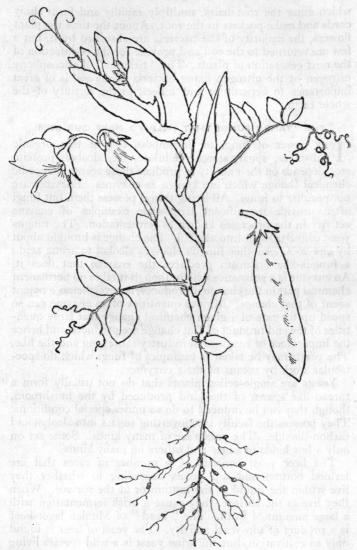

THE GARDEN PEA, SHOWING NODULAR SWELLINGS ON ITS ROOT

which enter the root hairs, multiply rapidly and form shiny cords and make pockets in the root. About the time the plant flowers, the majority of the bacteria are absorbed by it, but a few are returned to the soil and provide for the re-infection of the next generation of plants. The " fixation " of atmospheric nitrogen by the nitrogen fixing bacteria of the soil is of great importance to agriculture and indeed to the fertility of the whole earth.

THE "TAME" FUNGI THAT HELP TO MAKE OUR BEER

THE power of fungi to decompose this or that organic substance, sugar, starch, cellulose, fat, alcohol, protein, etc., depends on their ability to produce those agents of specific chemical change which are known as enzymes. Enzymes are not peculiar to fungi. All living things possess them but fungi often provide magnificent large-scale examples of enzyme activity in the processes known as fermentation. The fungus yeast converts sugar into alcohol. The change is brought about by enzymes. Another fungus changes alcohol to acetic acid : a fungus-like organism produces the enzyme that does it. An enzyme is a substance which, though it takes no permanent chemical part in the change it produces, is nevertheless a potent agent of that change. Minute quantities of an enzyme can so speed up the rate of a given chemical change that large quantities of the end product of that change are produced and hence the importance of enzymes in industry : brewing and the like. The yeasts may be taken as examples of fungi which do spectacular work by means of their enzymes.

Yeasts are single-celled plants that do not usually form a thread-like spawn of the kind produced by the mushroom, though they can be induced to do so under special conditions. They possess the faculty of converting sugars into alcohol and carbon-dioxide. The yeasts are of many kinds. Some act on only a few kinds of sugar and others on many kinds.

The beer yeast consists of a number of races that are termed bottom and top yeasts according to whether they live within the liquid at the bottom or at the surface. When they live at the surface, they cause a brisk fermentation with a large amount of froth. The " head " of Munich lager-beer is a product of top-yeast activity. The yeast of beer is found only in cultivation, but the wine yeast is a wild species living normally on the outside of grape skins. The flavour of particular wines is due to the particular variety of yeast used to

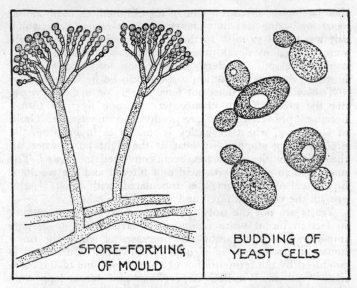

SPORE-FORMING OF MOULD

BUDDING OF YEAST CELLS

HOW MOULDS AND YEASTS REPRODUCE

Moulds possess special filaments in which spores are formed ; yeasts, of which there are many kinds, give off little buds which in time produce new chains of organisms.

ferment the grape juice. Every wine district seems to have its own particular form of yeast with a different kind of growth. Some yeasts, like the Burgundy and Champagne forms, settle quickly and leave a clear liquid while others remain suspended for a long time and take a long time to settle. Sometimes unwanted fermentation occurs and turbid diseases of beer result from the presence of unwanted yeasts.

THE LITTLE BACILLI THAT MAKE THE BREAD RISE

THE cultivated yeasts are probably among the oldest of all cultivated plants, as even in biblical times there was a distinction drawn between unleavened bread and leavened bread that had been " raised " by yeast. The leaven was a lump of dough kept from one baking to the next and contained the active yeasts, while unleavened bread was simply the tough mass produced by mixing flour and water and then baking the mixture. One of the old methods of obtaining yeast for baking was that known as " salt-raising," by which salt was added to milk so that the bacteria of the sour milk were delayed in development until the yeasts from the air could develop. Modern investigation of " salt-raising," however, declares the action to be produced by bacteria.

To-day the baker does not have to rely on brewers' yeast, nor the housewife on chance fermentation by wild forms because " pressed-yeasts " are produced commercially. Grain of either rye, wheat or barley is malted as in brewing, the process being stopped by heat at the right point when all the starch in the grain has been converted to sugar. The mash is then soured with acid and filtered and the resultant liquid, called a " wort," is inoculated with yeast. After growth the yeast is filtered and pressed into cakes.

Yeasts are not the only fungi concerned in fermentation ; in fact in recent years many fungi have tended to assume importance in many industrial processes of which the time-honoured production of alcohol is only one. Citric acid is produced by the fermentation of sugars with one of the common " mildews " called Aspergillus, and for a long time alcohols and vinegar have been produced on an industrial scale by means of the fermentative properties of bacteria. The use of bacteria in industry is, however, so specialised that it is a subject in itself. To show how wide are its possibilities it is only necessary to mention that the whole of the rubber industry depends on the fact that the milky-juice of the rubber tree is coagulated into rubber by a special bacterial flora.

GERMS THAT HELP TO RUN OUR CITIES: GUARDIANS OF THE WATER SUPPLY

QUITE apart from their uses in industry and their rather spectacular relations with human diseases, bacteria are important in everyday life. They cause foodstuffs to go bad, they sour our milk, " make " a cheese, and more notably still, they purify sewage. Indeed, we might almost say that without the bacterial processes by which sewage is purified, the civilisation of our big towns would be impossible.

It is obvious that crude sewage will contain very nearly as many bacteria as it is possible for it to hold. Under proper conditions of storage the bacteria will kill themselves by using the available food materials and give as a result water that is perfectly clear, and valuable substances that are used as fertilisers. The supply of pure milk has perhaps focused attention on bacterial activity in a way that nothing else could have done : we are told everywhere that milk has been " pasteurised," by which we understand that it has been subjected to a process of sterilisation which kills a large number of the bacteria normally contained in it. Further, we are told milk is supplied from " tuberculin " tested cows, by which we understand that the cows have been examined for the amount of tubercle bacteria they contain. We assume from the results obtained that our daily milk supply will not be infecting our bodies with large quantities of bacteria that will cause tuberculosis.

HIDDEN AND INSIDIOUS GUESTS: THE FUNGI THAT EAT OUR HOUSES

SUFFICIENT has already been said to indicate how closely the existence of microscopic fungi and bacteria are bound up with our daily lives. But the method in which they impinge on our domestic activities is no less startling. The whole process of cooking, for example, has as one of its objects, not merely the rendering of food more digestible or more palatable, but the sterilisation of it by the application of heat, so that it can be kept for a longer period before " going bad." " Going bad " is much more bacterial or fungal decay than an actual chemical breakdown of the food substances. We have to obviate the effects of fungi and bacteria in various ways. Tea is a dried leaf ; if kept moist it will develop an abundant growth of micro-organisms, and it is possible occasionally to find mildew developing inside the tea-caddy. The bottling of fruit depends for its success on sterilising the material by heat. When jam is made the product must have so high a concentration of sugars that micro-organisms are unable to grow in it.

"LEPROSY OF A HOUSE"

SOME mention should be made of fungus diseases that can assail the actual fabric of a house. If a house is damp, mildews will grow on the wall-paper and on pictures and books. They will cover boots in an undisturbed cupboard and will attack curtains, cretonne covers, furniture, towels and dusters. The sinister " dry-rot " disease of timber, which is caused by a fungus, is one that often proves expensive to harbour. It is invariably a product of damp conditions, as like all other fungi it cannot grow unless it is supplied with certain minimum quantities of air, moisture, heat and food-materials. The food material is the woodwork of the house, and from the point of view of the fungus all timber in a house is as one, whether it be a joint, floorboard, wall panelling or ceiling-lath; all can be attacked unless protected by a layer of creosote or some other preservative.

House owners are often puzzled to find that the point of attack is a long way from the source of the infection. The fungus will usually have some wet place as its base of operations from which the attack has commenced. When it has extracted from any piece of woodwork all that it can usefully extract, the fungus will form long cords that may travel considerable distances through brickwork, concrete, or inside pipes, until they find some more food-material—that is, unprotected wood.

It may be said in passing that paint offers but little hindrance to the triumphant progress of the fungus. The method of ridding a house of this dangerous pest is first to destroy all infected material by burning, to protect all unprotected woodwork and to take the necessary steps to secure an efficient ventilation by a circulation of dry air. The disease is so widespread that it is impossible to avoid infection, so to protect a house an effort must be made to ensure that infection cannot develop.

DELICACIES THAT ENGLISHMEN DERIDE

A QUITE casual examination of contemporary literature will show that fungi of various kinds have from a remote past been greatly appreciated as table delicacies. Naturally enough it is the larger fungi that have received attention in this way. Mildews, except those used in the ripening of special cheeses, such as Rocquefort, only appear on the table by accident. The larger fungi on the contrary are commonly used either as delicacies or for flavouring purposes, as, for instance, the manner in which truffles are used in *Pâté de foie gras*, or dried Boleti are commonly used on the Continent for flavouring soups. Those who have tasted or smelt many of the Continental dried mushrooms, however, may be astonished to learn that they are supposed to be edible.

Many fungi are commonly eaten abroad that in England

would not be looked at save with derision, as here, except in the houses of a few learned enthusiasts, mushrooms are practically the only fungi that find their way to the table. From time to time accounts are published of families dying from fungus poisoning because they had thought they were eating a mushroom, whereas actually they had digested one of the many poisonous varieties that abound everywhere. Punch's practical method of distinguishing between a mushroom and a toadstool by making the experiment of eating it is hardly one to recommend generally. There are many popular tests for distinguishing edible toadstools from poisonous toadstools, but they are uniformly quite valueless. Stories that poisonous fungi do or do not peel, do or do not turn silver coins black, or have some weird effect upon an onion are all discredited by competent botanists, who declare that the only way to tell a mushroom from a toadstool is to be able to recognise it from its botanical characters. A mushroom must be recognised and distinguished from its fellows in the same way as a daisy is told from a dandelion. There is no other safe way.

A SWIFT AND FATAL POISONER: THE MALIGNANT "DEATH-CAP"

QUITE apart from the fact that the empirical tests that are quoted again and again exclude many edible kinds, they are utterly useless because they do *not* exclude many very dangerous species. One of these, the so-called " death-cap " ought to be recognised before any attempt is made to eat any fungus. The " death-cap " is normally about five inches high with a cap some three inches or four inches across. It is olive grey and streaked with very thin dark lines. The underside of the cap is covered with white gills that remain white throughout and never become pink or black as do the gills of a mushroom. There is a ring around the stem, and close to the base, usually half-hidden in the ground, is a membranous cup-like structure that enclosed the toadstool in the " button " stage. A mushroom never has this cup at the base of the stem and any fungus possessing such a structure should be regarded with suspicion until more is known about it.

The poison of the " death-cap " fungus is swift and fatal. Usually the first symptoms are experienced six to twelve hours after the toadstool has been eaten and are the common ones of food poisoning—sickness, diarrhœa, vertigo ; later, muscular cramp may occur. Finally, the patient will die after some four days of agony and may be considered comparatively fortunate if his suffering is not further prolonged. There is rarely any recovery as the poison destroys the blood and the patient dies from the accumulation of his own bodypoisons, possibly after a long period of intense pain. There are other " killers " besides this fungus, that are eaten from time to time by ignorant people, but if this species can be excluded there is usually some hope for recovery.

While mentioning the " death-cap " it may be said that its ally, the red-capped fungus with white spots that grows under birch trees, is not nearly so virulent, and small quantities of it produce only an intense intoxication. It is said that at one time a regular trade existed with the Kolchaks for this fungus. It was used in religious ceremonies so that a whole tribe could enjoy mass drunkenness.

A DESTROYER OF FOOD AND FORTUNE: THE GREAT RUST SCOURGE

" Rusts " to a botanist implies a particular kind of fungus, of microscopic size, which is parasitic on green plants. The effect of the fungus is to produce a lesion on its host, which becomes in the course of time filled with spores of the fungus that, because of their colour, show like patches of ironrust on the plant. Frequently, as may be seen on juniper in this country, a large gall-growth is produced, and sometimes, as with wheat and other cereals, the result of an attack is that the plant is useless for normal purposes. It will readily be appreciated that when large areas of ground are cultivated with one crop, very serious loss may ensue if a disease appears. The very concentration of host material will lead to widespread infection once a disease has broken out, and the " rusts " in the world's wheat-growing belts causes enormous financial loss.

" Rust " is always present in the great wheat zones, but in some years it is more troublesome than in others. In 1916 which was a bad " rust " year, the wheat crop lost in Western Australia was valued at two million pounds; in western Canada twenty million pounds of damage was done and the story was repeated round the world. Thousands of acres of wheat were never even garnered as the yield could not possibly have paid for the labour and materials that would be spent.

Wheat and cereals are not the only crops adversely affected by rust. Apples, small fruit, forage crops and garden flowers all have their particular rust disease that, as in the famous instance of the rust of coffee in Ceylon, can become so menacing as practically to kill an industry. The rust of coffee that started in Ceylon and spread through the Old World reduced the value of the coffee exports of Ceylon from about three million pounds to twenty-five thousand pounds sterling—a drop to $\frac{1}{120}$ part of its original value in about thirty years. Even to-day the life-history of this dangerous disease is not fully known in spite of the fact that on the completeness of that knowledge depends the success of methods of controlling rust diseases.

"LIVE AND LET LIVE": THE PARASITE'S BEST POLICY

To appreciate the peculiarities of the life-histories of rusts it is necessary to consider the properties of parasites in general. First of all it is as well to avoid the moral threat this word implies when levelled at people whom we happen to dislike as a group, and to remember that biologically a parasite is a highly specialised organism that has come to conform fairly closely to the environment that is provided by its host. If we could endow a parasite with the power of thought so that it could be said to have conscious action, we should be justified in saying that its policy was very short-sighted if it so depleted its host that the host died. For, once the host was dead the parasite would be without a food supply. Again, the parasite endowed with thought might realise that the elaborate organisation it had built up to comply with the conditions inside a host might not only be useless, but even a source of weakness and therefore of danger in the great world outside. It would be wise, therefore, for a parasite to stop short of killing its host and to conduct itself on a " live and let live " principle merely with an eye to its own future.

However careful a parasite might be about this, hosts sometimes die, and this fact has to be reckoned with. Should a host incontinently die the parasite must either die with its host, or get out of its host's body—and get out quickly. A double problem then faces it. It might very probably stand a greater chance of survival if it could adopt quickly some other form, but it needs mobility to reach a new host. So long as a parasite is concerned merely with its own affairs these problems stand, but should it, may we say, elect to have some pride of race, to wish to produce " more and better parasites," these problems would become intensified. To produce more of its own kind to compete with it for food in its own particular environment would be foolish, so that a desire for reproduction implies a need for distribution. It must not be assumed that a parasite is capable of considering possibilities and acting accordingly. The fact is that it cannot appear otherwise than if it were so subtly governed, because death is the reward of error. If a parasite made a mistake, it would commit suicide.

One method of solving the problem of protection and distribution at the same time is to adopt an " alternative " or " intermediate " host endowed with the power of mobility. A notable example of this is to be found in malaria, which is a disease caused by the growth of a parasite in the blood of man. It is transferred from one person to another by mosquitoes which act as intermediate hosts.

THE FUNGUS THAT TAKES A "HOUSE FOR THE SEASON"

A SIMILAR state of affairs is found in the rust fungi. Some are confined to one host while others require two hosts, one of which is known as the principal host, and the other is called the alternate host. If the principal host happens to be an annual plant that will die at the end of summer the rust fungus is compelled to have some method of living during the winter and frequently finds an alternative host that is evergreen or at least perennial. Dispersal is made by the wind which carries off a large number of tiny spores. Whether the spores ever reach a suitable host must therefore be largely a matter of chance. It has been found that there are different spore forms, which according to their function have been distinguished as winter-spores and summer-spores. Summer-spores form pustules in the host that show red through cracks in the epidermis or skin. Sometimes a special form of " spring-spores " may occur and produce a rusted appearance. The winter-spore is a special two-celled spore that produces four spores, called basidiospores, on a special stalk or basidium.

All, some, or one form only may exist in any life-cycle. We may take the " rust " of wheat, which is typical of the life-history of a " rust ", as an example of what happens. When the wheat is about to produce flower spikes the rust appears as cracks on the leaves and stalks. That is the summer-spore stage, and several crops of rust may succeed each other on the wheat plant. Then in time the winter-spore stage, which is black, follows, and in this stage the rust endures the winter. Sometimes during late winter or early spring the winter-spore germinates and gives rise to an evanescent spore stage which is blown by the wind on to the alternative host, in this particular instance, the common Barberry. There, two forms of cups are produced on the leaves, one on the upper surface containing the spring spores, and one on the lower surface holding another spore stage, the function of which is still obscure, though it is connected with sex. The fusion of two nuclei from sister cells during the formation of spring-spores is probably not a sexual process as was at one time thought but a pseudo-sexual fusion that can replace sex. Recent evidence tends to suggest that the cells of the cup on the lower surface may produce male sexual cells.

It was at one time thought that this parasite had become so highly specialised that it would die if its life-cycle was broken by the disappearance of one host, but the disease occurs on wheat in countries where Barberry is unknown, and re-infection is continued by the summer-spores.

FUNGI THAT PREY ON MAN, BEAST AND PLANT

IT has been seen that fungi and their allies play a most useful part in the world but the adverse side of the balance-sheet has still to be considered. This is chiefly a disclosure of diseases that can affect both plants and animals. Disease may be said to indicate a condition when two organisms are constantly associated beyond mutual tolerance. The lack of tolerance means that some kind of reaction will occur in the host. There may be unhealthy enlargement at the site of attack. A rot may develop in a vital part, or in some bacterial diseases of plants (such as " crown-gall ") a tumour may develop at some distance from the seat of attack, in the same way as in cancer of the human subject. It is found that a number of disease-producing fungi are ones which usually live in dead organisms but which occasionally become virulent.

Little purpose would be served here in giving a catalogue of various diseases of plants and animals caused by fungi, bacteria or mycetozoa. It will probably be of greater interest to indicate the kinds of diseases that occur and the methods used to control them. We can hardly do better than continue to discuss the " rust " disease of wheat as it affords almost a typical example. It has been mentioned that efforts have been made to break the life-cycle of the " rust " disease of wheat by eradicating the intermediate host. This is a general method of attack on parasites living on two hosts, but it is not, unfortunately, successful. At the same time it had been noted for years by farmers that " rust " of wheat developed especially strongly when corn-fields were associated with Barberry. At this time the double life-history was unknown and botanists generally regarded the practical experience of the farmer as a piece of unscientific stupidity. Finally the farmers had their way and in various countries, particularly in France and the United States, laws were passed prohibiting a farmer from having Barberry on his land. This undoubtedly had a great effect in controlling the spread of the disease as it demonstrably led to its decrease in certain areas.

To-day the problem is dealt with in two ways. In the first place an effort is made to produce strains of wheat that will resist attacks of " rust ", and in the second, by good cultivation, strong healthy plants are produced ; it has been shown, for instance, that excessive manuring with nitrogenous manures tends to increase the susceptibility to disease. Apart from these methods, attempts are made to control the disease by the use of antisepsis in the same manner as disinfectants are used in hospitals to check the spread of human disease. To control rust of wheat is a large problem rather like trying to check a world-wide attack of influenza.

DISEASE ON THE WING: HOW 'PLANES PURSUE THE FLYING SEED

THE spores of rust are so small that when freed from the diseased plant they rise into the air by means of currents produced by alterations in atmospheric temperature, and can float through the air for a distance of some thirty miles before coming to rest after an initial rise of only a few feet. It has been shown by means of traps exposed from aeroplanes that spores can float through the air a mile above the earth. The aeroplane has also come into use in other ways. It has been found that various substances when sprayed in a solution on to the plant can kill the disease, and recently it has been demonstrated that fine dusts, chiefly of sulphur compounds, are particularly valuable in this respect. To-day in Canada low-flying aeroplanes spray clouds of antiseptic dusts over growing corn.

The farmer to-day has to sterilise his machines and tools in the same way as a surgeon has to treat his instruments, before operating on a patient. If a threshing machine is used on wheat that is even partially rusted, it may simply become a means of spreading infection broadcast wherever it is used unless carefully sterilised with some antiseptic. Chemical sprays have been in use for controlling fungus pests almost from the beginnings of plant pathology as a science. The well-known Bordeaux and Burgundy mixtures were originally used for spraying grapes in the French vineyards to prevent people from eating them. It was found subsequently that where crops had been sprayed grape mildew was kept within bounds. Since that time spraying has become a method of control for nearly all plant diseases. Immense quantities of spray are used to prevent the appearance of potato blight, a dangerous fungus disease that can so far affect man's affairs that it caused the Irish potato famine, the repeal of the Corn Laws, and the consequent fall of Peel's government in England.

It is not merely diseases of standing crops that can be caused by fungi. Many crops develop rots in storage, and in recent years with the increase of the fruit trade throughout the world, storage rots have come to be increasingly studied. Commonly, as with apples, a large number of these rots are shown to be due to common infections of orchards, so that here again aseptic and antiseptic methods will prevent trouble.

LURING A GERM TO DESTRUCTION: HOW INOCULATION WORKS

ANIMAL diseases are not so commonly caused by fungi, unless we count the diseases of the human body produced by bacteria; such diseases as tuberculosis, diphtheria and indeed the majority of the infectious diseases of humanity. In these instances the spread of the disease may be said to be due always to dirt. Dust blowing about can carry infection directly or can introduce infection into some carrying agent, such as milk, that merely provides for distribution. Strict attention to cleanliness has been found to control the development of most bacteria and hence the spread of disease.

A rather spectacular method of disease control has, however, been placed in man's hands through intensive research during

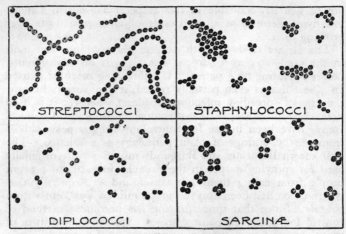

TYPES OF BACTERIA FOUND IN THE HUMAN BODY

Bacteria are the cause of the majority of infectious diseases, though some may not be harmful. Sarcina ventricula *is found in the human stomach.*

recent years. This is the method of acquiring immunity. If a disease is given to an organism in a small quantity, well below a lethal dose, the disease may be killed through " antibodies " that it provokes to form in the body of the host. Immunity bodies can therefore be created in this way and collected for use in an emergency. The method has been tried in connection with plant diseases but with no conspicuous success. Indeed it is hard to visualise how this method can be successfully used for plants because it depends for its success on the presence of substances in animal blood.

The whole of the modern science of immunology and the relation of toxins and anti-toxins is extremely complicated. According to some investigators a substance called " bacteriophage " is formed that is actually a living organism which is even smaller than the bacteria, growing and preying upon them. A dramatic account of this discovery is given by Sinclair Lewis in his novel *Martin Arrowsmith*. Other scientists remain incredulous and prefer to explain the facts in terms of physical chemistry. As, however, there are diseases called virus diseases, including those caused by vaccinia (small-pox) that seem to exist between the stage of chemical substances like enzymes and definite organisms like bacteria it can only be said that the whole subject is a developing one requiring further elucidation.

Unless the poisoning induced by poisonous toadstools can be called a disease it may be said that only certain microscopic fungi cause diseases of the animal body. There is a large group of fungi concerned in the formation of ringworm and allied diseases of the skin. These organisms have become so specialised in their host range that they are not found outside the diseased area which they characterise, but their nearest allies contain some that live normally as saprophytes on decaying fur and feathers. Presumably at some time there has been a rake's progress from one stage to another. Obscure intestinal diseases, such as the tropical " sprue ", are caused by fungi, and there are diseases, like " thrush," caused by a fungus growing on the throat-wall, and the well-known " pigeon-breeder's disease " where a fungus grows in the human lung. From time to time other parts of the animal body are infected. There is a normal fungus-flora of the alimentary canal of man and occasionally associated organs, such as the liver, are attacked. Experiments to render animal bodies immune from fungus diseases have not so far been successful.

NATURE'S CONSTANT QUESTION: CO-OPERATION OR WAR?

WE have considered one particular aspect of the relation between the association of two organisms which is called disease, but other combinations can be found and a study of any throws light on them all. There are for example a number of yeasts associated with certain insects, and this association is not merely an external one like the fungus gardens cultivated by the termites of South America, but is actually internal. Pocket-like yeast-glands associated with the alimentary canal are found, and apparently the yeasts play an essential part in the digestion of cellulose for the insect. Presumably the yeast feels the benefit of a sheltered life and feeds on food that comes drifting by. It can be seen that the change from such a condition to a parasitic relation might be very slight.

This type of association of fungi with other organisms is

known as "symbiosis." Originally by "symbiosis" was understood an intimate association of two organisms for the benefit of each. It has, however, to be admitted that " mutual benefit " of two organisms is a matter more often of conjecture than of proof. Nevertheless association of fungi with other organisms close enough to be " symbiotic " is frequent.

FUNGI THAT NURSE THE ORCHID'S SEEDS

TWO interesting examples that may be quoted are provided by the association of certain kinds of microscopic fungi of the soil and orchids, and by toadstools and the roots of many forest trees. The seeds of orchids are very small with an incomplete differentiation of parts and practically no arrangement for storing food. In some orchids, the majority of the seeds die as, unless a germinating seed encounters the right kind of soil fungus, further development does not occur. Apparently the meeting of seed and fungus results in a stimulation of activity in the seed, which then develops a swollen structure about one-eighth of an inch in diameter, containing the fungus in the basal cells. The fungus starts by destroying some of the cell contents of the orchid and then apparently the orchid asserts itself and prevents the fungus from destroying any further cells. The manner in which the fungus is restricted to a zone in which it can do no harm is indeed remarkable ; it is kept far away from the point at which the young orchid's shoot and root develop. Eventually the young root absorbs its way right through the zone where the fungus is in occupation, but the root is protected as it goes, by a special layer, and eventually finds its way into the soil. Here, in the course of time, the fungus hyphæ from the soil find their way into the outer series of cells of the root, and every orchid carries with it in this way the fungus that it requires for development of its seed.

This has become the basis of a spectacular application of biology to industry. An orchid grower contrived to take the fungus that he wanted from a number of cultivated orchids and grow them on nutrient jellies in the same way as an expert will cultivate bacteria. The fungus was then added to the orchid seed at the required moment, and so successful has this method become, that raising orchids from seed has been changed from a hazardous enterprise into a certainty. Of recent years, particularly in America, successful attempts have been made to imitate the action of the fungus by supplying certain chemicals to the orchid seeds.

Practically all the woodland toadstools of this country are concerned in an association with the roots of our forest trees. Typically fungus mycelium is wrapped round the ends of young tree-roots that lie close to the surface. Eventually, however, the fungus penetrates the tissue of the root, but apparently is never permitted to become a nuisance. It is obvious that if the conducting area that lies in the middle of a root became blocked with masses of fungus hyphæ the whole plant would suffer, as even from mechanical interference alone the streams of water and food substances, flowing through the root, would be stopped. In tree-roots, as in orchids, the fungus is restricted to the outer cells and is never allowed to interfere with the food stream.

So far as any judgment can be reached on such a matter as this purely from a study of the distribution of fungus hyphæ in a host, such associations were common in a remote geological past, as fossils from the Coal Measures have frequently been found showing masses in their root-cells that have been interpreted as fossilised masses of fungi. A striking fact that does emerge from an examination of these associations is that the flowering plant always seems to be well in command of the situation.

What these associations mean and how they are to be interpreted is a difficult matter to decide upon, and to-day we are far from any final view on the matter.

HOW PROLIFIC NATURE SPREADS THE FAMILY OF FUNGI

THE methods by which the spores of fungi are dispersed are both interesting and varied. Normally the spores are small and can travel long distances by air, and such distribution is only prevented by the natural barriers of mountains and seas. Small areas of water usually form no hindrance to travel.

The normal method of dispersal of spores of toadstools is by means of air-currents. The spore-bearing surface forms a lining to the gills on the underside of a toadstool and the spores are first shot from the surface into the tiny space between neighbouring gills. The spore then begins to fall vertically under the influence of gravity until outside the region of the cap where it is taken up by air-currents. It will be seen that it is important for a toadstool to maintain a perfectly erect position, otherwise a spore on its downward journey might foul a portion of an adjacent gill. The discharge of spores from an ordinary toadstool may continue night and day for a week or more.

Some of the hard bracket-fungi which grow out like shelves from the sides of trees are perennial and instances are known where a fungus has developed year after year in the same place for over eighty years. In fungi of this type the spore discharge may proceed continuously for perhaps a month every year. The total number of spores discharged reaches colossal figures. The number of spores that may be produced by a common mushroom averages about fifteen million million. In some fungi even higher figures than these are obtained, figures with such amazing rows of noughts that they seem to have strayed from an account of the national debt.

HOW A TOADSTOOL KEEPS ITS BALANCE: AN ENGINEERING ACHIEVEMENT

IN spite of the fact that the shape of toadstools seems so peculiarly to suit the function of spore discharge it must not be too hastily assumed that this function brings about their shape. There are toadstools where the gills are such an impediment in the way of spore dispersal that the spores cannot be freed until the gills have dissolved. Even here the toadstool shape is still retained. It is at least a stimulus to the imagination to consider these structures in the light of pressure and stability. It is generally conceded that some of the structural lines in animal bones revealed by X-rays are developed in response to the direction of thrust, and in the same way in general terms it may be said that animal skeletons correspond structurally to bridges where girders are placed along the main pressure and tension lines. If a toadstool is growing against the pressure of the earth that pressure might be expected to develop corresponding structures in the same way as in animals, and if the form of a toadstool is considered as being a compound arrangement of cantilever brackets (cap and gills) set in a wall (the stem) the shape of the toadstool becomes intelligible on engineering principles.

The air-drift method is not the only manner in which fungus spores are distributed, though it is certainly the main one. Invariably there is some kind of preliminary explosion, which may vary from the small one of a toadstool, to the larger one of a puff-ball, or of the sac-like bodies that comprise the fruit of one of the cup-fungi. These, although tiny, may in the mass explode with sufficient force to make a sharp hiss.

Occasionally, as with the well-known stink-horn, carrion-flies crawl over the surface and sticky spores adhere to their bodies. A common mildew on dung, called *Pilolobus* has an arrangement by which a " bullet " of spores can be shot off some six feet into the air after the " gun " has been carefully sighted towards the light. The spore-mass is sticky and adheres to grass, and if the grass is eaten by horses the cycle is completed. Another fungus called *Sphærobolus* throws out a spore-mass in a similar fashion, but in this fungus the mechanism is not sensitive to light and the projectile is exploded from a mortar rather than from a gun. All kinds of " creepies and crawlies," mites, insects and slugs play a part in distributing fungus spores so universally as to make them, as they are, the common organisms of everyday life.

The efficiency of these methods of distribution does not seem to be high. Fungi seem to be prodigal in spore production, but few spores are favoured by destiny. It may reasonably be assumed always that the saturation point of any environment is quickly attained, and the maximum number of organisms develop that conditions will permit. The pressure of competition may drive useful scavengers into parasitism, or not, according to the material we provide and the control we exercise, so that to a large extent it may be said that the future of this group of organisms lies in man's hands.

WHERE TO READ MORE ABOUT FUNGI

THE study of fungi has both gained and suffered from the fact that many of its advances have arrived incidentally from the separate aspects of the study of plant pathology and cytology and these characteristics are reflected in its modern literature. Formerly some scholarly books attempted to range over the whole subject, but partly owing to its growth and complexity, this now seems impossible. Amongst the best modern textbooks are E. A. Gaumann and C. W. Dodge's *Comparative Morphology of Fungi*, 1928, and H. C. I. Gwynne-Vaughan and B. Barnes's *Structure and Development of Fungi*.

The first is really an American version of a German book, but it departs from the original text and as it contains a considerable number of technical terms it is recommended only for the more advanced reader. The book by Gwynne-Vaughan and Barnes is more easily followed by English readers, but alone it might give the false impression that mycology is a series of evolutionary essays brightened by cytological anecdotes, and it is marred by the fact that a large group of fungi, the *Fungi Imperfecti*, full of economic potentialities, are barely mentioned. A slim volume by J. Ramsbottom entitled simply *Fungi* should be read at the same time as one of these, as it will bring back the breath of life and serve to show the interest of this group of organisms to the great world and to the small man, for the writer has achieved a philosophical approach in the manner of the older authors.

For more detailed information special books must be consulted. Of these *Penicillia* by J. Thom, *Yeasts*, a translation from the French by F. W. Tanner, *The Lower Fungi* by H. M. Fitzpatrick, and *Plant Rusts* by J. C. Arthur are typical. A work that must be mentioned is R. Buller's *Researches on Fungi*, now extended to six volumes, and those who have the courage and patience to cope with it will undoubtedly profit, as there is much information of general interest in it that is available otherwise only in scattered papers. The most recent edition of Muir and Ritchie's *Manual of Bacteriology* is a readable version of the development of modern bacteriology.

THE HUMBLEST CITIZENS OF THE ANIMAL KINGDOM

*by MAURICE BURTON, M.Sc., of the British
Museum (Natural History)*

FROM the study of plants we now turn to consider the next
highest group in the scale of living things—the animals. As
the science of Botany tells us how plants are built, how they
grow and feed and propagate, where they may be found and how
they may be distinguished from each other, so Zoology deals with
the animals. We shall see, in the sections which follow, how
animals are equipped to meet the conditions of their environment
and how they adapt themselves to changes. We shall learn of
their struggle for existence against their enemies, both man and
beast, of the special abilities and characteristics which enable
us to divide them into groups, and of how they use them ; how
they care for their young, and how the young reach maturity ;
and finally how animals have evolved throughout the ages.

Beginning with the lowest forms of animal life, the sponges,
star-fish and so on, we go on to consider that curious assembly
called Arthropods, among which are the insects, spiders, crabs,
centipedes and other familiar creatures. Going higher in the
scale we come to the backboned animals—birds, beasts and
fish—including the highest form of all—the mammals. In this
section some of the greatest glories of the Animal Kingdom are
described.

The following article " The Social Life of Animals " deals
with the extraordinary community life of creatures such as the
ants, wasps, and termites, with their complex cities, their social
castes, their roads, gardens, flocks and paying guests. In
" When Life Began " is unfolded the story of the animal life of
millions of years ago. Here we discover from what bizarre
ancestors some of the most familiar of present-day animals are
descended, and we catch astonishing glimpses of the mammoths
that were sovereigns of the earth long before the advent of man.
Finally, after a succeeding section on the working of the human
body, the problem of how certain characteristics are transmitted
from parent to offspring, and sometimes from more remote
ancestors, is examined in the section on Heredity, where also
the mechanism that determines these phenomena is explained.

In popular language an animal is something that moves on four legs and has its body covered with hair. Thus dogs, rabbits, bears and lions are animals ; but the rest of the Animal Kingdom is divided into birds, fishes, insects and a number of ill-defined and ill-conceived groups to which the layman often finds difficulty in giving a name. It may not be without profit, therefore, to emphasise at the onset that the Animal Kingdom includes a host of diverse creatures ranging from microscopic organisms, the bodies of which consist only of a single cell, to leviathans such as elephants and whales ; and that, strictly speaking, these microscopic one-celled creatures, together with a multitude of other lowly beings, rank equally with fishes, birds, insects and the quadrupeds as animals. Even man himself is compelled to swallow his conceit and admit that he is no more than a close relative of the beasts of the field.

Roughly speaking, an animal can be defined as any living organism capable of moving about, feeding on solid food and having an obvious nervous or muscular reaction to various stimuli ; or perhaps we could better express this last quality by saying that an animal possesses in a greater or lesser degree one or more of the senses—taste, sight, smell and hearing. And although there are exceptions to this, especially among the lower animals, the definition does serve as a broad means of distinguishing between the two great groups of living things—the Plants and the Animals.

The next point which should be emphasised at this juncture is what may be best described as the evolutionary sequence in the classification of animals, the manner in which they can be arranged in a series of increasing complexity. This sequence corresponds closely to that revealed in the fossil remains of animals as we progress from the oldest rocks down to the present day, and is probably closely comparable to the order and manner in which the higher animals have been evolved from simple and lowly ancestors. Thus, starting from the unicellular organisms, we have the Sponges, the Cœlenterates, including sea-anemones and jelly-fishes, animals with a very low grade of nervous system, without brain or any real centralised sense organs, and differing markedly in appearance and behaviour from the more familiar animals such as fishes, birds and mammals.

The next step takes us to that ill-assorted group commonly referred to as the Worms. These have a centralised nervous system, a rudimentary brain and definite sense-organs, while other details of their anatomy, the intestine, for example, bear a strong resemblance to those of higher animals. Following them, the Mollusca, Insects, Fishes, Reptiles, Birds, Mammals and Man form so obviously progressive a series, even to those uninitiated in the study of Zoology, that there is little to be gained by pursuing the subject further.

In the following pages, therefore, the various members of the Animal Kingdom will be dealt with in this sequence and some attempt will be made to bring out the salient features of their anatomy, behaviour and relationship to each other.

AMŒBA: THE ANIMAL THAT IS NOT WHAT IT SEEMS

WHAT is Amœba? It is one of the one-celled animals already referred to and may be readily taken as our starting-point in the sequence we are to follow : it is one of the simplest animals known, but is not so simple as it is often held to be. Amœba is usually described as " a colourless, shapeless speck of protoplasm, found in any fresh water, even in the supply cisterns of houses." Nearly every book devoted to natural history, and every book devoted to biology or zoology, says much the same thing about it. Yet Amœba is a fraud, or rather, some who write about it are unintentionally fraudulent and the popular conception of Amœba is not altogether correct. In the first place, Amœba is not colourless. It is nearly transparent, but not colourless. Secondly, it is not shapeless, although its shape is constantly changing. And thirdly, it cannot be found in just any fresh water—least of all in cisterns ; and those who set out to look for Amœba are likely to meet with many disappointments before, perhaps in some small pool or pond, they find it after much painstaking search.

But an even greater complaint has yet to be made. In the early days, when the doctrine of evolution was taking concrete form, Amœba was a perfect godsend to the scientist. It was a form of life that approximated closely to his idea of what the first living matter to appear on the earth looked like. It symbolised to him the primeval blob of jelly from which all living matter was assumed to have arisen, and whose evolution through the ages culminated in the advent of man himself. In this way it served a useful purpose, but this use of Amœba is now obsolete. Though a very lowly, very primitive organism, it is a well-developed animal with specialised organs and a

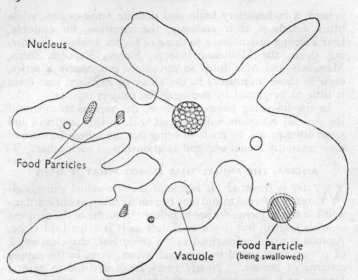

Nucleus

Food Particles

Vacuole

Food Particle
(being swallowed)

THE LOWEST FORM OF ANIMAL LIFE

Amœba, the most primitive form of animal we know, consists of a single cell and is a rounded mass of protoplasm too small to be seen without a magnifying glass. As the diagram shows, it eats simply by flowing round its food.

complex structure, and resembles to only a very slight degree the original speck of protoplasm from which all living matter is assumed to have sprung. For really low forms of life we have to turn to the bacteria, the lowest forms of plant-life, and by comparison with these Amœba is a well-advanced organism. Once we have disabused our minds of the old conception of Amœba we are in a position to realize that the lowest forms of animal life known to us have already reached quite an advanced stage in evolution.

The bodies of the great majority of animals are built up of thousands or even millions of living cells, each one of which bears a strong resemblance to the body of Amœba—in structure at all events, though not always in behaviour or appearance. The white corpuscles of the blood, for example, are really nothing more than Amœbæ imprisoned within our blood-vessels. It may, therefore, be of interest to consider closely the structure of the single cell that makes the body of Amœba.

The cell is, when at rest, a rounded mass of protoplasm, visible only under a strong hand-lens or under a microscope, with the interior granular, and suggesting, when magnified, a jelly impregnated with sand-grains. At the centre, or thereabouts, is a rounded body, the nucleus, which is the seat of control. As the animal moves, the substance of the cell is thrown out into finger-like processes, called pseudopodia, and the animal moves in a creeping way.

A CREATURE THAT FOLDS ITSELF OVER ITS FOOD

LIVING as it does at the bottom of muddy pools the animal is constantly coming into contact with all manner of fine organic debris and particles of mud. The indigestible mud is ignored, but the organic matter is ingested simply by the protoplasm flowing round it and engulfing it. The fact that a selection is exercised in the matter of what is and what is not taken in, points definitely to a sense of taste in Amœba, however feeble this sense may be. Once inside the body, a rounded space forms about the food particle and digestive juices are poured into it from the body proper. When digestion is completed, the indigestible remains are got rid of by a very simple process; the Amœba simply flows away from it.

An imitation of this simple animal can be made by mixing various fats and oils and allowing drops of the mixture to fall on a damp surface of glass. These artificial Amœbas move about in the same way as the living Amœbas and in appearance at all events are strikingly like them, but they cannot feed or reproduce themselves, and in this is demonstrated the fundamental difference between living and non-living things : non-living things can never reproduce themselves. It is true that reproduction in Amœba begins with an extremely simple process, a mere splitting in two of the original body to form two new individuals. It is no complicated union between two parents to produce an offspring, but a simple fission of the parental body. In other words, in this lowly animal we approach, theoretically, very close to true immortality since there is neither birth nor death in the sense used of higher animals.

ANIMALS MADE OF A SINGLE CELL

THE number of animals which, like Amœba, have a body composed of a single cell only is legion. Many are found in fresh water, and an even greater number in the sea, where

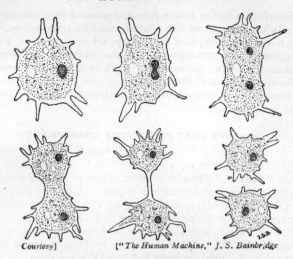

Courtesy]   ["The Human Machine," J. S. Bainbridge

A SIMPLE CREATURE THAT IS NEARLY IMMORTAL

The one-celled Amœba knows neither birth nor natural death. When it reproduces, its nucleus first divides into two, each going to opposite ends of the cell. Later the cell itself divides completely, thus giving two single-celled Amœbas.

the surface is often rendered phosphorescent for miles by the presence of vast shoals of *Noctiluca*, representing teeming millions of these animals. Some idea of the enormous quantities of unicellular animals that have inhabited the world in past times may be gained from the fact that many of the large masses of rock composing the earth's crust are composed almost exclusively of the limy skeletons of Protozoa, as all one-celled animals are called. The Nummulitic limestone, extending in a wide belt across Northern Africa, from the stone of which the pyramids were built, is a case in point.

Even to-day extensive deposits of similar skeletons cover the bottom of the sea for thousands of square miles, and the sandy beaches at many points on our coasts and the coasts of other countries throughout the world are composed mainly of the shells of Foraminifera, a group of unicellular animals. These shells are of surprising beauty and diversity, and few more fascinating diversions can be found than to examine a handful of sand under a strong hand-lens or under the microscope and to see the beautiful shells of Foraminifera among the sand-grains.

To a lesser extent, we may gain some idea of the infinite variety and the vast numbers of the Protozoa in the world by simply taking a dipping of water from practically any pond or stream, or, for the matter of that, from any stagnant pool or water butt, and examining a drop of it under a microscope. In it we shall see numerous small animals, some spherical, some oval, others pointed at each end. Some are crawling about with a slug-like motion, others swimming round and round, propelled by a coating of fine protoplasmic hairs covering the body, others moving forward in a straight line drawn along by a vortex created by the lashing of a single long, whip-like thread of protoplasm. In fact, a single drop of such water is as abundantly peopled with these unicellular animals as any garden is with insects.

Not the least important of the Protozoa are those that have forsaken a free existence for one parasitic in the bodies of other animals and of plants. Some of them do little damage to their hosts, but others are responsible for some of the most damaging and widespread diseases known to us. Dysentery, for example, is caused by the presence in the intestine of hosts of unicellular animals very closely related to Amœba. Malaria is due to the invasion of the blood cells by Protozoa that periodically set up a poisoning of the system, while sleeping sickness is the result of an infection of Trypanosomes, another group of Protozoa.

STRANGE ANIMAL: THE BATH-SPONGE AND ITS THOUSAND RELATIONS

THE next group of animals to be considered consists of the Porifera, or pore-bearing animals ; also known as the Sponges, although the word sponge should probably be restricted to one only of these animals—the Bath-sponge. Indeed, in the minds of most people there is only one thing meant by this word : the familiar article of toilet use. But in actual fact, and using the word in its more liberal sense, it includes some ten thousand or more different kinds of animals. All of these live in water, and most of them in salt water. They are found in large numbers all over the world, in the shallow seas as well as the ocean deeps ; in ponds, streams and rivers, even to the lakes formed in the craters of extinct volcanoes ten thousand feet or more above sea-level. Their form is varied, from thin crusts growing on rocks and seaweeds, to irregular masses, often several feet across. Many are fan-shaped, or branching and looking like leafless trees. Others are cup-shaped, funnel-shaped or tubular. Those growing in the shallow waters are coloured in a variety of hues and rival in this respect the better-known corals.

The bath-sponge, as we know it in the home, is merely the skeleton of a once living animal, which in life was covered by a jelly-like flesh and a tough purple skin ; and although so many different kinds of sponges are known, only the one is of commercial value. In most of them the skeleton is built up of minute bodies, known as spicules, composed either of lime or of silica, and these spicules, although exhibiting a great beauty of form when examined under a microscope, render them useless for the usual purposes. To wash with them would be akin to washing with a handful of very minute tin-tacks. There are many, it is true, which have a fibrous skeleton, but only in one case, that known and used as a bath-sponge, are the fibres sufficiently fine and delicate to allow of vigorous contact with the human skin.

Sponges in life show little sign of activity and are, moreover, extremely plant-like in appearance. Consequently, it was a very long time before scientists could make up their minds whether they should be regarded as plants or animals, and it was not until the discovery that they were in a state of constant activity that anything approaching a decision was arrived at on this point. Anatomically, sponges differ markedly from any other group of animals. In place of the usual mouth and digestive tract, which is a feature of practically all other animals, the body is fed through a complicated system of fine canals. Water is drawn in through numerous minute pores in the skin and makes its way through the body of the sponge and out again through a number of larger, crater-like vents at other points on the surface. The motive power is supplied by numbers of cells grouped at various points along the system of canals, which, by the lashing movements of long protoplasmic threads extending from their upper surfaces, draw water in through the pores and drive it out again through the vents. In other words, sponges are living pumping-stations, and the water during its course through the body of a sponge gives to the animal oxygen and food particles and carries out with it all effete matter.

HOW SPONGES GET NEW BODIES FOR OLD

ONE of the most interesting features of the behaviour of sponges is their truly remarkable power of regeneration. If we take a piece of living sponge and squeeze it through fine silk, the cells composing the tissues will become completely separated from each other and will flow through the pores of the silk in the form of a fine emulsion. When this emulsion is examined under a microscope the separate cells can be clearly seen, but a remarkable change has taken place in them. Instead of having its distinctive shape, according to its function, as it has in the undamaged sponge, each cell has become irregular in outline and is seen to be wandering about on its own.

A still more wonderful thing is yet to happen, however. If we take a few drops of this emulsion as it flows through the silk, place it in a small vessel containing sea-water, and watch it at intervals under the microscope, we shall see that after a time the cells have ceased their disordered wanderings and that they have begun to congregate together in a loose mass. In the course of a few hours this loose mass gives place to a small irregular mass of jelly, and if we now leave it for a longer period, we shall find on our return that this small mass has become a complete sponge. Guided by some influence which we can no more than doubtfully guess at, the various cells have come together again, after a brief spell of independence, have each taken on a definite place and a function, with the result that a complete new sponge is created out of the disintegrated remains of the piece originally taken.

In other words, the cells of sponges are capable of assuming the form and behaviour of independent Amœbas for a brief space of time, but ultimately are compelled to come together for mutual well-being. If then the first animals in the world were something in the order of the present-day Amœba, it is probable that we have in the behaviour of sponge cells a suggestion as to how the many-celled animals were evolved from the one-celled, by a co-operation on the part of separate and independent cells and a living in harmony for the welfare and progress of the race.

THE MANY-ARMED HYDRA OF OUR PONDS

THE recuperative powers of sponges are shared to a hardly lesser degree by a few other of the lower animals. There is, for example, a small creature to be found living on the leaves and stems of the plants growing in our ponds which goes by the short and elegant name of Hydra. Whether so-called because it lives in water or whether on account of a resemblance to the Hydra of Greek mythology is not known. If, however, the latter is the case the name is doubly apt.

According to the legend, it fell to the lot of Hercules to conquer a loathsome creature living in the marshes which, in addition to its other terrifying attributes, possessed nine heads, each capable of inflicting considerable injury on anyone attacking the owner. Each head was carried at the end of a long neck and, to make matters worse for those who incurred the creature's wrath, as fast as one head was cut off another grew in its place. The Hydra of our ponds, though doubtless as formidable an enemy to the smaller creatures with whom it shares the pond, is from a human point of view inoffensive and innocuous. It can, on the other hand, replace lost parts with something approaching the ease displayed by the monster of the legend. This power, which is called regeneration, is strongest among the lower animals and is gradually lost as we ascend the animal scale—that is, as the organism becomes more complex and highly organised, until the only vestige of it left is the ability of wounds to heal themselves.

The body of Hydra is built slightly more on the plan familiar to us in the higher animals than is that of a sponge, but even so is sufficiently peculiar to merit some attention being paid to its structure. There is a definite digestive cavity and a mouth, but that is all, and the waste products of digestion are passed out through the mouth. Further, instead of three sets of tissue being present, as in practically all multi-cellular animals, there are only two. Hydra may, therefore, be described as having a tubular body, the wall of which is composed of two layers of cells. The cavity of the sac so formed constitutes the digestive cavity, and while there is a mouth at the upper end, the lower end is completely closed. Food is captured and conveyed to the mouth by tentacles grouped in a ring on the summit of the body around the mouth.

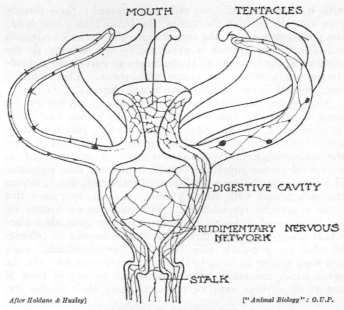

MOUTH   TENTACLES

DIGESTIVE CAVITY

RUDIMENTARY NERVOUS
NETWORK

STALK

After Haldane & Huxley]   *[" Animal Biology" : O.U.P.*

THE MANY-ARMED HYDRA

*Slightly more complicated than Amœba, the Hydra is still a
very primitive animal. It is here cut in half to show its digestive cavity and mouth, the only internal organs it possesses.
Its waving tentacles are armed with poisonous stinging cells
with which it paralyses its living food before drawing it into its
mouth and digesting it.*

CREATURES THAT POISON THEIR FOOD

PERHAPS the most distinctive feature of the Cœlenterata, the
group to which Hydra belongs, is the means by which it
is able to catch its food. The tentacles, more particularly,
and the surface of the body are armed with stinging cells ;
each of these contains a reservoir of poison and a coiled-up
tubular thread connected with it. The base of the thread is
armed with barbs, and at the summit of the cell, protruding
outwards, is a small pointed trigger. The lightest touch on
the trigger and the cell is shot out, the thread uncoils rapidly
and with some force. Therefore, whenever one of the smaller
animals inhabiting the same water as Hydra comes in contact

with it, numerous stinging cells are released ; their threads penetrate the body of the victim, the barbs take a firm hold, the poison flows down the threads into the victim's body, and the unfortunate creature is paralysed by the poison. At the same time, the tentacles of Hydra begin to curve over towards the mouth, carrying the victim with them. The victim is then pushed in through the mouth and digested.

Among the numerous relatives of Hydra, and having the same fundamental structure, however much they may differ in appearance, are the corals, sea-anemones, jelly-fish and a host of other animals of less familiar names. In most of these the resemblance to Hydra is obvious. A sea-anemone is, except for certain superficial details, little more than a gigantic Hydra, having the same fundamental form and, like it, having the skin armed with stinging cells. Corals, too, have this same superficial resemblance. The hard, stony masses we are accustomed to seeing in museums or in glass cases elsewhere are nothing more than the skeletons formed by colonies of what are popularly referred to as " coral-animals," each one very similar in form to Hydra or sea-anemones. On the other hand, the relationship of jelly-fish to any of these is not at all obvious until we come to study their life-history.

THE INFANT JELLY-FISH

TO appreciate fully the close relationship between a jelly-fish and any other of the Cœlenterates, such as Hydra or the sea-anemones, two things must be borne in mind : that there are two distinct phases in the life-cycle of a jelly-fish—a sedentary stage when the animal resembles them strongly, at least superficially ; and a free-swimming stage, the jelly-fish proper which, appearances notwithstanding, is built on the same radial plan and has essentially the same organs as they. The familiar sting of a jelly-fish is due to stinging cells also. The sedentary stage of the life-history of a jelly-fish begins with a small white opaque object about three-eighths of an inch long, consisting of a compact cylindrical body and a short stalk at the base of it. The surface of it has a scaled appearance reminiscent of that of a half-opened cedar cone, and at either end is a ring of tentacles, the ring at the base being situated at the junction of the scaled body and the stalk. The only sign of life is a somewhat lethargic movement on the part of the tentacles. After about twenty-four hours in this sedentary stage the body increases in size, becomes more transparent, the scaled appearance becomes more pronounced and the upper ring of tentacles disappears.

Strong pulsations begin to take place spasmodically at different points in the body, as though it were made up of a number of separate parts each of which was trying to free itself from the rest. This, indeed, is the case, for after a while, beginning at the top, a number of small eight-pointed stars become detached from the body, the process going on until only the stalk is left.

The reason why jelly-fish are found in such abundant shoals is that this process is repeated again and again, until the sea around is infested with them. To make matters worse, the rate of multiplication is increased by budding. The stalk remaining does not die but grows longer and swollen in the upper part, and fresh stars are budded off. In addition, the stalk may give rise to others like it, by budding, and each of these is capable of producing its own crop of eight-pointed stars. Thus each scyphistoma, as these stalked bodies are called, is capable of producing several hundreds of medusæ, or eight-pointed stars, simply by the repeated division of its own body or the production of other scyphistomæ budded off from it. The small eight-pointed medusæ gradually lose their star-like appearance and, by a process of growth extending over several months, become converted into the familiar umbrella-shaped jelly-fish.

In the life of a jelly-fish, therefore, there are two distinct phases : the hydroid phase, represented by the scyphistoma, and the medusoid. In the first, multiplication is asexual, by budding and fission, and in the second it is a sexual process wherein male and female cells, carried on the under-surface of the umbrella of the jelly-fish, unite to form a larva, which in turn becomes fixed to the sea-bottom and is converted into a scyphistoma. This alternation of generations is, generally speaking, found throughout the Cœlenterates. In corals and sea-anemones the hydroid phase has become dominant and the medusoid phase almost completely suppressed. In the jelly-fish the medusoid phase is dominant. Thus the scyphistoma or stalk of a jelly-fish corresponds to the familiar sea-anemone in anatomical details, to a lesser extent in appearance, but differs considerably in size, so that although sea-anemones and jelly-fish appear to differ so markedly that a blood-relationship would hardly be suspected, closer study of them reveals the fact that they are very closely related.

THE STRANGE FOSTER-CARE OF THE JELLY-FISH

FADS and fancies are not the monopoly of human beings, and all living things whatever their rank in the animal or vegetable kingdom have their likes and dislikes. Some of these fads involve the intimate and often lifelong association of two totally unlike creatures. In some cases a mutual benefit results and to this we give the name of commensalism. In many cases of commensalism the two partners are never found apart and, we may assume, are unable to exist for very long on their own. Often the special blessings derived from living together are far from obvious. Stranger still, however, are the cases where creatures live together in an association from which only one partner derives any benefit : stranger because it is difficult to see why the partner that gains nothing should tolerate such a state of affairs. A striking case is that concerning the association of certain large species of jelly-fish and certain small fishes that seek their protection.

It is no uncommon sight, to those who study the life in the oceans, to see a large jelly-fish floating about the surface with a crowd of small fishes sheltering beneath the ample expanse of its umbrella-shaped body. From time to time the fishes sally forth to feed or exercise, but as often as danger threatens they scuttle back into the safety of the jelly-fish's body. On the face of it there is nothing remarkable about this, for fish are past-masters at the art of utilising any nook or cranny—the spaces between rocks or the interstices in a coral bank—for a refuge, but the strange part of this association is that jelly-fish often feed largely on fish ; even if they do not feed on them they have the power to make it extremely unpleasant for even a big fish to come within range of their trailing tentacles.

Like the sea-anemones, jelly-fish are armed with batteries of stinging cells, as bathers in the sea have often found to their cost. If the sting of a jelly-fish can be painful to human beings, even fatal in the case of some of the larger forms found in tropical seas, how much more deadly must it be to the smaller creatures ? A mere touch is sufficient to call forth a fusillade of these poisoned darts and it would be difficult to believe that these crowds of little fishes, constantly swimming around and under the jelly-fish, scuttling this way and that among the bush of tentacles suspended from the underside of its body, never at any time touch the tentacles. Yet the fact remains that, so far as can be seen, they are never harmed by their strange guardians.

WHEN REAL CHIPS OFF THE OLD BLOCK COME TO LIFE

IN animals that exercise no parental care multiplication is attended by an enormous mortality in the offspring. In the sea there are not only living enemies to be reckoned with, but the elements take toll to a greater extent than is the case on land. The familiar example of the codfish which is said to lay millions of eggs in one season, out of which only one or two are destined to give rise to adult individuals, the rest being eaten or otherwise destroyed at some stage of their career, is only too true of practically all the lower invertebrates (animals without backbones). Constantly, the breeding season sees the production of enormous quantities of larvæ, most of which are practically certain to be destroyed by one means or another before reaching maturity. In the lower invertebrates, too, it is not unusual to find fragmentation used as an auxiliary means of reproduction, the animal breaking up into a number of fragments each of which is capable of producing a new individual. This method is very common among sponges. The more fragile sponges are torn asunder or lacerated by wave action, or pulled to pieces by crabs, the fragments so formed giving rise to fresh sponges.

Some sea-anemones have the power of reproducing themselves by unconscious self-laceration. In other words, they are able to take " cuttings " of themselves. Cases are known of sea-anemones which as they move about—even sea-anemones do this occasionally, strange as it may seem—leave behind fragments of their own bodies adhering to the surface of the rocks, and these fragments grow into new anemones. The early naturalists thought that eels dashed themselves against the rocks and that young eels were produced from the bits of skin rubbed off in the process. This was the only way they could think of to explain why eels' eggs could never be found. We smile at such notions now that the breeding-grounds of the eel have been traced to the mid-Atlantic, but the old ideas were not so extravagant after all, if we are to believe some of the modern investigators. It is said that some sea-anemones will choose the sharp edges of rocks and stones, almost purposely it would seem, in order to lacerate their bodies for the purposes of multiplication.

THE MANY-HEARTED WORM:
BENEFACTOR OF MAN

WHEN we speak of worms, we are referring to a group of animals that is a hotch-potch of living creatures, of very different types, having in common the fact that their bodies are long and thin, that there is little difference between the head and tail ends, and that they crawl about without the aid of legs. Thus, under the headings of worms the uninitiated will include earthworms, shipworms, tape worms, flat worms and an almost infinite variety of unrelated creatures. We have even gone so far as to talk about the blindworm, which is simply a legless lizard. To most of us, however, the earthworm would be regarded as the typical example of a worm, and this will suffice for our present purpose.

The outward form of an earthworm is familiar to all, and calls for no detailed description, but the internal anatomy forms a striking contrast to that of any other animal so far discussed. From the sponges, sea-anemones and jelly-fish, all without intestine or any other of the organs of digestion with which we are familiar in the higher animals, all without a heart or blood-vessels, without brain or nerves or any real sense-organs, we take a big jump in considering the worms, for in them we meet for the first time an anatomy which can be to any degree compared with our own.

The ringed appearance of an earthworm bears a close relation to the rest of the features to be discussed. For example, each ring or segment of the body bears four pairs of short bristles with their bases implanted in the skin and directed outwards, and locomotion is effected by the concerted action of these four rows of bristles which run lengthways along the lower surface of the body. If we pass an earthworm through the thumb and forefinger from the head end backwards these bristles impart a rasping sensation on our skin.

Internally each segment is partitioned from its neighbours, and passing through them all, from the mouth to the hinder end of the body, is a straight tube, the intestine. There is a well-defined central nervous system, with the main nerve running immediately under the intestine, and in each segment this is swollen into a ganglion from which several pairs of nerves are given off to serve the organs in the segment. There is a sort of brain, a simple structure it is true, lying above the intestine in the front end of the body. In addition the body is served by a system of blood-vessels consisting of three main vessels running longitudinally through the body and connected in front with five pairs of " hearts," or short pulsating vessels.

EARTHWORMS : THE GARDENER'S GREATEST FRIEND

MANY people are inclined to brand the earthworm as a useless creature of disgusting, or even revolting, appearance and to regard it rather in the light of a nuisance. Their ranks are recruited mainly from those who have inherited, or acquired, a distaste for any animal, no matter how interesting or inoffensive, whose body is cold and somewhat clammy to the touch ; and they do not trouble to inquire further into the matter. Yet the earthworm, like the toad, " ugly and venomous, bears yet a precious jewel in its head."

It would go ill with mankind if earthworms were suddenly and completely exterminated. The agriculturalist and the horticulturalist can hardly claim or hope for a stauncher ally than is found in these lowly and insignificant creatures. Their normal method of feeding is to swallow large quantities of earth, digest the organic matter contained therein, and to void the indigestible matter as worm-casts. It has been calculated that there are some fifty thousand earthworms in an acre of arable land and that these bring to the surface more than twenty tons of soil annually in the form of casts. Much of this comes from the deeper layers of the soil since in dry weather the worms go down quite deep in search of moisture. This constant tunnelling and movement of the soil not only turns the ground over in the course of years, but allows it to be aerated and drained and, in general, to be exposed to the sweetening action of air and rain.

The regenerative powers of earthworms have become almost legendary and, as is usual with the growth of legends, strict accuracy is not always maintained. It is true that an earthworm cut in two becomes two individuals, the front half growing a new hinder end and the hinder part developing a new head. It is not true, however, that the swelling commonly seen near the front end of a worm is the scar formed from the healing of a wound, nor does it mark, as is often suggested, the spot where the two halves of a bisected worm have become joined together again. It is true that, under artificial conditions, the two parts of a cut worm can be made to graft together, but it is doubtful whether this ever happens under natural circumstances. The so-called scar is better known as the " saddle " and is in reality a large glandular area which secretes a cocoon around the eggs as they are laid.

WORMS THAT ARE BELLES OF THE OCEAN BED

IN contrast to the somewhat commonplace, perhaps almost dull, appearance of worms living on land or in fresh water, those living in the sea are often remarkable for their beauty and the unusual forms they assume. Many are brightly and variously coloured, others are luminous. Some burrow in the sand, others swim about habitually, and yet others build homes of sand or mud which in themselves are interesting objects for study. Perhaps the most remarkable of all the marine worms is that which goes by the name of Aphrodite, or the Sea-mouse, and which may be seen, often in large numbers, on the sandy beaches around the shores of the British Isles.

The body of a Sea-mouse is four inches or so long and nearly two inches across at the centre, and from there tapers away to end in a rounded head and tail. The animal creeps about over the sand with the smooth and easy movement characteristic of a mouse. Its upper surface is covered with a pile of fine bristles which change colour with the movement of the animal's body and gives the impression of being a coat of iridescent fur. This strange beast, often seen on a sandy shore as the tide is going out, is sometimes the cause of considerable speculation as to what it really is. If, however, we turn it over on to its back all doubt and guessing is put at rest. The under surface is ringed in exactly the same way as the body of the common earthworm, and there too are the pairs of bristles of which mention has already been made. In fact, the Sea-mouse is merely a worm whose body has become much enlarged and in which the upper surface has become obscured by a dense coating of bristles similar to those used by all worms as organs of locomotion.

THE LITTLE WORM THAT LIVES IN A PEBBLE

WE may frequently pick up on the seashore stones that are marked on the surface with a number of small, slit-like holes, as if they had been persistently stabbed with the sharp end of the blade of a penknife. Similar slits may also be found on the surface of the shells of oysters, mussels and other shellfish. These are made by a small worm known as Polydora. On examination the slits prove to be in pairs and to be the openings of narrow tunnels which penetrate the rock and meet in the middle to form a U. In this retreat Polydora hides with its head protruding from one slit and its tail from the other ; an admirable protection for such a soft-bodied animal. In addition, small chimney-like tubes of mud are often constructed over the slits to protect further the protruding ends of the body.

How such a hard material is bored by so small an animal is as yet uncertain, but it is possible that the skin gives off a fluid capable of dissolving the substance of the rock or shell. Among the oyster-beds considerable damage is done to the stocks by the boring habits of this marine tunneller, not because of actual injury to the oysters but because the shell is spoilt in appearance and the bivalve rendered less marketable. A Polydora living in the Red Sea, however, goes even further. This one enters the shell of an oyster, pushes its way between the soft body of the oyster and the inner surface of the shell, and irritates the oyster until it almost completely covers the worm with a layer of mother-of-pearl. Then, in the safe seclusion of the oyster's shell, in a burrow obtained without labour or trouble, it feeds on the small animals living in the currents of water drawn in by the oyster's gills.

For a striking contrast to the parasitic habits of the Red Sea Polydora we may turn to the evidence of commendable industry found on our own shores. Many worms build for themselves tubes of mud or sand-grains. Often these are of most delicate workmanship, the grains of mud or sand being carefully arranged in the walls of the tube and cemented together with as much precision as the bricks in the walls of human habitations. Some of these worms live singly, others in colonies, and on some parts of our coasts the colonial forms build reefs of sandy tubes several square yards in extent. Although the individual tubes are of such seeming delicacy, the reefs are capable of withstanding the battering of the surf four times a day as the tide rises and falls.

THE TUBE-BUILDER: A WORM WHOSE VIRTUE IS PATIENCE

WHEN the tide goes out on a sandy shore it leaves little behind to reveal the secrets of the sea's inhabitants. There are no rock-pools, as on the more rugged parts of the coast, rich with a profusion of sea-anemones, sponges, shrimps and crabs ; but disappointing as a sandy shore may be there are yet some things to be seen by those interested. Not least among these is the little sand-mason worm, a creature of lowly station and meagre abilities yet which, nevertheless, is able to build itself a beautiful tube of sand, small pebbles and fragments of shell. We can see these tubes at low tide, lying limply on the damp sand, but we find no trace of the owner for it has disappeared below to await the return of the tide.

If we could watch the sand-mason worm at work we should see a rather wonderful sight. This worm has a crown of tentacles surrounding the head which can be extended for a long distance, and as they grope about they grasp the sand-grains or the pieces of shell which come within their reach. These then pass down the length of the tentacles as though moved by invisible hands until they reach the mouth ; actually they are passing along a groove in the tentacle specially provided for the purpose, and propelled by fine protoplasmic hairs lining the grooves. Each particle so obtained is taken into the mouth, moistened with an adhesive fluid, and then ejected and placed into position by the lips. So grain by grain the tube is built up, a monument to tireless energy and patience.

There are many difficulties in the way of seeing the sand-mason worm actually at work, but it is fairly simple to see a similar process being carried on, provided a microscope is available, by a small animal living in freshwater. This is one of the Wheel-animalcules, or Rotifers, known as Melicerta, which grows in ponds and streams on the leaves of water-weeds. When fully extended the body of Melicerta is less than an eighth of an inch long, cylindrical, and bearing at the summit a four-lobed head with a mouth set in the centre. The margins of the lobes are fringed with protoplasmic hairs in a constant state of rhythmic motion giving the effect of four continuously revolving wheels. Normally the body is enclosed within an upright tube built up of minute spheres of a dark material arranged in a remarkably regular series. When feeding, the animal's head is protruded beyond the tube, but at rest the whole body is drawn inside.

To see how this exquisitely formed tube is made we have only to wait for Melicerta to protrude its head from the tube, when the action of the " wheels " sets up a continuous stream of particles into the mouth. The transparent nature of the animal enables us to see the further fate of the particles.

Some are passed on to the stomach, others, the indigestible fragments, pass into a small cavity within the head and are there revolved until they are compacted into a small, round pellet. This is then passed back to the lips and, with a convulsive jerk of the head, the lips are protruded and the pellet placed in position on the wall of the tube. Regularly and with never-failing precision, the pellets are formed and placed into position, the wall of the tube being built up, a row at a time, as though composed of microscopic beads.

WORMS THAT HAVE GOT INTO BAD HABITS: THE PARASITES

EVOLUTION has come to be regarded to-day as a synonym of progress, but while in the main it signifies a forward movement, the word is equally applicable to retrogressive or degenerative trends. The evolution of living things has been on the whole a process of increasing organisation and efficiency, an advancement from the simplest and lowliest forms to the higher and more complicated. But many striking cases of evolution can be cited in which the movement has been in the reverse direction. As often as not, retrogressive evolution is associated with a change from an independent to a parasitic mode of life. Sometimes this leads to a complete degeneration of the individual, but in other instances this degeneration is accompanied by a specialisation, which is in itself a progressive evolution in so far as the individual becomes remarkably well adapted to fit its new surroundings and mode of life.

Perhaps the best illustration of this is found in the tapeworms. A typical tape-worm has an elongated body, with a head beset with a crown of hooks, enabling it to obtain a fast hold in the tissues of its host. Sense-organs are wanting, and the nervous system is much reduced. The body is covered with a cuticle or outer skin to withstand the action of digestive juices, since most of these parasites are found in the gut of their host, but capable of absorbing the products of digestion elaborated by its host. There is no need for a blood-system, since the sole purpose of this would be to distribute the food material arising from digestion, and in the case of a parasite the whole body is bathed in its food. Excretory organs are, however, present. The remaining organs—those of reproduction—are enlarged out of all proportion to the rest.

In order that the race may survive it is necessary for eggs to be laid and for some at least of the young resulting from them to find their way to a new host. In the case of parasites the chances of this happening are infinitely more remote than those of free-living animals that can choose the season for laying, can select a suitable site to deposit the eggs, can lay by a store of food for the young when they are hatched, or even guard the young until they are able to look after themselves. With parasites it is a much more haphazard affair. This means that a vast number of eggs must be laid in order to ensure that a few shall survive and the young from it find a suitable host.

A tape-worm's body is divided into segments each of which is filled very largely with the reproductive organs. As the eggs are fertilised and ripen, the segments containing them become detached from the rest of the body and pass to the exterior, usually with the fæces of the host. As old segments are thrown off, new segments are budded off from just behind the head. A tape-worm is, therefore, in effect, nothing more than a reproducing machine, living on the energies of another animal and devoting all its time and energy to producing fresh tape-worms to bother other animals of the same species. Truly one of the strangest freaks of evolution imaginable !

STARFISH AND THEIR WEIRD COMPANIONS

PROBABLY no other animals present such bizarre forms as those collectively grouped under the heading of the Echinoderms, and including the starfish, sea-urchin and sea-cucumber. Many of the sea-anemones and other polyps of a like nature have quaint forms, but they are on the whole so reminiscent of plants that they do not appear unfamiliar to us. Were we, however, to be suddenly faced with drawings of a starfish or sea-urchin, without having previously seen or heard about these animals, it is probable that we should regard the pictures as figments of an artist's imagination. The star-like build of the starfish, with no apparent head or tail, and little externally to suggest the possibility of its being an animal, or even a living thing, except the ability to move about, is surpassed for quaintness only by the box-like body, covered with a closely-set crop of spines, of the sea-urchin. It is obvious from the attitudes of deep concentration maintained by visitors to the seashore as they stoop watching a stranded starfish that many questions and speculations are passing through their minds as to what these strange beings are and how they live.

The organisation of a starfish's body is really quite simple. The central disc contains the essential organs, the stomach, intestine and so on, and the arms are purely organs of locomotion or used in the capture of food. The mouth is on the under surface of the central disc and can be seen by turning the creature over on to its back. In animals with so unusual an exterior we should naturally expect to find some unusual anatomical features, and in this we shall not be disappointed.

Once the starfish is turned on to its back, we shall have our attention drawn to the rows of suckers, hundreds in each row, running down the centre of each of the radiating arms. It is in the possession of these more than in any other respect that the starfish, and other Echinoderms, differ so markedly from all other animals. These suckers are known as tube-feet and are connected up with a series of tubes within the body, forming a hydraulic system. By throwing the tube-feet well out and fastening them on to the surface of a rock, the starfish is able to pull itself along, the tube-feet working in unison. While some are maintaining a hold others are being retraced to pull the body along and others are being thrown out to obtain a fresh hold farther ahead.

HOW A STARFISH TRAVELS AND COLLECTS ITS MEALS

WHEN a starfish is lying on its back the tube-feet wave about in different directions, apparently quite independent of each other, but when the animal is right side up and moving along, the feet move with one accord and in one direction, for the reason that they are all connected by a continuous system of tubes. Their efficiency as feet depends on this that they can be converted into suckers when necessary. When the terminal discs, which are hollow also, touch the surface of a rock they flatten against it and the floor of each is raised by the manipulation of slender muscles operating inside the foot. Thus a vacuum is created between the disc and the surface of the rock. The combined pull of the suckers is sufficiently strong to enable the starfish to cling to a rock in the roughest of seas, or to climb up the face of a vertical obstruction.

Another use of the tube-feet, quite an important one, is in pulling apart the shells of mussels and other shellfish on which the starfish feeds. The two shells of a mussel are held together by a powerful muscle running from the inside of one shell, through the body of the animal, to the opposite shell, and the strength of this muscle may be gauged by the amount of prising open that is necessary before the morsel inside may be extracted. The starfish, having nothing with which to prise, has another method of accomplishing this end. Wrapping its arms round the shell, it takes a firm hold with its tube-feet and begins to pull until it has pulled the shells apart. Then it everts its stomach, wraps it around the body of the mussel and proceeds to digest it.

Not only are the tube-feet used as organs of locomotion and as weapons of offence, but they also serve as respiratory organs. Through them oxygen is absorbed from the sea-water, but in spite of their numbers the amount of oxygen they can absorb is insufficient to meet the requirements of the starfish ; consequently some means must be found of augmenting the supply. The starfish's skin offers few possibilities in this direction since it is studded with numerous plates of lime and constitutes an effective barrier to the passage of oxygen. An interesting compromise is, however, effected. Between the limy plates the skin grows out at intervals in groups of small, finger-shaped folds all over the surface of the body, and through these oxygen can be absorbed.

Having to adopt a second-best alternative, however, something more than the bare skin is necessary to ensure complete respiration, and an ingenious device is therefore used. These minute folds of skin are coated both inside and out with extremely fine protoplasmic hairs, constantly waving in one direction. Those on the inside keep the fluid of the body moving, so that as soon as one lot is saturated with oxygen it is passed on and another lot devoid of oxygen can take its place. The sea-water, also, is kept in constant movement by the protoplasmic hairs on the outside so that as soon as one lot of sea-water is deprived of its oxygen it is driven away and a fresh supply takes its place. By this combined action the maximum amount of respiration can take place.

THE SEA-CUCUMBER'S INDELICATE RETORT

THE power of regeneration already noted in some of the lower animals is present to a considerable extent in many of the Echinoderms. The sea-cucumbers are close relatives of the starfish but have plump, elongated bodies covered with a warty skin and look, in fact, like cucumbers except in colour.

They, too, have longitudinal rows of tube-feet running along the body. Their mere appearance is sufficiently repulsive, but their methods of protecting themselves are even more to be deplored. An irritated sea-cucumber will not hesitate to eject the whole of its internal organs, an evil-smelling mass, squirting them at whoever may be the cause of the annoyance. Such wholesale self-mutilation is not so injurious as might appear to be the case since the sea-cucumber is able to regenerate all the lost parts in a short space of time. Starfish, also, have been known to eject the whole of their digestive organs when they have swallowed something that does not agree with them, and to re-grow the lost organs—a truly novel cure for indigestion !

The occasions when such drastic remedies for mistakes in diet are necessary are probably few and far between. On the other hand, the ability to repair and replace lost limbs is an ever-present need with starfish, owing to the depredations of crabs of all sizes and descriptions, who do not hesitate to attack a starfish, wrench off a portion of one of its arms and depart to enjoy the feast at leisure. Starfish may often be found in which the arms bear as many as a dozen or more scars, each scar representing an occasion on which a part or the whole of an arm has been lost and has been replaced. How great is this power of replacement may be judged from the fact that so long as the central disc and one arm remain intact the other four arms may be damaged again and again, and as often replaced, without causing the animal's death or causing, so far as can be ascertained, any great inconvenience.

HOW THE CUTTLEFISH AND LIMPET BECAME RELATIONS

JUDGED purely by external appearances one would hardly suspect anything in the nature of a close relationship between a limpet and a cuttlefish. The one small, inoffensive, appearing hardly ever to move, its body completely enveloped in a hard shell ; and the other large, active, belligerent, with a naked body differing markedly in general features from that enclosed within the limpet's shell. Yet these two and many more creatures almost equally diverse in form are grouped together under one heading : the Mollusca. For general purposes it is convenient to describe the molluscs as animals with soft bodies usually enclosed in one or more shells, but this, like all rules, has many exceptions. That it is applicable to the limpet is quite obvious, but to find the shell of a cuttlefish it is necessary to cut the beast open. In fact, the familiar cuttlebone corresponds to the shells of other molluscs.

The three main groups of the Mollusca are the Cephalopoda, including the octopus, squid and nautilus ; the Gastropoda, or univalves, including snails, whelks and limpets, which move about on a broad muscular expansion of the body, known as the foot, and have a single shell usually spirally coiled ; and the Lamellibranchiata, or bivalves, including oysters, mussels, cockles and others of their kind, with the body usually enclosed within a shell formed of two parts, or valves, and hinged along one side.

The last two groups are well known to us in a general way, even to those who, zoologically speaking, are the least initiated and none will fail to recognise in them creatures of a sluggish habit. In fact, so characteristic is their slow rate of locomotion that the very word sluggish is derived from the name of a shell-less Gastropod mollusc. And has not the snail's pace at all times been regarded as the epitome of the slowest rate of locomotion ?

THE ATHLETIC COCKLE: A HIGH JUMP EXPERT

YET even the ranks of the Mollusca can boast members of no mean athletic prowess. Scallops, for example, are vigorous swimmers, travelling backwards through the water, when alarmed, in convulsive jerks, propelled by the expulsion of water as the two valves of the shell are alternately opened and brought forcibly together again. Cockles, too, are expert at high jumping and, when left stranded by the receding tide, are capable of leaping four or five feet into the air in a series of bounding movements as they make their way downshore to the edge of the water. For the most part, however, the Gastropoda and the Lamellibranchiata are content to travel very little or even not to travel at all. Oysters, for example, swim vigorously in the larval, or young, state, but once they have settled down they become almost literally rooted to the spot.

To understand the movements of molluscs, whether the slow creeping movements of a snail or the leaping of a cockle, it is necessary to make clear what is meant by the foot, as all locomotion is effected by means of this organ. This is not

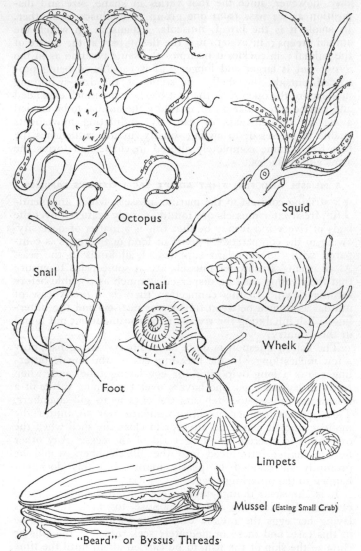

Octopus

Squid

Snail

Snail

Whelk

Foot

Limpets

Mussel (Eating Small Crab)

"Beard" or Byssus Threads

SOME MEMBERS OF THE MOLLUSC FAMILY

easy, however, since the foot varies in shape, size and disposition as we pass from one group of molluscs to another. In snails it is the broad, muscular expansion on which the animal creeps ; in oysters it is the fleshy part at the centre of the animal ; in cockles it occupies the same position as in the oyster but is larger and longer and is capable of being protruded outside the shell ; in some of the free-swimming molluscs of the open seas, the foot has become much expanded and can be spread like a sail, enabling the animal to be carried along by the currents or can, by undulating movements enable its possessor to swim ; finally, in the cuttlefishes the foot has become completely altered in shape and forms the arms and tentacles.

A MUSSEL AND FISH THAT ADOPT EACH OTHER'S FAMILIES

IN striking contrast to the marine mussels, which are plentiful, freshwater mussels are found sparsely scattered over the beds of rivers and it may be that this is a matter of necessity, owing to the comparative scarcity of food in the rivers as compared with the abundant supplies of all kinds in the seas. At all events, freshwater mussels are at some pains to ensure that their young shall be dispersed as much as possible before settling down. In this connection there is a pretty case of mutual assistance between freshwater mussels and the bitterling, a fish inhabiting the rivers of the continent but not found in this country.

The fish in question is quite an ordinary-looking fish, only a few inches long. In the breeding season the female bitterling grows a long ovipositor (or egg-laying tube) and, when ready to lay her eggs, she hovers over the gaping valves of a freshwater mussel and deposits the eggs in its gill-chambers. This appears neither to inconvenience nor to injure the mollusc since it makes no attempt to close the shell when the ovipositor is inserted nor to get rid of the eggs. Any other foreign matter introduced into the gill-chambers would be promptly surrounded by pearly matter, but this does not happen to the bitterling's eggs.

It is almost as though there were a mutual understanding between the bitterling and the mollusc, for while the first is laying her eggs the mussel discharges its own brood, larvæ in this case, and these immediately seek refuge in the gills or cling to the skin of the fish, to be carried about until the time comes for them to grow a pair of valves and live at the bottom of the stream like their parents. Then they release their hold on the tissues of the bitterling and drop off, leaving their unwitting benefactor none the worse for the service rendered.

How such an association, or mutual exchange, came into being and what are the influences that bring about the exact timing necessary for its success are matters for speculation, but the upshot is, almost certainly so far as the mussel's side of the bargain is concerned, that its young are scattered more effectively over the bottom of the river, and have, therefore, a greater chance of survival, than would otherwise have been the case. It is significant that the British pearl industry should have flourished around the swiftly-moving streams, and one can only suppose that the rapid movement of the water carrying the larvæ about and scattering them broadcast, results in the same end as the passenger transport service provided by the bitterling in continental rivers.

Associations of this sort, between animal and animal, between animal and plant, and between plant and plant, are very numerous ; not only are they of absorbing interest, but they serve to show, what is only too often overlooked, that Nature is not entirely " red in tooth and claw." On the contrary, progress in the evolution of both animals and plants has been more often due to co-operation than otherwise. Some of the associations are quite commonplace, and call for little comment. Others are of so strange an order as to place them in the realm of tall stories had we not fairly convincing proof to the contrary.

CREATURES THAT CAPTURE THEIR ENEMY'S "GUNS"

CERTAIN marine molluscs, belonging to the Gastropod group, known as sea-slugs, have lost their shells either partially or completely in exactly the same way as the land-slugs. Their bodies are naked like those of the land-slugs, which they resemble in many ways, but they are more beautiful in colour and their backs usually bear a number of warts or small, finger-shaped folds of skin. Some burrow in the sand, others swim in the open waters, but most of them crawl about over the seaweeds, sponges, hydroids and other animals, feeding on them in the same way as land-slugs are found infesting and feeding on the land-plants. As a rule they take on the colour of the seaweed or animal on which they are feeding and for this reason are frequently overlooked.

One of the sea-slugs, owing to the peculiar manner in which

the skin of the back is folded, presents a striking resemblance in miniature to a hare and is known in consequence as the sea-hare. When interfered with the sea-hare pours out from its skin a dense purple fluid, an indelible dye, and this not only obscures the animal's movements, in the manner of a smoke-screen, but is also distasteful to its enemies. It has been said, without truth of course, that a human being coming in contact with this fluid would lose all the hair from his head. Sea-slugs, having lost their shells must find some other method of protection, and this is how the sea-hare accomplishes it.

A still more remarkable method of protection is found in the plumed sea-slug. This animal is about three inches long and its back is covered with numerous rows of erect, cylindrical folds of skin. These are partly used for breathing purposes and, in addition, each contains a small organ corresponding to an extent with the liver. The plumed sea-slug often lives on the same ground as certain sea-anemones, resembling them in colour and appearing the more like them by reason of the similarity of the respiratory plumes to the tentacles of the anemones. The anemones being armed with stinging cells are treated with considerable respect by fishes and other carnivorous animals, and the sea-slugs share in this immunity from attack by reason of their resemblance to the anemone. Curiously enough, and as a very poor return for the immunity enjoyed, the slugs feed on the anemones.

Now comes the strange and almost incredible part of the story. Not content with the immunity they already enjoy, the slugs actually arm themselves with the weapons of their victims and use them against foes that may attack them when they are away from the shelter of the anemone's stings. And this is how it is done. Undigested remains of the anemone's tentacles pass up into the livers situated in the plumes ; the stinging-cells contained in the tentacles remain undigested, pass out of the liver and take up their position in the skin of the sea-slug, whence they can be shot out at enemies when the occasion arises. The truth of this story has often been doubted, but the matter has been investigated again and again and there is no reason now for not accepting it.

In passing, it may be noted that, in addition to this strange method of arming itself, the sea-slug, when pursued, has a habit of throwing off some of its plumes to distract the attention of an enemy while it makes good its escape, new plumes being eventually grown in place of those thrown off.

THE SPINNING SLUG THAT SWINGS FROM TREES

ANYTHING in the nature of acrobatics would hardly be accredited to slugs and snails ; nor indeed does one ordinarily associate them with spinning, an industry of which the monopoly is usually believed to be held by spiders, and to a lesser extent by certain caterpillars. Nevertheless, although they do not perform these things as a matter of habit, certain slugs are capable on occasion of spinning threads and suspending themselves from the branches of trees, or even of swinging from one branch to another. The material used in the spinning of such threads is the same as the mucus given off from the body as the slug travels over the ground and which gives rise to the tell-tale silvery tracks. The significance of this form of spinning is obscure, but in some cases it is associated with mating, the two slugs hanging suspended side by side and mating in mid-air.

An example of spinning may be seen in the bladder-snails living in ponds and streams. They often spin a thread a foot or more in length and reaching from the surface of the water to the bottom, or with the lower end hanging free. A few inches of the upper end of the thread are allowed to lie free on the surface to give the necessary grip. With the thread in position the snail can travel from the bottom of the pond to the surface and *vice versa* with a minimum of effort, crawling up and down the thread instead of having to swim.

What is perhaps more remarkable, is that, when the snail wishes to move to another part of the pond, it eats the thread inch by inch, digests it and uses the material again to construct another thread in the new quarters. In this case, the thread is so fine that it cannot be detected when the animal is in its natural haunts. Only in an aquarium, and under special illumination can it be seen.

HOW MUSSELS HELP MAN TO PROTECT THE SHORE

THE Mollusca vie with the insects, among the backbone-less animals, or invertebrates, in their abounding numbers and more particularly, in the extreme variety of situations in which they are found ; in and on the ground, on lowland and highland, in marsh, moor and heath ; in pond, stream and river, on the shore, in shallow water or in the abyssal depths of the ocean in every sea the world over. Yet for all their abounding numbers the Mollusca are of surprisingly little direct use to man. Some like the oysters, mussels and cockles serve for food, but even these are, in civilised countries at least, to be counted as delicacies. Cuttlefish also are eaten in some parts of the world. Apart from this, however, molluscs merely supply pearls and mother-of-pearl, for buttons, studs and such things.

Surprisingly enough it is the mussel that should be looked upon as the greatest benefactor to man, if such a phrase may be used for unwitting service. In addition to its value as food and as a bait in long-line fishing, its strongly gregarious habit and method of attaching itself to timber and masonry have a quite unexpected value. The byssus, the tangle of brown threads by which a mussel is attached, serves to bind the sand and mud, and mussel-beds are often an important factor in preserving the foreshore against the shifting action of tides and currents. The masses of mussels on breakwaters, pier-piles and quaysides also serve as fenders against the force of the waves. Although this can hardly be quoted as a case of direct use to mankind, it is interesting to recall, if only to illustrate its strength in relation to its power to bind a shifting foreshore, that the threads of the byssus have occasionally been used to weave a cloth from which small articles of human apparel, such as gloves, can be made.

THE BRITISH SNAIL THAT THE ROMANS ENJOYED

IT is a curious fact that there appears to be a certain reluctance in this country to use the members of the Mollusca as food. Oysters, it is true, are not disdained, but whelks and mussels are by no means fashionable dishes, while snails are regarded as quite outside the pale of human consideration, although they are eaten with relish in other countries. Yet although no one would think of scorning crab, lobster, or prawn, these in fact rank very little higher in the animal scale than the Mollusca.

There can be little doubt that the Romans were particularly partial to snails—not to the common or garden snail, but to a larger variety, known as the Roman snail or apple-snail, found in abundance in certain parts of England. This has led to the belief that these large snails were introduced into the country by the early invaders. As is usually the case where information is uncertain, legend steps in with an enthusiastic if misguided attempt to fill in the gaps.

The origin of the belief appears to be two-fold. In the

first place, in excavations of the sites of Roman camps and dwellings, the empty shells of this particular snail are often found associated in quantities with the remains of Romano-British pottery. Secondly, the snails are usually found to-day within a fairly short radius of a Roman site, implying, it may be supposed, that the descendants of those snails that survived the gustatory onslaughts of the early invaders still cling to the ancestral haunts.

In this country, the Roman snail is confined to the southeast corner of England, and even here is local in its distribution. Usually it is found only on chalky soil, though sometimes thriving on sand, and when it is remembered how thickly the chalk areas of the south-eastern counties are studded with Roman remains, it is easy to see that no local patch of snails could be far from one of them. To associate them with the Roman occupation, then, was natural and the idea once having been started, an observer would be influenced to search more closely for them in such areas, overlooking them, as a consequence, in those areas where no Roman relics had been found.

Fortunately, the geologist is at hand to give us enlightenment in the matter. The Romans may have introduced some snails to augment the numbers already here, or even to replenish depleted stocks, but *Helix pomatia*, the Roman snail, was here before Cæsar cast covetous eyes on the cliffs of Britain. Their fossil remains are associated not only with eoliths, that is with the very earliest flint tools fashioned by man, but also with deposits of earth that were probably laid down before man had even begun to throw off his brutish mantle. If any further proof that the Romans were not responsible for their introduction were needed, it is that the snails are not found around the sites of Roman camps elsewhere in this country than in the south-eastern counties.

The Roman snail is sometimes called the apple-snail because it is wrongly assumed that *pomatia* in its Latin name *Helix pomatia* means apple. Actually, however, it is derived from a Greek word, *poma*, meaning a pot-lid. In winter, or in very dry weather, all snails tend to bury themselves under dead leaves or decaying vegetation, or to creep into a cleft in a rock, under stones or, indeed, under or into anything that will give them shelter from the desiccating powers of the sun's rays. In winter, or in prolonged drought, the garden snail not only buries itself but, to preserve what little moisture it can and to prevent undue evaporation from its own body, closes the opening of its shell with a film of mucus, which hardens on contact with the air. Snails may often be turned out in the garden with the shell sealed up in this manner. A small aperture is left in the film to admit air, but otherwise the snail is well-protected both from the elements and from its smaller enemies. The Roman snail, under similar circumstances, also withdraws into its shell and seals the opening, but this it does with a thick, chalky plate, the pot-lid—not perforated to admit the air but porous like plaster of Paris, which it closely resembles.

Just as in the higher vertebrates, including man himself, provision is made for protecting the more vulnerable organs, such as heart and lungs, with a strong skeleton, in their case the ribs, so in the Mollusca these organs are always found under the shell. For example, in the snails the lungs and other organs are permanently lodged within the shell, so that not only can the body be withdrawn into the shell at the alarm, but the vital organs are always protected by it. The carnivorous slug, on the other hand, has so small a shell, which it carries at the hinder end of its body, that it could not withdraw the whole of the body into it. But we find that the pulmonary chamber, heart, and other organs are immediately underneath it. Further, the vegetarian slugs that harass our gardens, and which appear to be devoid of a shell, have a shell of sorts hidden underneath the warty skin situated near the front end of the body and under this, too, the vital organs are lodged. In the last-named, owing to the lack of an external shell, we may see the opening to the lung, or pulmonary chamber, on this same warty patch of skin, varying in position according to the species examined.

All marine molluscs breathe by gills, but all land molluscs, and practically all of those living in freshwater, have a pulmonary chamber ; this is not a lung in the sense of a spongy mass of tubes such as is found in the higher animals but merely a cavity with walls richly supplied with blood-vessels and opening to the exterior by a single aperture.

SOME LAUDABLE CUSTOMS OF THE SLUG

SLUGS are regarded by most people with abhorrence ; they seem repulsive to the touch and sight, are regarded as despoilers of the garden, of little use in any way and fit only to be trodden underfoot or otherwise destroyed at the very earliest opportunity. In a few outlying districts, it is true, a particular type of slug boiled in milk is still regarded as a sovereign cure for consumption, but even those who recommend this cure can easily be made to admit that they regard the supposed cure as little better than the disease itself. Nevertheless, as is usually the case with supposedly noxious animals, there is something to be said in favour of some slugs at least, and indiscriminate killing by gardeners is not the best method of dealing with them.

The carnivorous slugs, however unattractive their appearance may be, are among those with some claim to virtue in human eyes. To begin with, they do not eat vegetable matter except when it has reached an advanced stage of decomposition, and in this they may be classed as effective scavengers, especially as they will devour garbage and scraps of all kinds, vegetable or animal, including dead bodies of small animals, insects, or even the carcases of their own kin. Other slugs feed largely on toadstools and help to keep the countryside clear of the decomposing remains of these fungi which are often obnoxious. One of them, about three inches long and readily recognisable because the hinder end of its body is broader than any other part and bears a small shell, not only feeds on worms, actually pursuing them into their burrows, but will even feed on other slugs and snails.

It not infrequently happens that the estimable qualities of the carnivorous snails become perverted. In this case their predatory and scavenging tendencies work contrary to human desires and needs. Some take to feeding on paper, with dire results if they become established in the house of a bibliophil. Let loose in a dairy, they will feed on cream or butter or whatever else may be available ; and in a larder will do similar damage, having even been known to attack the family joint.

A MOUTHFUL OF TROUBLE: THE SLUG WITH FIFTEEN THOUSAND TEETH

SLUGS capable of hunting and killing worms would naturally be expected to be possessed of specially constructed jaws or some other apparatus for seizing and holding so wriggling a prey, but actually the mouth of a carnivorous slug differs little from that of other Gastropods, and not at all in the principle of its construction. In Gastropods there is a small horny plate which is dignified by the name of jaw, but this only serves to cut off the food. More rarely two such plates are present. The process of mastication is performed by the tongue, or more properly speaking, the radula. This consists of a thin ribbon of a horny substance known as chitin and is covered with numerous teeth of the same material. The pattern, size and ornamentation of the radula vary enormously in different species. In the sea-slugs, for example, there are often few more than a dozen such teeth on the radula, but in the garden slugs there may be nearly fifteen thousand set in rows of about a hundred each, the whole looking under microscope like a very irregular file. The action of using the radula is precisely a filing motion, the food being rasped up into pieces sufficiently small for the stomach to deal with.

In the cuttlefish there are a pair of horny jaws and a radula, but the latter is reduced to extremely small dimensions whereas the jaws are much enlarged and strengthened and curved to form a formidable beak, like a parrot's beak in shape and having similar powers. The Lamellibranchs (oysters, mussels, cockles, etc.), on the other hand, have neither jaws nor radula and the head has become practically nothing more than an opening into the gullet, for the simple reason that they feed on small plants and animals of microscopic dimensions carried in by the same currents of water that bring oxygen to their gills. In this case the food is trapped on the gill-plates and carried up to the mouth by rows of fine protoplasmic hairs.

The feeding mechanism of the Lamellibranchs is not at all easy to describe in a few words, but by dealing in round terms with the anatomy of the oyster, it may be possible to make clear the general principles on which it works. An oyster is roughly comparable to a book of which the valves form the covers. Immediately within the valves, and actually responsible for their formation and growth, are two broad flaps of flesh known as the mantle. Within the mantle are the gills, delicate plate-like organs composed of a fine lattice-work plentifully supplied with blood-vessels and covered with countless fine protoplasmic hairs. The gills constitute what is known popularly as the " beard ". At the centre, between the pair of gill-plates on either side, is the muscular foot containing the vital organs. In life the protoplasmic hairs covering the gills are in constant and concerted action, driving a current of water across the gill-plates, the edges of the mantle being so arranged that water can be drawn in at one point and driven out at another. In many bivalves the process is assisted by siphons, or tubular prolongations of the edge of the mantle, one siphon for drawing the water in and the other serving as a waste-pipe.

THE SHIPWORM, DESTROYER-IN-CHIEF

IT IS the enormous over-development of the siphons that has enabled the shipworm to pursue its destructive activities. The shipworm bores into the timbers of piers and breakwaters and, before the days of copper-sheathing, was a source of considerable trouble to shipping. It consists of quite a small body proper, enclosed in the usual bivalve shell, from which extend backwards a pair of long siphons. In some species the siphons are up to two or three feet long. The manner in which the boring of timbers is carried out has not yet been fully elucidated so that it is only possible to say what the shipworm does and not how it does it. The tunnels are driven into the wood with the grain and a piece of timber well-infested is excavated with longitudinal tunnels, many of them separated from each other by the thinnest partitions of wood imaginable, so that what appears to be a mighty baulk of timber is really a fragile mass, ready to fall to pieces at the buffeting of the waves.

A close relative of the shipworm, the piddock, bores into limestone rocks, and evidence of its work may be seen in the limestone pebbles, sometimes picked up on the shore, which are riddled with holes into which the finger can be inserted with ease. The piddock, however, has not undergone the change seen in the shipworm. It is a normal bivalve with the front ends of the shell ornamented with rows of rasp-like teeth, to assist in the boring, and a pair of siphons only slightly elongated. Some piddocks bore into driftwood, and samples of their handiwork may, again, be picked up on the shore.

WHAT CAN THE SHELL CREATURES SEE, HEAR AND FEEL?

ALTHOUGH in general construction, in the possession of highly organised digestive and respiratory systems, and in their habits, the Mollusca show a considerable advance on the backboneless animals or invertebrates considered so far, the development of their nervous system does not appear to have kept pace with the development of the other parts of the body. They have nothing comparable with the highly organised and centralised brain of the vertebrates. Their nervous system consists of a series of nerves with various ganglia, or masses of nerve cells, at the junctions of the main nerves. Certainly many of them, as for example, oysters, show very little sign of intelligence—little more, in fact, than the more primitive animals, such as sea-anemones and jellyfish. But it would be wrong to brand the whole group on the attainments of a few of its members. Some show quite a high degree in the development of the senses, and the cuttlefish, as will be shown later on, compare favourably in this respect with some of the lower vertebrates.

In oysters and many others the sense of sight is feeble and the organs doing duty for eyes are little more than shallow pits in the edge of the mantle, filled with pigment. Slugs and snails, on the other hand, have well-developed eyes, as everybody knows, since from early childhood we must all be accustomed to seeing these animals draw in their stalked eyes when touched, and protrude them again after we have left them alone for a short while. But even slugs and snails have a very limited field of vision, extending to little more than a fifth of an inch. The use of their eyes is rather for the perception of moving shadows, warning them of the vicinity of a potential enemy. In cuttlefish, however, the eye has a lens and retina and is undoubtedly a very efficient organ of sight, a strict necessity in animals depending as they do on the hunting of swiftly moving prey.

The sense of hearing is very slight in all molluscs, although they are capable of appreciating sound, as experiment has shown. But apart from the cuttlefish, it is undoubtedly on the sense of smell and touch that they depend for their food and for escape from enemies. Whelks are caught by baiting them with rotting fish; slugs and snails will smell out an apple or a dish of cream and make their way directly to them, showing that they have smelt them from a distance; and even the supposedly stupid oyster will close its valves on the approach of its arch-enemy, the starfish. Experiments have shown that a little of the juice of a starfish placed in the water near an oyster will cause it to close. That the sense of touch is acute needs little proof, as anyone who has tried to insert a small pebble into the gaping valves of a mussel or has touched a snail and seen it withdraw into its shell will testify. Even a very slight touch on the shell of a snail is instantly communicated to the animal's nervous system and is sufficient to make the snail withdraw.

YOU WILL FIND THE SNAIL AT HIS PERMANENT ADDRESS

IT WOULD hardly be proper to leave the question of the senses of Mollusca without saying something of the homing instinct, not uncommon among animals of all types, but particularly striking in certain molluscs, perhaps because it is least suspected there. The most beautiful example is seen in the limpets. The young limpet settles down on a spot on a rock, and that spot remains its home for the rest of its life. As its shell grows, the edge takes on the contour of the surface of the rock and fits exactly to it, with the result that it is difficult to get anything underneath to prise the limpet off. A limpet feeds on seaweeds and often travels quite considerable distances in search of food, yet, unless some accident overtakes it, it will always return to its "home." Moreover, it always orientates itself in such a way that it takes up precisely the position it had before embarking on its excursion, with the result that it fits on to the rock, as closely as though it had never left it.

With most other molluscs there is not such a need for this extreme precision, but even they have their preferences for particular corners in which to lie up when resting. Snails and slugs will often travel long distances in a single night and return before dawn to the spot they left. Experiments have been made to test the truth of this. Snails have been taken from certain crannies in a wall, their shells have been marked with distinctive dabs of paint and the animals then hurled for yards, often over a garden fence or a wall. Sure enough, the next morning they have been found again in the same places from which they were taken the night before. Again and again this has been done with the same snails and just as persistently they have returned except when they have suffered injury in falling after being thrown, or disaster, perhaps in the shape of a thrush, has overtaken them.

ANIMALS THAT HAVE THEIR SHELLS INSIDE

CUTTLEFISH, of which the Octopus is a familiar example, are so different from other molluscs that it is difficult to believe that they are closely related to them. They are by far the most highly organised of the group. The body is usually distinctly divided into a head and a trunk, and the head is surrounded with a crown of arms and tentacles, each of which is beset with numerous suckers for laying hold of prey. The shell is internal (the familiar cuttle-bone of the octopus is a good example), and the foot has become modified and much altered in shape to form the arms and tentacles. The eyes are large and have much the same appearance and structure as the eye of a vertebrate, and there is a concentration of the nervous ganglia which is the nearest approach to a brain found in the Mollusca.

Just behind the head is seen the opening of a pouch, formed by the mantle being wrapped around the body, and from this protrudes the end of a siphon, known as the funnel. The funnel is the organ of locomotion, a stream of water being constantly driven out from it in a regularly pulsating manner. When the animal is stationary, the discharge from the funnel is of a mild character and directed first this way and then that in order not to disturb the surrounding water too much and to keep the body in the same position, but the moment the cuttlefish is alarmed, or wishes to pursue its prey, water is driven out in strong jets and these have the effect of driving the animal backwards through the water at a rapid rate.

INK THAT LASTS FOR THOUSANDS OF YEARS

CONNECTED with the funnel is a structure peculiar to cuttle-fish, the ink-sac. This is divided into two portions, the first holding the main supply and the outer portion containing a diluted store ready for use, so that at the moment of alarm, the valve leading into the funnel is opened and each jet of water comes out as a cloud of dense black ink, under cover of which the cuttlefish retreats from its foes. Ink-sacs are commonly found as fossil remains and even now, after the lapse of countless thousands of years, it is often possible to make a usable ink from them.

Small octopus and squid are commonly met with off the coasts of the British Isles. Sometimes they may be found in rock-pools, left behind by the receding tide, although sharp eyes are needed to see them, since they possess the power, more familiarly associated with the chameleon, of changing their colour according to the background they are on. But such examples are usually very small, perhaps an inch or two across. Further out, in the deeper waters, larger examples are found, while, at rare intervals, squid, measuring five, six, or even twelve feet long are cast up during storms, particularly on the east coast.

A FEARSOME SPECTACLE: FIFTY FEET OF WRIGGLING TENTACLES

STORIES of giant squid and octopus abound, but it not infrequently happens that the dimensions of the beasts are exaggerated beyond all reason. At the same time we cannot be certain how plentiful these animals are nor what is the largest size they may attain. In some parts of the world cuttlefish must be present in very large numbers, yet dredging and trawling, the usual methods of investigating the inhabitants of the sea, have been singularly unsuccessful in landing more than a few. This is almost certainly due to their agility in dodging the nets. Nevertheless, they must be plentiful since they form the food of the sperm whale, an animal whose appetite presumably takes a lot of satisfying.

From the remains of tentacles found in the stomachs of whales and from trustworthy reports of specimens actually seen that have escaped capture, the largest probably measure up to fifty feet. Possibly individuals larger than this exist, but the bodies of cuttlefish are so soft and fragile that specimens are seldom hoisted aboard whole, even when captured, and those cast ashore are as often as not in a very damaged condition. But fifty feet, or even less, of struggling cuttlefish, with a writhing mass of muscular tentacles, ten, twenty or thirty feet long, each beset with numerous suckers edged with rims of sharp, horny teeth, is sufficiently fearsome for the stories of their greater size to be excusable if not acceptable.

BOOKS FOR THE STUDENT OF PRIMITIVE CREATURES

THE brief outline of the lower animals given in this account can be augmented by reference to such books as *The Royal Natural History* (Warne), in several volumes, profusely illustrated but having the disadvantage of being somewhat out-of-date, especially in the matter of classification. A more modern work, by the same publishers, *The Standard Natural History*, again well illustrated, contains the same information, abridged and brought up-to-date. This has much to recommend it as a work for general reading and, perhaps more particularly, as a work of reference. Articles on special groups will be found in any edition of *The Encyclopædia Britannica*, always worth consulting where an especially full knowledge is required on a particular subject. For the more academic information concerning classification and anatomy, text-books of Zoology such as those by Parker and Haswell (Macmillan), Shipley and Macbride (Cambridge University Press) and J. Arthur Thomson should be consulted. Books dealing with special groups of the lower invertebrates are extremely rare, except for those dealing with the Mollusca, and here no better recommendation can be given than *Shell Life* by Step (Warne). For the lower marine invertebrates, *The Seas*, by Russell and Yonge (Warne), is always worth reading, as well as for general accounts of the modern methods of marine investigation.

THE CRAWLING WORLD OF CRABS AND INSECTS

by C. HORTON SMITH, B.Sc., D.I.C.

CRABS, insects, centipedes and spiders together form a group called the Arthropoda or animals with jointed legs. The first three of these form quite a definite series and appear to be sharply separated from the spiders. In addition there is another animal called Peripatus—a primitive, worm-like creature, retiring in habit and living in damp places in the tropics of Africa and America, in Australia and New Zealand. It is an interesting animal, because it shows affinities with worms on the one hand and Arthropoda, especially the insects, on the other ; we shall say no more about Peripatus, but it should be remembered as one of those synthetic sort of animals which combine the qualities of two or more widely separated groups and whose very existence enables us to build up a fairly accurate knowledge of how higher groups may have evolved from the lower.

The arthropod body consists of a series of rings and, theoretically, each ring or segment carries a pair of legs. This is well shown in the centipedes. When we come to the higher forms, these legs tend to disappear from some of the segments, fusion of the segments takes place and specialisation for various purposes sets in. Some of the legs are no longer used for walking but become modified as jaw-feet. On account of changes of this kind, we shall find it convenient to describe the legs and similar structures as appendages, a term which can include antennæ or feelers, claws of crabs, claw horns or cheliceræ of spiders as well as the modified jaw-feet of crustacea (lobsters, crabs, shrimps, etc.) and of insects.

Arthropods may be recognised by their strong, horny armour which would greatly hamper their movements were it not for the many-jointed limbs from which the group gets its name. The possession of antennæ or feelers is quite characteristic. Like practically all other groups of the animal kingdom, and as we should expect from their great diversity and numbers, the Arthropoda has representatives in every sphere of animal activity ; they flourish in the air, on and in the earth, and in the seas, rivers and ponds. It is interesting to recall that even the typically water-loving crustacea have sent a few representatives to the land as in the case of the land crabs and wood lice. This almost universal distribution is the outcome of success in evolution brought about by a remarkable adaptability on the part of the organisms—there is, for example, a shrimp which lives in concentrated brine !

In the life histories of two great sub-groups of the Arthropoda—the Crustacea and the Insects—there is rarely a direct change over from egg to adult comparable to the way in which a hen's egg gives rise to a chick of more or less the same form as its parents ; there are phases interpolated, each phase being marked by a stage in the life history which is quite characteristic in form and structure. In other words, the young arthropod may look very different from its parents. Such a series of changes is referred to as metamorphosis and the complexity of the metamorphosis may vary very much in character and degree in the different members of the group. Unlike many of the lower animals, the sexes are usually separate.

The Crustacea, which includes the Crabs and Lobsters, is typically a water-inhabiting group breathing by gills. The Insecta, which typically dwells on the land, breathes by means of air-tubes.

The arthropod group has a particular claim to man's attention, for it is important to him in a variety of ways, pleasant and otherwise—it may afford him food like crabs and shrimps ; it may destroy his possessions as the termites do ; it may ruin his crops in the way the Colorado beetle does ; it carries disease through the house-flies, mosquitoes and lice ; it supplies the bees which pollinate his flowers.

THE CRAB FAMILY AND ITS CONNECTIONS

WHEN we speak of crustacea, we think at once of the crabs and crab-like animals which are really the highest and largest members of the sub-group. There are, however, a host of small forms which are quite unlike the crabs both in structure and habit. Most of the newly hatched young are quite different from their parents and only attain to the parent form after a series of immature stages—i.e. the life-history of most crustacea includes a complicated metamorphosis. The Crustacea group can be divided into two parts : one which contains all the familiar forms like the crabs, lobsters and shrimps, and a second, including all the other forms. Anyone who has collected in ponds knows the water flea, the little Cypris, which looks like a bivalved shell-fish, and the Cyclops ; a microscope must be employed to see the details of structure of these tiny creatures.

Water fleas are the most abundant of the fresh water crustacea. They live in a sort of transparent bivalve shell from which their heads project. The popular name of water flea was given to it on account of its jumping actions when swimming. If you watch one under the microscope, you can see its method of swimming. It is carried through the water by backward strokes of its two antennæ. Four to six pairs of legs act as paddles to create a current of water between the valves of the shell from back to front, and this carries small food bodies towards the mouth. The head bears a large eye. Between the shell and the animal's back there is a space, which in the female is used as a brood-pouch ; this is usually filled with developing but unfertilised eggs, for males are never found during the greater part of the year. These eggs give rise to tiny water fleas, so that there is no metamorphosis.

When the males appear, as they do at certain seasons, the females lay eggs which cannot develop without fertilisation, and if these eggs are examined, they are seen to be enclosed in a protective case which shelters them from the adverse conditions of the outer world. In this condition they can be transported either by the wind or by birds from one pond to another without injury. Not infrequently, water fleas suddenly appear in ornamental garden pools and are no doubt carried there by one of these agencies.

Cyclops is another common denizen of ponds, and its life-history includes a metamorphosis. Cyclops has a pear-shaped body which gradually narrows down behind to a forked tail. The head carries a single eye of a reddish colour. Unlike the water fleas, Cyclops has two pairs of antennæ, the second being much shorter than the first pair. It has mouth-parts which are jaw-feet, and four pairs of forked legs used in swimming. In contrast to the water fleas, Cyclops pass smoothly through the water. Females carrying long egg sacs can frequently be collected from ponds. The eggs, however, do not give rise to small replicas of the adult, but hatch out into little oval larvæ (an immature stage which is unlike the adult) with three pairs of limbs and a single eye. This larva is called a *nauplius* and it eventually develops into the adult.

The relatives of Cyclops are numerous and diverse. Many of them are marine, living near the surface of the sea. Some are economically important as food for herring ; others, such as fish lice, are parasitic. Some, through their parasitic habit, degenerate into immobile, shapeless masses. Others are numbered amongst the most beautiful creatures of tropical seas.

AN ANIMAL THAT KICKS FOOD INTO ITS MOUTH

ANOTHER well-known creature in this group is the barnacle, so common above low-water mark on the rocks of our coasts. Older naturalists thought barnacles were shell-fish, which is not surprising ; later, it was seen that the eggs gave rise to a nauplius larva which linked them up with other crustacea. This nauplius larva swims about for a time and then changes into another larval form which resembles the bivalved cypris already mentioned and is therefore called the Cypris larva. It possesses six pairs of legs, and the antennæ carry suckers with which the animal eventually attaches itself to a rock, when the shell falls off and development proceeds. Huxley described the barnacle as " a Crustacean fixed by its head and kicking the food into its mouth with its legs." If an acorn barnacle is watched, these feet will be seen at work sweeping the surrounding water for prey. Little valves of the adult shell open and close to allow the legs to protrude.

A relative of the barnacle is the parasite Sacculina, which is frequently found under the abdomens of crabs. It sends root-like processes through the crab's armour, and these eventually penetrate to every organ of the body and absorb nourishment. Sometimes the presence of the parasite changes the sex of the crab. Through parasitism, great degeneration has taken place and there is not the slightest hint that the adult Sacculina is an Arthropod at all—but the life-history gives it away and we find the characteristic stages of a crustacean's life.

The life-history of Sacculina is given in the following scheme:

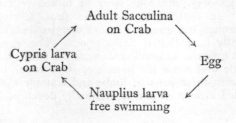

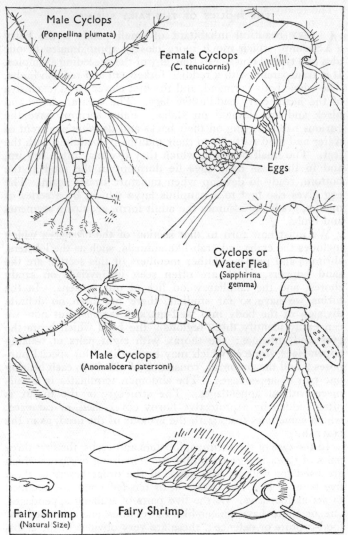

Male Cyclops
(Ponpellina plumata)

Female Cyclops
(C. tenuicornis)

Eggs

Cyclops or
Water Flea
(Sapphirina
gemma)

Male Cyclops
(Anomalocera patersoni)

Fairy Shrimp
(Natural Size)

Fairy Shrimp

SOME MINUTE RELATIVES OF THE CRAB
*Cyclops, Water Fleas and Fairy Shrimps are all crustacea,
the family to which the Crabs and Lobsters also belong.*

THE FROLICS OF THE FAIRY SHRIMP

A VERY beautiful inhabitant of small ponds is the Fairy Shrimp, which much more closely approximates to our idea of a typical crustacean than any of the preceding examples. It is transparent, with a reddish forked tail and reddish limbs. The whole body is ringed, and the first eleven rings (exclusive of the head) carry paddle-like legs. The eyes are large and black and are elevated on stalks. Fairy shrimps have the curious habit of lying on their backs and drawing a current of water and food particles to their mouths by paddling with the feet. The small ponds in which they live may often dry up, and in this case their eggs lie dormant in the mud at the bottom, ready to develop when moisture comes again. The egg gives rise first to a nauplius larva which, by a series of moults, gradually assumes the adult form, acquiring segments and limbs.

We must now turn to that section of the crustacea which includes the crabs and crab-like animals, such as the lobsters, shrimps and prawns. Other members of this section are the sand hoppers, which are often seen in myriads on sandy shores, and the familiar wood lice of our gardens. In the forms we have so far studied, there has been no definite division of the body into well-marked regions, but now we can easily identify three regions : the head which bears the eyes and antennæ ; the thorax with eight pairs of walking appendages, some of which may be modified for special purposes ; and the abdomen, consisting of six rings, each bearing one pair of appendages. The abdomen terminates in a tail-piece without appendages. The structure of the thorax is often hidden by a protective horny cover-shell, or carapace, which sometimes fuses with the armour of the head, as in the crayfish.

In the case of the shrimps, lobsters and crabs, the first three pairs of thoracic legs are unlike the remaining five pairs which are used for walking (the name of the order describes these five pairs of legs, i.e. *Decapoda* or ten feet) and are modified to act as foot-jaws. Of the five pairs of walking appendages, one or more have pincer-like extremities and are used for food-capture or defence ; these are very obvious in the crabs. The gills are feathery structures at the bases of the legs ; the blood passes through the filaments of the gill and exchanges its carbon dioxide for some of the oxygen dissolved in the water. By placing a little powdered dye near the last walking legs, one can perform a simple experiment on the crayfish which will show the way in which a current of water is created by the paddle-action of the mouth-parts. The water passes under the shell near the last pair of legs and out again near the head in such a way that a constantly changing stream of water passes over the gills so that the animal's oxygen supply is continually being replenished.

The tendency in this order (Decapoda) is towards the reduction is size of the abdomen. In the crabs, the abdomen is very small and is tucked under the thorax ; in the shrimps, however, it is quite large and its swimming limbs are the principal locomotory organs. These changes are connected with the walking habits of the crabs and the swimming habits of the shrimps. In view of these characteristics, we could speak of the crabs as the Short-tailed Decapods and the lobsters and shrimps as the Long-tailed Decapods. The Hermit crabs come into a different category, as their tails are asymmetrical. The crab-like animals can therefore be split up into three sub-orders :

THE MACRURA or long-tailed forms like lobsters, with strong abdominal limbs.

THE ANOMURA or irregular tailed forms like the hermit crabs, with a twisted abdomen.

THE BRACHYURA or short-tailed forms like the true crabs with small abdomens and few abdominal limbs.

The long-tailed Macrura include swimming and walking forms like the prawns, shrimps and lobsters. Prawns and shrimps are frequently seen in the rock-pools left by the receding tide ; the shrimps lie on the sandy bottom of the pool, half-covered in the sand, and it is only when the water is disturbed that they can be seen darting about in search of a new retreat. Many of the prawns possess the power of colour change.

The lobsters lurk in crevices in the rocks ; their habits can be studied in the aquarium at a zoo. They back into these little caves, and often only the large, pincer-like limbs can be seen, waiting to seize any suitable prey. The large pincer claws differ from one another in size and shape, one pair of pincers being large and knobbed, the other smaller and saw-like. The large one is used for breaking up shell-fish, the other for clasping and tearing the prey. If a lobster is caught by one

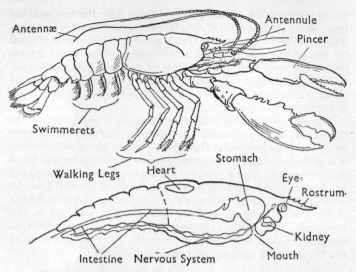

Antennæ

Antennule

Pincer

Swimmerets

Walking Legs   Heart   Stomach   Eye   Rostrum

Intestine   Nervous System   Mouth   Kidney

THE LOBSTERS LEGS ARE USED AS WEAPONS

The lobster's two " pincers," used as weapons of defence and to capture food, are really one of its five pairs of walking legs. The order of crustacea to which the lobsters, shrimps and crabs belong—the Long-Tailed Decapoda—takes its name from these ten legs characteristic of all its members. In the lower diagram, the lobster is drawn in section to show its internal organs.

of its legs, it has little compunction about leaving its leg in your fingers and making its escape. This is not so drastic a measure as one would think, for its legs are provided with special breaking points for this purpose and, what is more, it can grow another leg to take the place of that which was lost—in other words, the limbs can be regenerated. The eggs of the lobster give rise to little transparent larvæ which swim near the surface of the sea—this in contrast to their parents' habit, which is to remain on the bottom.

The Crayfishes are fresh-water relatives of the lobsters, and they live in some of the English and Irish rivers ; they burrow holes in the banks and either await their prey there or go hunting along the bottom. When alarmed they retreat with great rapidity by means of strong strokes of their tail fans and contraction of the abdominal muscles. The young crayfishes are like their parents and spend their early days in clinging to the swimmerets of the mother's abdomen. The green crayfish of England is seldom used as food, the red continental form being specially imported for this purpose.

THE CRAB THAT TAKES A PAYING GUEST

THE hermit crabs or Anomura are soft-bodied and so for protection use empty gastropod[1] shells as houses. The gastropod is spiral and, consequently, modifications in the body form of the crustacea have taken place. In habit they are extremely active and may be seen running over the sea-weed-covered stones in rock-pools, carrying their acquired shelters with them. When alarmed they withdraw into this shelter. One of their pincer-claws is much larger than the other, and serves as a door to close the entrance to the shell when they are inside. Not infrequently the shell carries a sea-anemone, which shares the crab's meals and, in return for board and lodging, protects the crab by means of its stinging cells. A little crab, which lives in the Indian Ocean, actually carries a living sea-anemone in each claw and uses them as weapons.

The true crabs are usually broader than they are long, the abdomen being merely a small flap which is folded under the thorax, and there is no terminal tail fan. The abdominal appendages are only developed to any extent in the female, where they act as organs of attachment for the numerous eggs —a condition spoken of as " being in berry." The life-history of the crab is complicated and consists of three main stages, two of which are larval. The typical larva is called the zoea. It is a characteristic helmet-shaped creature, with large spines and foot-jaws, slender, ringed abdomen and tail-fork. This becomes a megalopa larva which resembles the adult except for the abdomen, which is large and bears true swimming legs. The zoea and megalopa are surface-living stages, at which these creatures are often obtained in tow nets. The adult crab develops from the megalopa larva.

THE SPIDER CRAB'S WARDROBE: DRESSES FOR ALL OCCASIONS

THE Crabs show us a diversity of habits. The long-legged Spider crabs dress themselves up in costumes of sponge and seaweed, which they gather and stick on their backs and legs

[1] See p. 214.

to make themselves inconspicuous against the vegetation of their environment.   They will change their dresses to suit their surroundings !

The largest living arthropod is a spider crab, living in Japan; the legs outstretched may together measure so much as ten feet. Crabs, like the Velvet crabs, swim quite easily by means of the paddle-shaped terminal joints of their last legs.   Then there are the land crabs of tropical countries, which have large gill chambers lined by a membrane, through which oxygen is absorbed—the chambers act as lungs.   They always keep in touch with the sea, for their young are marine and the adults go down to the shore at the breeding season.

The wood lice are the only crustacea adapted for a life spent entirely on land.   Their general appearance is well known.   Most of the relatives of the wood lice are marine and some are inhabitants of fresh water, like the common *Asellus* of our English ditches ; others show an intermediate state between the marine and terrestrial forms, and occur in rock-pools and between tide limits, one living just above high-water mark and yet within reach of sea spray.   Others are fish parasites, some of which are peculiar in that they transform themselves from young free-swimming males into parasitic females.

The brown Oniscus and blue Porcellio are the common garden forms, which live in moist situations under stones and wood.   They show the beginnings of an air tube system comparable to that of insects—but, in other respects, the wood lice are far removed from insects.   One of the wood lice is sometimes found as a guest in the nests of ants.

The sense of sight in crustacea is well developed and they possess two kinds of eyes ; these will be described when dealing with insects, since they are similar in the two groups.   Like insects, too, crustacea appear to appreciate differences or qualities of colour.   For example, green light rays appear to attract water fleas more than other colour rays.   They move towards light in preference to darkness ; this is a practical measure, for they feed on minute floating plants which require light for growth and multiplication.

Some crustacea have balancing organs in the form of pits lined with stiff hairs which rest on nerve cells.   The Crayfish, for example, collects sand grains and places them in the pit in such a way that they rest on the hairs.   As the Crayfish changes its position from the normal, the pressure of the sand

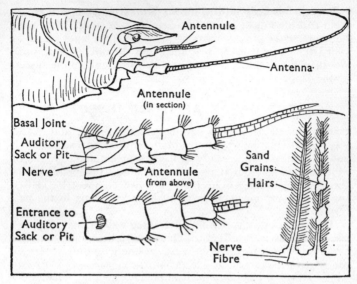

HOW THE CRAYFISH KEEPS THE RIGHT WAY UP

The diagram shows the mechanism enabling the Crayfish and some other crustacea to recognise their position in space. In each antennule, at the end where these join the head, there is an opening leading to an auditory sack or pit, which is lined with stiff hairs resting on nerve cells. The Crayfish tosses sand grains into this pit and is made aware of any change in its position by variation in the pressure of the sand on the pit hairs.

grains on the hairs varies, and a message is passed on to the nervous system and the necessary correction made. If iron filings are substituted for sand grains, the position of the Crayfish can be controlled by means of a magnet ; the Crayfish will swim along quite happily on its back under these conditions.

CREATURES THAT CARRY THEIR OWN LAMPS

OTHER crustacea possess light organs ; some exude luminous secretions ; the Euphausids—transparent, shrimp-like creatures living near the surface of the sea—actually possess little lamps complete with lens and reflector.

Enough has been said to show the great range of crustacean form and life in salt and fresh water and on land. In point of numbers, as well as in parts of their structure, they could be called the insects of the sea, and from the insects of the sea, we must turn to the vaster assemblage which are the insects of the land.

THE GREAT ARMY OF INSECTS

THE Insecta is a group so large and diverse and yet so specialised that the study of it requires special methods and knowledge. The study of insects, or entomology, has its roots in zoology, but it now flowers almost independently of the mother science. The blooms, however, must be viewed together to appreciate their mutual contributions to the pattern of life.

The insect body is divided into three well-defined regions : the head, a division called the thorax, and the abdomen. The head carries such organs of sense as the eyes and antennæ ; the thorax, the locomotory limbs or appendages—the legs and wings—while the abdomen is completely devoid of such structures, any appendages which it bears being connected with pairing. The cavity of the thorax is almost completely filled by the wing muscles, while that of the abdomen is occupied by the digestive glands, fat body and such parts of the alimentary canal as the crop and gizzard, and the reproductive organs. If the external features of an insect are examined, it will be seen that the rings or segments of the abdomen are much more complete and more easily made out than those composing the head and thorax. In the adult, the rings of the head and thorax have fused in connection with the special functions of eating and flight, etc. As already mentioned, each ring of the primitive arthropod carries paired limbs, so that the presence of paired limbs is evidence of a segmental origin which is otherwise hidden in such regions as the head and thorax.

On this evidence, coupled with other observations relating to the arrangement of the nervous system, we find that the head is composed of six or seven rings or segments, four of which are indicated by the antennæ, and three pairs of jaws. The thorax is made up of three rings which are identifiable by the three pairs of legs which they carry, the wings being borne on the middle and last of these segments. The abdomen

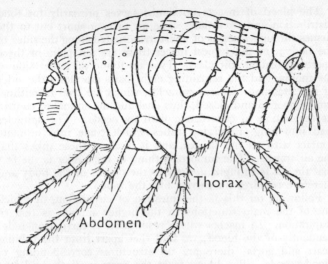

THE HUMAN FLEA

The human flea, here drawn twenty-two times natural size,
is an insect possessing three clearly marked regions : head,
thorax and abdomen. Although wingless, the flea is classified
with the winged insects, because it has lost its wings only through
its mode of life. Its ancestors were winged. Note how the
body is divided into segments.

is composed of eleven rings, which are much less specialised
than those of the head or thorax. Any apparent reduction in
the number of rings towards the tip of the abdomen is due to
telescoping and specialisation in connection with the organs
of reproduction.

THE INSECTS' SHORT CUT TO DEEP BREATHING

INSECTS have a peculiar method of breathing. Quite a lot of
the lower animals breathe either entirely, or in part, by the
surface of the skin, but the thick horny covering which is
present in insects makes this impossible. Unlike higher animals, they have no structures at all comparable with lungs,
where the blood of land vertebrates is oxygenated and from
which the oxygen is carried round in the blood circulation to
the various tissues of the body. No such carrier of oxygen
exists in insects.

The blood of insects no doubt serves primarily for food distribution and excretion. The air takes a short cut to the tissues through a series of apertures situated along the sides of the body ; in the typical insect there are ten pairs of these apertures (called spiracles). Two are found on either side of the thorax, and the remaining eight pairs are along the sides of the abdomen. These spiracles, which are oval in outline, can be opened and closed, thus enabling the animal to control its respiration in accordance with its needs. The spiracles lead into long, ramifying tubes which come into intimate contact with all the tissues, and it is along these tubes that the air travels. The important thing to remember is the fact that the air is brought *directly* to the organs of the body and therefore requires no carrier like the blood.

Following on this is the question of circulation, of which one of the main functions in the higher animals is that of respiration. In insects where respiration is carried on independently of the blood, we find that apart from the tubular heart and aorta, there are no structures corresponding to blood-vessels. The blood from the aorta is discharged into the body cavity—in other words, no well-defined blood system exists.

SEEING IN SECTIONS : THE INSECTS' MANY-SIDED EYE

THE eyes of insects are usually very prominent, and, if looked at under a lens, are seen to be divided into numerous six-sided areas or facets. Each facet is supposed to focus on its visual cells a portion, say of a flower, in such a way that the flower is broken up into as many parts as there are facets and the separate images so made combine to form the whole. It is as though the pieces of a jig-saw puzzle were uniform, each piece corresponding to the image of a facet and fitted together to give the complete picture. As a result of the minute pictures supplied by the cells of each facet, extremely keen vision obtains, and the slightest movements in the insect's environment are detected. Every novice in the art of insect collecting knows this only too well.

The larger the facets the less detailed will be the combined image. In some insects, the eye is built up of large facets dorsally-placed (that is, on top), which probably indicate differences in illumination and movement, and small ventral ones which give detailed vision—a shadow falling across an insect sitting on a leaf will be registered by the dorsal or upper half of the eye with its large facets, while the insect perceives in detail the surface of the leaf with the smaller faceted lower half of the eye. An eye composed of numerous facets is known as a compound eye in contrast to another eye structure in insects called the simple eye or ocellus, which consists of a single undivided area of modified skin or cuticle forming a lens which can register a simple picture ; this type of eye is found in insect larvæ where the compound eye is usually absent. Both types of eye occur in the adult where the ocelli are borne dorsally, but in the larva they are found at the sides of the head.

The whole question of vision is a complicated one. Before leaving the subject, it should be pointed out that clarity of vision not only infers an efficient eye but a well-developed nervous system as well.

It is often assumed that flowers have evolved attractive colours for purposes of pollination by insects, from which it would follow that insects themselves possess an æsthetic appreciation of colour. Such an assumption is extremely doubtful, and it is much more probable that a flower which stands out from its fellows by contrast will be the one which attracts the insects—brightness is probably more important than shade of colour. Reds and purples attract some butterflies more than whites. Experiments in this connection have been performed on bees, and one series, designed by C. II. Turner, may be described.

A number of coloured discs fixed to sticks were set up amongst flowers which were constantly visited by honey bees ; the bees still visited the flowers, in spite of the huge amount of honey with which the discs were covered. But if the bees discovered the honey on a coloured disc, they would still visit the same colour even when the honey had been removed, and this despite the fact that a honey-laden disc of another colour was in the vicinity. Such experiments show that neither scent nor colour alone are sufficient to guide bees to a food supply. Turner concluded that both vision and scent are necessary to guide the bees to a source of honey.

THE INSECTS' GREATEST ALLIES : TOUCH AND SMELL

THE hard coat with which insects are covered obviously necessitates the provision of special organs of touch to connect the outside world with the nervous system so that the insect may react in the way best calculated to meet external stimuli.

The insect body is covered with hairs which rest on sensory cells, and when these hairs are touched, the stimulus is passed on to the nervous system by the sensory cells.

Touch to insects probably means something more than touch to man, for they often show in their reactions discrimination between types of touch other than degrees of pressure. For example, a caterpillar passing over a leaf may have its sensory hairs depressed by the leaf hairs and it shows no visible reaction ; on the other hand, should it be touched by something new to its experience, it exhibits a definite response. As in other animals, heat and cold are distinguished by the sense of touch. There are also other hairs capable of detecting chemical stimuli. The sense of touch is very important to social insects like ants which spend much of their time in the dark.

The insect smells with its antennæ. In the bee, the smelling or olfactory organ is composed of an oval plate overlying sensory tissue, the whole being borne by the antenna. If the organ is cut away, the bee exhibits no power of smell. The social insects recognise members of their own colony by nest-smell. Since we have been speaking of the olfactory sense, this is the place to draw the reader's attention to the fact that many insects are able to produce scents. These may be protective and are then used to deter enemies, or they may perform the function of attracting opposite sexes—male or female. Male moths are often attracted to a female in this way from quite a considerable distance.

THE INSECT WHOSE VOICE IS IN ITS LEGS

YOU have often heard grasshoppers on the commons ; they are not calling to you but to each other. The grasshopper's note is obtained by drawing its hind-legs across the edges of the fore-wings ; the inner edge of the leg bears a row of pegs which are rubbed against the wing to produce a high-pitched note by friction. The frictional method by which one part of the body is rubbed against another part is by far the commonest method employed in calling. The vibration of wings in the bumble bee produces sound. The Deathwatch beetle in old furniture taps its head on the wooden floor of its tunnel and produces a noise like the ticking of a watch.

Sound may be used as an attracting or warning signal in insects. Insects calling to each other implies some sort of hearing apparatus in the group. The grasshopper's ears are

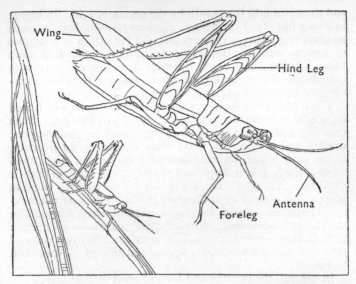

Wing

Hind Leg

Antenna

Foreleg

FIRST FIDDLE IN THE INSECT ORCHESTRA

The grasshopper produces its high-pitched note by drawing its hind-legs—the inside edges of which are equipped with a row of pegs—across the edges of its fore-wings. It hears by means of ears situated in its abdomen ! The grasshopper at the bottom left of the picture is about life size.

in its abdomen ! These ears are complicated structures but they are easily recognised. An oval membrane is found at the sides of the first abdominal ring ; sound waves cause it to vibrate, and these vibrations are passed on to the appropriate nerve. There are other methods of sounding and hearing, but these examples will serve to show that ways exist.

A FEARSOME ARMOURY FOR BITING AND SUCKING

THERE are two methods of feeding employed by insects— biting and sucking. Primitive insects show the typical biting condition, and a study of their mouth-parts reveals three pairs of jaws : the strong, tooth-like mandibles and two other pairs called maxillæ or accessory jaws. They are well seen in the cockroach. A biting insect is able to feed on solid particles of food which are torn up by the mandibles and shovelled into the mouth by the accessory jaws. In higher insects which feed on nectar, the mouth-parts have become adapted to sucking. We may cite the butterflies as examples of insects with mouth-parts considerably modified to meet these requirements. Other insects have mouth-parts with both biting and sucking constituents and are therefore intermediate between these two extremes.

The mandibles have a crushing surface in insects which feed on plants ; in carnivorous insects they are pointed. Such crushing and pointed mandibles are found in grasshoppers, sawflies and beetles. In many male insects, as, for instance, in the Stag beetle, the mandibles are very much larger than those of the female and are used as weapons in addition to their usual function. The wasp has mandibles for chewing wood to pulp, and in general form these are similar to those of the cockroach ; the bee, on the other hand, has club-shaped mandibles used in comb-building. Similar modifications in connection with feeding occur in connection with the other two pairs of jaws and in the more highly specialised insects the two tend to fuse.

In general, the mouths and jaws of most mature insects are more highly organised than those of the primitive biting type of the cockroach and larvæ. In butterflies, the second pair of jaws (maxillæ) are prolonged into a sensitive sucking tube for reaching down to the nectaries of tubular flowers. In bees and flies, the third pair of jaws (second maxillæ) are similarly modified. The mouth of the female mosquito shows us quite a set of implements for piercing the skin and sucking the blood. The mandibles and maxillæ are prolonged into fine blades ; the maxillæ are furnished with little saws at their tips, and there is also an unpaired lancet and sucking tube for drawing up the blood. The male mosquito, which does not suck blood, is devoid of these specialisations.

All these modifications have interesting biological reactions : an insect whose mouth-parts have undergone little specialisation can feed on widely different things, and hence its distribution is not seriously hampered by the scarcity of one particular kind of food. As specialisation increases, the insect's distribution depends upon food factors and its range becomes limited by these, until we find certain insects confined to localities where a particular plant grows ; blood-sucking flies, like the tsetse fly, are confined to regions inhabited by the animals upon which they feed.

FROM YOUTH TO AGE : A COMPLICATED BIOGRAPHY

HAVING learnt something of the ways in which an insect can live and react to its environment, it is now possible for us to turn to the types of life-history and its stages. Primitive wingless insects like the springtails, which are commonly found amongst the grass of certain meadows, hatch out from the egg in a form very like the parents, so that there is no metamorphosis. The complications of metamorphosis arose with the development of wings. There are two types of wing development : first, that in which they develop gradually as *external* buds, and second, where they develop *internally* during the early stages of the life-history and are later everted and remain in a half-grown condition for a definite period when, after a sudden change, they become fully grown.

There are two orders of insects, the lice and the fleas, which are wingless and are yet included amongst the winged insects in classification, the reason being that their winglessness is a secondary modification due to their mode of life : their ancestors were winged. As already pointed out, in the true wingless forms like the springtails and bristletails, the life-cycle is direct, the egg hatching out into a young insect not very dissimilar from the adult into which it will grow. There is no metamorphosis.

In the case of insects whose wings develop as external buds, there is a partial metamorphosis and the life-history consists of three well-defined stages—the egg, nymph and adult or imago. A nymph is the name given to a young insect which is hatched in a fairly advanced state of development but whose wings are only partially developed. The nymph possesses compound eyes and tissue identical with that of the adult. The change from nymph to adult is really a very slight one. This three-stage life-history occurs amongst cockroaches, crickets, stick insects, earwigs and bugs.

The life-history of those insects whose wings develop internally is more complex and is made up of four stages : the egg, larva, pupa and adult or imago. Young insects within the egg feed on the yolk and, where this is scarce, as it is in the eggs of many of the higher insects, the young have to emerge much earlier than those which have plenty of yolk on which to feed. The result is that they hatch out at a much earlier stage and consequently differ very considerably from the parents in general shape and make-up. This young stage is called a larva, and it differs from the imago or perfect insect in the possession of simple eyes and special larval tissue differing from that of the adult. Metamorphosis could be defined as the change from larval to adult tissue. The larval tissues ultimately break down, and buds which give rise to adult tissue are found throughout the body.

A very active larva with well-developed legs is characteristic of the beetles ; the soft, cylindrical and much less active caterpillar of the butterfly and the well-known maggot of the fly are both larvæ. They vary in shape, size and habit, but they all have this in common, that they are the effective feeding and growing stage of the life-history.

Following on the larval stage comes the inactive pupa or chrysalis, a stage of internal reconstruction, during which the adult tissues are being built up. This is a helpless phase, often seeking protection in a silk or earth-cemented cell or cocoon. Pupæ vary as much as larvæ : the legs and wings may be free from the body as in beetles and bees ; they may be closely attached to the body and the pupal case rigid, with the exception of the abdomen, as in butterflies and moths, or a definite puparium or capsule is formed from the larval skin as in flies.

The final stage of the life-history is the imago or perfect insect whose principal function is that of reproduction. It may become so specialised to this end that the feeding mechanism degenerates altogether. In some cases the life of an adult varies from one hour to a fortnight, but, in the case of insects which emerge from the pupa in the autumn, the whole winter may be passed in hibernation until the spring heralds the time for egg-laying. In many examples very resistant eggs are laid at the end of the summer or in early autumn, which hatch in the spring and serve to carry the species over the inclement winter months.

The imago has rarely any personal interest in the food plant of its larval days, and yet she invariably chooses a similar kind of plant on which to lay her eggs, thus making provision for her offspring. The Cabbage White butterfly does not eat cabbage but her larvæ do, and so she always lays her eggs on cabbage leaves.

The larva and nymph, then, are the stages of growth, while the imago is essentially the unit in the life-history which makes for increase both in numbers and range—for its wings enable it to cover much wider areas than a wingless form could negotiate and so a wider distribution of eggs is possible.

INSECTS THAT CAN LIVE IN WATER

ALTHOUGH there are many insects which have taken to water, comparatively few of them are entirely aquatic; they have to come to the surface at intervals to breathe atmospheric air. When we speak of an aquatic insect, we do not necessarily mean one which spends its whole life in the water; in fact there are very few which do so, although a bug and a fly which live entirely in the sea are known. No, we speak of an insect as aquatic if any part at all of its life is spent in water. In the case of an aquatic insect whose wings develop externally, it is usually the nymph, but in the higher aquatic insects the larva is the stage which lives in water, and it is these stages which are adapted for a water existence.

The eggs are laid or dropped into the water, or else they are laid on vegetation verging the selected pond or stream. The female of certain species pierces the stems of aquatic plants with her egg-laying organ, or ovipositor, and lays her eggs in the internal tissues. When eggs are laid beneath the surface of the water, they resemble frog spawn in that they are cemented together by a gelatinous, water-absorbing material or mucilage.

The nymph is the aquatic stage in stone-flies, mayflies and dragon-flies. The larva is the aquatic stage in alder flies. In caddis flies, mosquitoes and gnats, all stages except the adult live in water. The big carnivorous water beetles live in water as adults and yet are dependent on atmospheric air for breathing. They carry a supply of air to the bottom of the pond in the form of a bubble at their tails, and draw on this supply by means of their abdominal spiracles. The grown larva leaves the water and undergoes metamorphosis under the soil and is therefore terrestrial. Even the adult is not confined to water, for it can leave it to fly from one pond to another. Space forbids us to discuss each of these examples, so let us look more closely at the life-histories of the mayfly and the gnat.

GROWING UP IN TIME TO DIE: THE MAYFLY'S CURIOUS HISTORY

THE female mayfly drops her eggs into the water and the subsequent development extends over a long period. The nymphs which ultimately hatch out are quite different from their parents in that they possess large biting mouth-parts and are entirely aquatic. The nymphal phase is a prolonged one, and may last for three years. The nymphs feed on small aquatic creatures and vegetation. Their principal adaptation to aquatic life lies, as one would expect, in their breathing mechanism. They breathe by filamentous or thread-like gills which are penetrated by the air-tubes ; these gills are paired and are arranged along the sides of the abdomen.

As we have seen, the nymph is unlike its parents, but contrary to the usual sequence of events in such a case, the metamorphosis from nymph to adult is incomplete. When fully grown, the nymph leaves the water; its skin splits down the back and a winged insect emerges. This is not the adult, but a peculiar and unique condition called the sub-imago which has been interpolated between the usual stages of nymph and imago. The sub-imago flies away and moults once before reaching maturity. These discarded sub-imaginal skins are often found on fences near streams. The adult mayfly is easily identified by the three long streamers which project from the abdomen. An adult which may have taken three years to develop may only live long enough to lay eggs—a matter of a few hours.

The gnat lays masses of eggs on the surface of ponds, and these eggs are so placed that on hatching the larvæ can immediately take to the water. The larvæ or " wrigglers " are commonly found in outdoor water butts and troughs in the summer. The larva is dependent upon atmospheric and not dissolved air, and a special breathing structure is developed near the tail. This takes the form of a tube which is thrust through the surface film, the larva itself hanging head downwards from the surface film during the process of breathing. From the air tube, the air is drawn into the tracheæ (internal air tubes) as in other insects. The larva of the allied mosquito Anopheles, which differs from the gnat larva, suspends itself horizontally and not vertically from the surface film. In the pupal, which follows the larval stage, the breathing is carried out by means of thoracic trumpets which connect up with the air tubes (tracheæ), and in the act of breathing the pupa floats at the surface with its breathing trumpet erect above the water.

In countries where malaria is widespread, the mosquitoes of the Anopheles type carry the parasites of the disease from one human being to another, and the mosquito itself is a necessary host for part of the life-cycle of the malarial parasite. As the parasites only occur in other animals, the best way of checking them is to destroy one of the hosts, and in this case, as we are men, we destroy the mosquito in preference to man ! Now, it is easier to destroy localised larvæ than widely-spread adults, and, in view of their breathing mechanism, it is possible to drown them by preventing their breathing tubes from reaching the air ; this can be done by spreading oil over the surface of the water. The oil forms an effective barrier between the air-tubes and the atmospheric air, with the result that hundreds of larvæ are drowned.

The stone-flies have aquatic nymphs which may or may not have gills. If they have not, they breathe through the skin at certain points. The dragon-fly nymph carries gills and is quite unlike its parents. A characteristic contrivance called the mask is formed by the considerable development of the lower lip. The mask is arm-like and jointed so that it can be folded below the head or extended. At the end of the mask, two curved spines are carried for securing prey. The aquatic larvæ of the caddis fly build cases of sand or shells and débris which are carried about with them. These are so well known to collectors of pond life that further description is unnecessary.

BARGAINING FOR A PLACE IN THE SUN : THE PARASITES

MANY insects can behave as parasites or, alternatively, can harbour parasites at every stage of their life-history. Some insects, such as the ichneumons, lay their eggs in the larvæ of other insects, and, when the eggs hatch, the young larvæ feed on the tissues of the host larvæ. The important parasites are included in the groups of beetles, ants, bees and wasps, and flies. An insect may be parasitised by another which is also parasitised and so *ad infinitum*, and a balance may exist which ranges between limits favourable to all the parasites in question. Two parasites on the same insect have to bargain for a place in the sun, even if the bargaining entails force and the subsequent annihilation of one or other of the bargainers.

The presence of parasites on an insect host tends to control the numbers of that host, and as parasites are often limited to one kind of host, their range is limited and the host species tends to become more and more infested with the parasite until it is exterminated or the parasites cancel themselves out. Where parasites have other parasites living on them, the parasites themselves are controlled, with the result that the host survives. Parasite control has been used by entomologists for the control of insect pests ; the process has been spectacular in its success in some cases, but great dangers and complications may attend it—for example, a parasite introduced into new conditions for the purpose of controlling a pest may fasten on another and beneficial species instead, thus becoming a pest itself.

Much might be written about the question of parasitism, for there are grades of it each with different implications. Certain insects change their habit of living very easily, and when they do this, corresponding changes take place in their structure to enable them to carry on their new mode of life successfully. In this way new races are formed, and these races, which may be interchangeable, are referred to as biological races, since change of habit brings about structural changes. The body and head lice of man is a case in point. The difference between these two varieties lies chiefly in the structure of the claws. One can be converted into the other in two or three generations.

LODGERS THAT DO NOT PAY FOR THEIR KEEP

IN addition to body parasites, there are what are called social parasites—solitary insects which take advantage of the social insects by living in their colonies and receiving board and lodging at their expense. They may indeed actually acquire a superficial resemblance to their hosts. There are solitary bees which build cells and provision them with pollen for their larvæ. There is another solitary bee which builds no cells but exploits the cell-building bee by laying eggs in its cells. This habit is a parallel case to that of the cuckoo which lays its eggs in the nests of other birds, and hence the bee is called a " cuckoo bee." The larvæ of the cuckoo bee hatch before those of the host, and they live on the pollen which the host bee had collected for its young. When the host's larvæ hatch, the cuckoo bee's larvæ attack and consume them.

Certain beetle larvæ are found in flowers, and one, Melöe, lies in wait for a visiting bee. When one arrives, the larva clings to hairs of its legs and is carried to the bee's nest ; the bee brushes it off with the pollen with which the hairs are covered. The larva continues its development at the expense of the bee's provisioning and young.

INSECTS AS FRIENDS OR FOES OF MAN

MANY insects act as scavengers. Others seek out dead animals and lay their eggs upon them—both larvæ and adults feeding on them. Some beetles excavate the earth below a dead rat, bury it, and proceed to lay eggs upon it. The larvæ complete the process by consuming it. Ants will pick a skeleton clean. Other insects pollinate our flowers, and an interesting example is the Yucca moth which lays her eggs in the ovaries of the Yucca flower.

Many flowers have structural devices for ensuring cross pollination by insects ; others pollinate themselves, but the Yucca flower does neither. As the caterpillar of the Yucca moth requires the pod in which to feed, it is essential from the moth's point of view that the ovary should be fertilised, and this it sets out to do by means of special mouth-parts ; the moth collects a mass of pollen and actually places it on the stigma of the flower. This is beneficial to the flower, to the insect, and indirectly to man.

We have already seen how some insects are useful to man by parasitising harmful ones. Some are also useful in destroying weeds—a two-winged fly has destroyed the Canadian thistle in Indiana.

Then there are the harmful insects of medical, agricultural and horticultural importance. Lice transmit the germs of typhus from one person to another. Mosquitoes are responsible for the transmission of malarial and yellow fevers. The tsetse fly is responsible for the spread of sleeping sickness. The Colorado beetle has created havoc amongst the potatoes of the United States of America. The Hessian fly is a serious grain pest. The depredations of Aphis on the fruit trees, roses and beans of our gardens are only too familiar.

INSECTS THAT ARE EXPERT MIMICS

CERTAIN insects, which make good eating for birds, mimic other insects which have a nasty taste. Palatable insects try to look like unpalatable ones to warn off the birds. The Stick insects, both in their colour and attitudes, closely resemble the plants on which they live. Some unarmed insects simulate the colours of wasps, and, in this connection, we might note that insects armed with stings are often very brightly coloured, e.g. the warning colours of yellow and black. Anyone who does any work at all in the field is bound to come across examples of mimicry, and there is abundant evidence of its quite wide occurrence.

We must now leave the insects and pass on to the remaining two groups of the Arthropoda—the Myriapoda (centipedes and millipedes) and the Arachnida (spiders, scorpions &c.).

A MILLION MANY-LEGGÉD ROGUES

THE centipedes and millipedes (forming a class technically known as Myriapoda) are confined to the earth, there being no aquatic forms. The body is composed of a complete series of rings, and all the rings behind the head carry one or two pairs of legs. The head is quite distinct and bears a pair of antennæ. There are two or three pairs of mouth-parts—one pair of mandibles and one or two pairs of maxillæ. The centipedes and millipedes form two well-defined groups. The centipedes carry one pair of legs on each body ring ; they possess poison fangs, and are compressed. The first four rings of the millipede body do not carry limbs and, as these creatures are vegetarians in contrast to the carnivorous centipedes, they possess no poison fangs, and the limbs are cylindrical. The centipedes are hunters and move quickly ; the millipedes have little occasion to move quickly and very rarely do so.

HOW THE CENTIPEDE POISONS ITS VICTIMS

THE brown garden centipede which lives amongst the fallen leaves and rubbish of our garden is very active throughout the summer, searching for the insect larvæ upon which it feeds ; in the winter it hibernates beneath the soil. The prey are seized by the poison fangs and injected with poison which is immediately fatal. The centipede lays its eggs from June to August, and the female quickly conceals the eggs, or else the male eats them. The egg, which is covered with a sticky substance, is rolled about by the female until soil particles have adhered to the whole surface and it is quite indistinguishable from its surroundings. The young centipede has poison fangs but only six pairs of legs—other legs and rings are added later.

The common millipede or wireworm is black in colour, relatively inactive, and feeds on the roots of cultivated plants. It has no poison fangs, but in defence it can secrete a fluid with a nauseating smell. A spherical nest is made beneath the ground by building up a mixture of saliva and soil particles. Through a hole at the top of the nest, the female deposits anything up to one hundred eggs. When this is accomplished she seals the nest, leaving the eggs to hatch and the young to their own devices. The eggs hatch in about a fortnight and three-legged young emerge—as in the centipedes the rest of the legs are added at a later stage.

The centipedes and millipedes are not very important economically, though centipedes can be beneficial in destroying certain insect larvæ, and wireworms harmful on account of the damage they do to the roots of crops.

SPIDERS AND THEIR EIGHT-LEGGED RELATIVES

THE members of the Arachnida series, to which belong spiders, scorpions, harvesters and mites, differ from the Crustacea and Insects in that their bodies consist of only two parts—the head and thorax are usually fused to form what is called a cephalothorax, and the abdomen. They have simple eyes, no antennæ, and eight legs and, except in mites, the life-history shows no metamorphosis. Their breathing is carried out by special devices situated in open pits on the under side of the cephalothorax. Into these pits thin, flat processes project like the pages of a book—whence they are called lung-books; the blood circulates in the leaves of the book and the air between them. Breathing tubes are present in spiders but differ from those of the insects. Very few members of the group live in water; most of them live on land and only rarely live in colonies. They are usually active by night and are carnivorous. The sexes are separate, the males usually being smaller than the females.

The largest Arachnida are the Scorpions which commonly live in holes in the sand and hunt insects. They may be as long as eight inches. The head and thorax are evident as separate units, as the head has no rings in contrast to the complete segmentation of the thorax and abdomen. The head carries a pair of strong claws which give the animal the appearance of a crustacean. The abdomen has six rings, the last one carrying a sting. When attacked, the scorpion adopts a menacing attitude, with its tail reared over its back with the sting pointing forwards. The prey are paralysed by the sting and pulled to pieces by the claws. The poison is strong and is immediately fatal to small creatures like insects; but if the scorpions inject their poison into each other, nothing amiss happens.

Although scorpions may look ferocious, they are really more retiring than pugilistic in habit and much prefer to pass unnoticed. This is true of their relations with all animals other than their own kind, and only courtship or hostilities bring them together. The young are well developed when born, and are carried on the mother's back for a time, during which time they never feed. Later they leave the mother and live their lives quite independently.

Spiders are the big order within the Arachnida. In addition to the general characters of the group, they possess silk-producing organs or spinnerets at the tip of the abdomen. The production of silk plays a most important part in the habits of the spiders. Much has been written about spiders, and, in spite of the fact that a study of their habits reveals a marvellous world of instinct and by-play, imagination on the part of observers has no doubt added colour to the already vivid pictures of the spiders' private lives.

SPIDERS THAT BUILD THEIR OWN AIRCRAFT

A NEWLY hatched spider climbs up to a point of vantage on a plant, and there it sits and drops a thread of liquid silk which is drawn out by the breeze ; the spider feels the tug, releases its hold of the leaf and is carried away by the wind, supported by its gossamer thread. It may go many miles before landing. With the exception of the burrowing spiders, most spiders adopt this means of aerial transport.

The wolf-spiders of the fields are speedy and hunt their prey on foot ; others hide under plants and pounce upon passing insects. The crab-spiders which walk sideways like crabs may hide in flowers of the same colour as themselves. Some have the capacity for changing their colours to match the surroundings and they catch insect visitors.

The garden spider traps prey in webs ; the struggling of the victim causes the threads to vibrate, and the spider, feeling these vibrations, rushes to the spot and proceeds to tie up the prey still further with bands of silk. As a rule the web-building spiders tackle larger prey than the hunting spiders which have no silken threads with which to bind their victims.

The poison of spiders is injected into the prey through the fangs. Certain exotic spiders are dangerous to man. The spider usually is regarded as the aggressor, but quite often it is preyed upon by birds and mammals ; its cocoons may be parasitised by the ichneumon-flies. Consequently spiders employ various protective devices, such as protective colour-ation, mimicry, etc. Some are streaked with the warning colours of yellow and black ; others display striking colours when they run about, but conceal them when they crouch, so

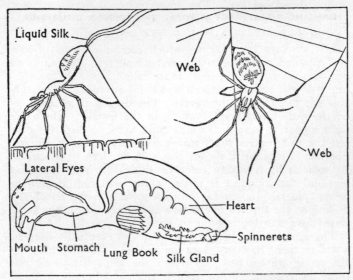

Liquid Silk

Web

Web

Lateral Eyes

Heart

Spinnerets

Mouth Stomach Lung Book Silk Gland

HOW THE SPIDER SPINS ITS WEB

The spider produces liquid silk from organs situated at the tip of its abdomen, known as " spinnerets." Besides its use in building a web, the silk, drawn out by the breeze, supports the weight of the spider and allows it to be carried for miles by air. Note the position of the internal organs.

that to all intents and purposes they become invisible. They may mimic other animals like snails, beetles and ants—the last being the commonest type of mimicry. In addition to these imitations, we all know how some spiders feign death when touched.

Tropical spiders are parasitised by ichneumon parasitic flies and birds attack them in their webs ; it is up to the spider to protect itself and this it does by introducing imitation spiders into its webs ! One method is to place a number of pellets shaped and coloured like itself on the threads in such a way that its enemies do not recognise the real thing when they see it. Others manufacture mats of insects bound together by silk, place them at the centres of their webs and conceal themselves behind them. About twenty different methods involving the use of protective devices of this kind have been observed.

DANCING TO ATTRACT A WIFE: THE SPIDER'S COURTSHIP

A MALE jumping spider dances before the favoured female. He displays his charms—which consist of tufts of hair and coloured patches—to the best advantage. He waves to her with his front legs, and circles round her; she watches him with the greatest interest and if his advances are acceptable she too joins in the revels. The display of decorations by the male infers good eyesight in the female; where the sight is poor, as in spiders which build webs, no display occurs but the male enters the female's web and makes it vibrate. She knows it is not a fly for she waits for him to approach. As soon as he is within reach he tickles her with his front legs and the conquest is made. This behaviour is seen in house spiders. In others, the male signals to the female by pulling on the threads of the web and she replies in the same way—their courting is done by wire, so to speak.

The eggs are laid in a cocoon which is eventually fixed to a wall or tree. In many cases the mother is dead by the time the young are hatched; in others she helps the young out from the cocoon. Some spiders play a definitely parental rôle and guard the cocoon and young. There is an English spider which carries her cocoon about with her. Most of us have seen wolf-spiders in the fields carrying their cocoons on their backs. The cocoons are really attached to the spider's spinnerets. The young hatch and are carried on and may completely cover the mother's back. Newly hatched spiders can spin no webs and are often without eyes.

Some spiders make their nests beneath the ground with an entrance leading to the outside world; this entrance is guarded by a door to keep out undesirables. These are the so-called trap-door spiders. Related to the trap-door spiders are the large bird-eating spiders of South America, etc., whose bodies may reach nearly four inches in length. Insects are their usual food, but they have been known to tackle humming birds with success. Their bodies are covered with stiff hairs and it is related how these may break off when handled and cause irritation by getting into the creases of the human skin. A number of these big spiders can usually be seen in the Insect House at the London Zoo; they are not infrequently found in bunches of bananas at the English docks. The writer has collected them in South America, but the cooler climate outside the tropics brings on a torpid state in which they seldom feed, and are therefore difficult to keep in captivity without very special care.

In heaps of manure, cracks in woodwork and the like, a widely distributed and interesting order of small spiders is found. These are the False Scorpions which are very retiring in habit and in consequence are little known. They have huge palps or foot-feelers for attack and these give them a scorpion-like look. The abdomen is ringed. They live on insects and mites. The eggs and early young are carried by the mother. The adults build round silken nests to shelter in during the winter.

The Harvesters or Harvestmen are widely distributed spider-like animals with very long legs ; they are frequently seen in the fields. They do not spin webs, since they pursue insects, spiders and mites. They differ from true spiders in their very compact, globular bodies. The males may be seen fighting for the possession of females at the mating season. The eggs are laid under stones and in holes in the ground ; the young are like their parents.

TINY AGENTS OF IMMENSE DESTRUCTION : THE MITES

MITES are widely distributed all over the world. Economically they are as important as the spiders. They are, as a rule, minute creatures and can only be studied adequately with the aid of the microscope. Many mites exhibit little differentiation of the body into regions. Their habits vary enormously and in consequence their structure is often extremely modified ; the mouth-parts especially differ in accordance with their feeding habits, but differences in habitat are quite frequently reflected by the legs which may end in bristles, hooks or suckers. They may be blind or alternatively they may possess a variable number of eyes. The life-history usually shows a metamorphosis consisting of egg, larva with a reduced number of legs—a nymph may or may not be present—and the adult. Mites may be free-living and live either in the earth, sea or freshwater streams and ponds ; or they may be parasites on other animals.

The snout-mites are soft-bodied animals with long legs and are able to run rapidly in pursuit of insects. They live in cold, damp localities, and in the winter may be found beneath fallen leaves. Some, the spinning mites, produce silk ; some have beaks which contain needle-like mandibles. Big appendages carrying comb-like claws serve to capture prey. The harvest mites attack man, causing severe skin irritation and inflammation ; farm labourers are frequently attacked while gathering the harvest. The Red " Spider " of our gardens is really one of the spinning mites and should it occur in great numbers much damage to foliage may result. Another of the spinning mites is a parasite of birds.

The water mites are nearly all confined to fresh water, though some live in brackish water, and a few in the sea. The adult water mites are usually free-living, but one is parasitic and lives on the gills of the freshwater mussel. They are beautifully coloured—green, blue and yellow, and yellow and black being the more usual combinations. They are larger than the average run of mites. Many of them live in rapid streams ; some are social and are found together amongst pond weeds. They are carnivorous in habit.

WAITING FOR A MEAL TO WALK PAST

THE ticks are of the greatest interest to man as they are all parasitic and live on the blood of their hosts. In the East they occur on many different kinds of small animals like squirrels. Ticks may also be the carriers of disease. They lay thousands of eggs in the soil of fields, and these hatch into six-legged larvæ which climb up the grass and sit tight until a suitable animal passes their way. When such an animal appears they become excited and should it pass near enough to them they will leave their grasses and cling to its hair. Having secured a foothold, they push their beaks into the host's flesh and gorge themselves with blood. This meal has to last them a long time, for when their hunger is appeased they drop off and burrow into the ground and digest it at their leisure. Later, the larval skin is shed and they enter upon a nymphal stage with eight legs. Once more they climb up the grass and repeat the performance of waiting for a suitable host, finding it, feeding, and again dropping to the ground and moulting. This moult produces the adult males and females which search for a third animal on which to feed and pair, after which the female once more seeks the ground and lays her eggs.

This is an extraordinarily complex life-history for an arachnid. The number of risks run by each batch of young ticks is enormous, and so we find that these risks are met to some extent by the large numbers of eggs laid by one female so that the chances of a few young finding a host on which to feed are much increased. The period of waiting for a host and thus for a meal may be long, so we find they have a capacity for undergoing prolonged fasts without incurring any damage.

The itch mites include that species parasitic on man. The human itch mite in former times caused terrible trouble amongst armies in the field. The itching which they cause is said to be intolerable. The fertilised females burrow into the skins of their hosts and line their burrows with dozens of eggs. In this way they block up their only exit to the outer world, and so they die at the ends of their tunnels. As only a month is taken from the hatching of the egg to the fully developed adult it will be realised how quickly infection spreads by contact with infected persons.

The familiar cheese-mites are related to the itch mites. One of this group of mites lives in the breathing tubes of bees and causes a virulent disease amongst them. Some members of this group are responsible for mange in mammals, and others are vegetarians which cause galls on plants.

So ends our review of the vast group of the Arthropoda with its infinite number and great diversity of forms.

METHODS THAT MAKE THE GOOD COLLECTOR

GOOD collecting is an art which is not easily acquired and experience in it counts for a lot. The *good* collector is not only a collector but a naturalist as well ; he must know the habits of his animals—where they live, the plants they feed on, etc., in addition to the methods of preparing them for his collection. A beginner in entomology is well advised to collect insects fairly generally rather than to specialise in the members of one order. This fosters a broader outlook and at the same time gives the worker a good practical know-ledge of different kinds of insects, their haunts and habits. This knowledge contributes towards a more intelligent appreciation of the problems with which he will be faced at a later stage when he is more or less in possession of the principles of his study and can therefore select a group in which to specialise.

The ordinary butterfly net and a sweeping net are the chief pieces of apparatus required by the insect-hunter. The butterfly net is used for catching insects on the wing as well as those which frequent flower heads. The sweeping net is made of strong material like unbleached calico and is used for sweeping vegetation which might tear the ordinary butterfly net. By sweeping we mean the dragging of the net to and fro amongst the herbage in such a way that insects, such as weevils, for instance, fall off the plants into the net. Another homely, but useful, instrument is an umbrella which can be inverted beneath the leafy boughs of trees ; when the leaves are gently struck with a stick a rich haul of insects tumbles into the umbrella and can be captured. This process is known as beating.

CAPTURING INSECTS WITH LIGHTS AND TREACLE

EVERYONE knows how moths are attracted into lighted rooms at night ; this foible can be employed to the advantage of the collector. If he sits by an open window at night, and puts a lantern outside, quite a number of insects are attracted by the light and all the collector has to do is to collect them as they come. An attractive bait for many insects is made from brown sugar, treacle and a little beer plus a little aromatic essence of aniseed. This mixture can be painted on the sheltered sides of palings and trees at dusk ; when visited an hour or two after application a goodly company of insects will reward the collector for the labour involved. This operation is called " sugaring."

Flower heads, hedges and bushes yield many insects when swept with the net in the summer months. Patches of cow-dung should be examined for beetles. Rich winter sources for beetle-collecting are the mosses torn from the bark of trees and the decaying leaves on the ground. Moths and butterflies can be reared from the pupa which are frequently found round the roots of isolated trees and have to be dug for with a trowel. Butterflies and moths can be transferred from the net to pill boxes with glass bottoms, and for most other insects glass tubes may be used.

Before passing on to the question of killing insects it must be emphasised that no locality should be ignored as useless until it has been examined—rarities may be found in the least likely of places.

THE RIGHT WAY TO KILL AN INSECT

THE process of killing must be a painless one which allows only the minimum of struggling on the part of the victim, so avoiding damage to wings, etc. Probably the most-used killing agent is the wide-mouthed cyanide bottle which can be purchased from any dealer. An insect stiffens when killed but it can be relaxed in an air-tight box containing a cork damped with hot (and therefore sterilised) water and a trace of carbolic acid to kill any mites or parasites which would destroy the specimen.

Wood-lice, centipedes, spiders and mites can be collected in tubes filled with methylated spirits. Shrimps and larger crustacea may be killed and kept in 10 per cent formalin. Whatever you collect should be carefully labelled as to locality and date at once and identified later. The insect is there but your memory may fail you as to when and where you obtained it.

It is a wise thing for naturalists to collect and rear larvæ as there is still much yet unknown in regard to life-histories. Eggs, too, should be collected and their subsequent development on their food plants followed through the various stages to the perfect insect : such experiments are of supreme value and interest and assist the naturalist towards a more complete understanding of the various phenomena connected with metamorphosis.

SOME BOOKS FOR THE STUDENT OF INSECT LIFE

THERE are a number of books about insects and other forms of life mentioned in this article which the student and collector will find attractive supplements to practical work, and stimulants to fresh experiment. *Insects, Their Structure and Life* by G. H. Carpenter (Dent) gives an outline sketch of the whole subject of entomology and has interesting chapters on insects and their surroundings and pedigrees. There are also descriptions of the various orders of insects. The same author has written a delightful little book called *The Life-story of Insects*, which is one of the Cambridge Manuals of Science and Literature.

British Insects and How to Know Them by Harold Bastin (Methuen) is a readable account written from the natural history point of view. For an advanced and comprehensive survey of insects, the reader should turn to *Text Book of Entomology* by A. D. Imms (Methuen). *Social Behaviour in Insects*, by the same author, and published in Methuen's series of Monographs on Biological Subjects, is a valuable review of work done on social insects, and should be consulted. This also applies to another book in the same series called *Mimicry* by G. D. Hale Carpenter.

In addition to these insect books there are three interesting works published in Benn's Sixpenny Series—*Insects* by F. Balfour-Browne, *Insects and Industry* by J. W. Munro, and *Ants* by Julian S. Huxley. Other admirable books are published in the *Wayside and Woodland* series (Warne). A most readable account of the crustacea is given in *Life of Crustacea* by W. T. Calman (Methuen).

BIRDS, BEASTS AND FISH

by H. M. BELL

THE whole of creation has been divided by scientists into six sub-divisions of which one contains the Vertebrates—that is, all those animals which have backbones. These creatures are again divided into five great classes according to whether they are fish, amphibians, reptiles, birds or mammals.

The term vertebrate may be taken to include all animals which have a symmetrical form on both sides. The body is divided by an imaginary axis into a right and left half, and the nerves and muscles in each are correspondingly formed and placed. The main masses of the nervous system lie along the back, and are always shut off from the internal organs. The nerve axis is underlaid by a structure known as the " notochord," which is a supporting rod, and in the adult stage is generally more or less replaced by the bony axis known as the " vertebral column." There may be no limbs, but when present there are never more than two pair of them.

Fish form the largest class in point of numbers and are among the most ancient of vertebrates, whilst its members exhibit the greatest variety of structure. All fish have gills throughout their life ; the structure of the heart, when present, is usually simple ; the limbs are in the form of fins. The shape of the body is largely based on its suitability for rapid movement in water, and for the avoidance of friction. To help further in this direction, an outer layer of mucus, or slime, covers the skin.

The structure of the scales is of four kinds. The scales may be, first : thin, bony and flexible (as in the fish, and the most familiar form to the majority of us) ; secondly : thin, bony, horny plates with spiny or comb-like projections ; thirdly : scales covered with a hard, polished enamel ; or, fourthly : detached plates or tubercles, which are often covered with spines.

Fish are essentially inhabitants of water, either fresh or salt, though a few live in both impartially. Fish like eels can live a considerable time out of water owing to the narrowness of their gill slits or because they have a special arrangement for keeping the gills moist.

With notable exceptions, some of which are mentioned below, fish reproduce by external fertilisation. The female discharges her eggs into the water near the male, who, about the same time, discharges sperm, also into the water. In this way some of the eggs are fertilized and, unless destroyed by other creatures, eventually hatch out into young fish.

THE SEA IS A WORLD OF COLOUR

OF all animals living fish are probably the most brilliantly coloured. Many have the power of changing colour, in some cases very rapidly. It is impossible to describe adequately the immense variety and striking colour effects present in some species. At the other end of the scale may be placed the uniform sombreness of certain fish inhabiting the depths of the sea.

Fish possess great variety of bodily shape. Compare, for instance, the serpent-like eels with the flattened skates and rays living on the sea-bottom, or the spherical globe-fish with the strange rectangular coffer-fish. In some fish there is great disproportion between the parts of the body, the head usually being the most varied in appearance. Mention may be made of the phosphorescent organs of some deep-sea fish, which enable them to find their prey in the dark abysses they frequent.

Contrary to general belief, certain fish are capable of producing sound, in some cases by rubbing together bony joints, or grating their teeth, or through muscular control of the air bladder. The sound has been described as a deep drumming, whilst in other cases it is like the grunting of a pig.

THE SIX BRANCHES OF THE FISH FAMILY

FISH have been divided into six orders :

1. LANCELET.
2. LAMPREYS AND HAG FISH.
3. BONY FISH.
4. GANOID FISH.
5. SHARKS AND RAYS.
6. MUD FISH.

The first two orders have no biting jaws, but have instead a highly specialised tongue in the form of a rasp. The lancelet is the only representative of its order ; it is a very curious animal, of exceedingly simple construction, found in sand-banks, especially in the Mediterranean. It is transparent, pointed at both ends, about two inches in length, with hardly a vestige of brain. The lampreys and hags are also very primitive—they are eel-like, slimy creatures with rudimentary eyes.

The bony fish are comparatively modern, but they are now the dominant class and the most numerous. This order includes most of the edible fish with which we are familiar. In their case the skeleton, instead of remaining more or less gristly throughout life, is more or less bony. In one small group the gills are arranged in a little tuft instead of in the usual form of plates. To this group belong the sea-horses, often seen in aquariums. They have the additional curious feature that the male has a sort of pouch, into which the eggs are placed by the female, and to which the young can retreat when threatened by any danger. Another species is just like a piece of seaweed in appearance, whilst the pipe fish, one species of which is British, are an allied group.

The sturgeons make up the majority of the fourth order. They are large fish inhabiting the rivers and seas of the north temperate zone. They have rows of large, bony shields on the body ; the mouth is toothless and the upper lobe of the tail is the larger one. This order has declined in numbers in recent geological times.

GIGANTIC TERRORS OF THE DEEP

THE sharks and rays constitute an order whose members have no swimming bladder. Some species bring forth their young alive. With the sharks there are often many rows of teeth, which are continually growing forward to replace the outer rows as they are worn out. Owing to the position of the mouth, a shark may have to turn over when seizing any animal—a man, for example—swimming on the surface, but this is not its normal method of feeding. Many sharks have been accused of man-eating when doubtless not guilty, but the big White Shark, which grows so long as forty feet, is one of the terrors of the sea.

Some species are truly remarkable, as for instance the Thresher or Fox Shark, which is distinguished by the great length of the upper lobe of the tail fin. This is often as long as the rest of the body, the creature measuring about fifteen feet in all. It is inoffensive as regards man, but is a voracious destroyer of other fish, and has been known to attack whales. Extraordinary, too, are the Hammer-headed Sharks, which have the head prolonged horizontally on either side, with the eye at the end of each lobe. They often attain a length of fifteen feet.

The Basking Sharks include the largest of all living fish, specimens measuring fifty feet in length being known. They have, however, small teeth and are harmless to man. The Dog Fish are also of the Shark family. They are much smaller, and the British species are familiar to fishermen by whom they are much disliked owing to the damage they cause to the nets.

The true Saw Fish are also remarkable. They measure ten to twelve feet long, their " saws " being six feet by a foot across the base. By powerful strokes of this weapon they are capable of lacerating the bodies of other animals and tearing off pieces of flesh to devour.

The Skates are allied to the Rays. Some of the Rays carry terrible stinging spines at the end of a long, whip-like tail. This, joined to their enormous size, makes them truly fearsome creatures. The giants of the race are found in the West Indies, and are often known as " Sea-bats " or " Devil-fish." They sometimes measure twenty feet across. At times they rise out of the water and for a short time skim along through the air ; when they fall back into the water, the sound is like the firing of a cannon.

Lastly there is a decreasing and intermediate order, the mud fish of the Amazon and Australia. At certain seasons these fish burrow in mud, breathe through their lung, and can exist a long time without water.

CREATURES THAT LEAD DUAL LIVES : THE AMPHIBIANS

AMPHIBIANS are creatures midway between fish and reptiles, and are adapted for a life both on land and in water. They all possess arangements for breathing air dissolved in water, and in the adults true lungs are always developed. Their limbs are never in the form of fins, and the skin is usually soft and moist. Instead of drinking in the usual manner, they absorb moisture through the pores. Their respiration is of importance : all have gills in their early stages and lungs in later life. The higher forms develop two sets of gills and

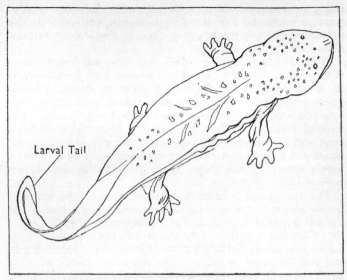

Larval Tail

THE GIANT SALAMANDER OF JAPAN
*This animal can live on land or in water. It does not drink
as other animals do, but absorbs moisture through the pores of
its skin. Because it retains its larval tail throughout its life,
it is known as a Tailed Amphibian.*

when gills are kept throughout life it is the external set which
is retained.

In all cases the lungs are of simple construction and when
the gills are retained they are the principal breathing organs.
The moist skin also plays an important part in the process.
As a class, amphibians are universally distributed, but none
of them are found in the sea. They are divided into those
that live in fresh water and those that are mainly land-dwellers.

THE LEGEND OF THE SALAMANDERS

In what are known as the Tailed Amphibians the larval tail
is retained throughout life ; such are the Giant Salamanders
of Japan and China. In the past many strange ideas were
current about salamanders. They were supposed to be able
to pass unharmed through fire, and were held to be so poisonous that nothing could save anyone who was bitten by them.
Actually, both these beliefs are groundless. They do, however,

exude a poisonous fluid from the skin which injures any small creature taking hold of them in its mouth, and possibly this protective moisture might enable them to pass quickly through a moderate fire.

Water Salamanders, or Newts and Efts, are lizard-like in shape with a flattened tail. The fore-feet have four toes and the hind-feet five. The Common Newt is abundant in the ponds and ditches of Britain and is about three inches long, brown above and orange spotted with black below. The Crested Newt is nearly twice as long. Only the male has a crest and in the breeding season is quite gay in colour. All newts are able to replace a lost member, such as a tail or a leg—a faculty which shows them to be rather low in the scale of life.

The true Land Salamanders are rather like the newts in bodily shape, but they have comparatively thick bodies and the tail is rounded instead of being flattened. In the case of the Common Spotted Salamander of Europe and North Africa the young, on leaving the mother, have external gills and are deposited in water. On the other hand, with the Black Salamander of the mountain districts of Central Europe, only two embryos are hatched at a time, and these are retained in the mother's womb until development is far advanced. While inside the mother the embryos have very long external gills, but they do not leave the mother till these disappear, and they start their outside life as genuine land creatures.

Lastly there are those strange creatures the axolotls, of which all the known species—about twenty in number—are to be found in the United States and in Mexico. The name Axolotl is really only applicable to the larval form, which in some cases is never changed. When this is so, the creature is aquatic in habits. Should its surroundings, however, not be suitable to this mode of life, a terrestrial form is assumed, and this is known as an Amblystome. The reason for the arrested development of many axolotls is that they have inadequate thyroid glands. It has been discovered that artifical feeding of the thyroids will at any time produce this change.

HOW THE TADPOLE BECOMES A FROG

MOST people are familiar with the development of the common frog, which in this respect may well be taken as representative of the higher amphibians. The eggs are

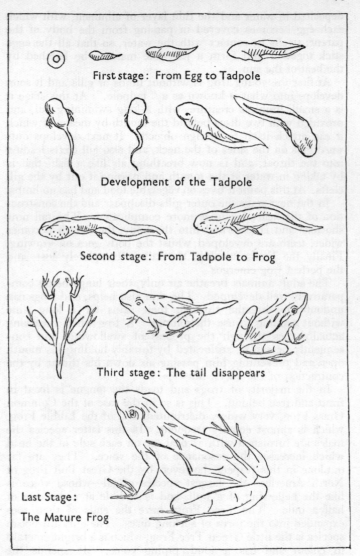

First stage: From Egg to Tadpole

Development of the Tadpole

Second stage: From Tadpole to Frog

Third stage: The tail disappears

Last Stage:

The Mature Frog

TADPOLE INTO FROG

Showing a change typical of the higher amphibians

deposited in water and the thin layer of albumen, with which each egg becomes covered in passing from the body of the parent, swells in contact with the water, so that all the eggs stick together and form a jelly-like mass to be hatched by the heat of the sun.

At first the young frog is without limbs or gills and it soon develops into what is known as a " tadpole." At this stage it is a small, limbless creature, with a long swimming tail, and provided with two discs behind the mouth by means of which it can attach itself to foreign objects. It next develops outward gills on the sides of the neck, and also gill clefts leading into the throat, and is now breathing air like a fish, that is by taking in water at the mouth and passing it out by the gill clefts. At this point it lives on vegetable food and has no limbs.

In the next stage the outer gills disappear and the construction of the heart becomes more complicated. The tail now shortens and is absorbed into the body, the mouth becomes wider, teeth are developed, whilst the body goes on growing. Finally the limbs develop, the tail is completely lost, and the perfect frog emerges.

The adult animals breathe air only, their lungs being comparatively well developed. The skin also helps, and frogs can undoubtedly breathe through their skins for a long time without needing to use their lungs. A frog when breathing actually goes through the process of swallowing, and consequently he can be suffocated by forcibly holding his mouth open and preventing him passing air down his throat by the contraction of the cheek muscles.

In the majority of frogs and toads the tongue is fixed in front and free behind. This is so in the case of the Common Grass Frog, very widely distributed, and of the Edible Frog, which is almost equally frequent. In this latter species the males are furnished with a vocal sac on each side of the head which increases the resonance of the voice. They are far outdone in this respect, however, by the Great Bull Frog of North America—the largest species of all—whose voice is like the bellowing of a bull, and is audible at a distance of half a mile. The Tree Frogs have the ends of their toes expanded into the form of sucking discs. The only European species is the little Green Tree Frog, which is a bright emerald in colour and has a loud, piping voice. It spends the summer in trees searching for insects, but in the winter retires to the water to spawn and hibernate.

WHERE THE FROG AND TOAD DIFFER

TOADS are a very widely distributed family, though of about a hundred known species only three are European. Two of these are British, the Common Toad and the lesser-known Natter Jack Toad. Toads differ from frogs in having no teeth ; their legs are shorter and stouter, the head is more blunt, the skin very warty, and the hind feet are only partially webbed. Toads do not lay their eggs in a mass but in a string, and the tadpole's are smaller than those of the frog.

They are often kept in gardens where they prove themselves very useful by devouring countless insects. They have been the subject of many superstitions on account of their appearance but the beauty of their eyes does much to redeem their undoubted ugliness. Their only means of defence is to exude a bitter moisture from the skin, which will often prevent a dog from seizing them in his mouth.

COLD AND CREEPING ANIMALS : THE REPTILES

THE blood of reptiles is cold—that is to say, only slightly warmer than the outside atmosphere. The body is supplied with a mixture of blood from the veins and arteries in place of pure arterial blood, and in consequence of this imperfect aeration of the blood reptiles are normally of a sluggish disposition, though capable on occasion of great energy. They are dull, inert creatures very different from warm-blooded mammals. Existing reptiles are divided into four orders : first, the tortoises and turtles ; secondly, the snakes ; thirdly, the lizards ; and finally, the crocodiles and alligators.

THE ONLY REPTILES THAT HAVE SHELLS

IN the first order, the tortoises and turtles, the body is enclosed in a kind of bony case or box, covered sometimes with a leathery skin, or more usually, with horny plates. These creatures possess no teeth and the jaws are encased with horn to form a beak. The true turtles may be known by the flattened form of the outer shell and by the adaptation of the limbs to act as paddles. Turtles all live in warm seas and visit land only to lay their eggs, which they deposit in holes scraped in the sand.

The Green Turtle, which is imported to this country for

making the well-known " turtle soup ", is found abundantly in the Atlantic and Indian Oceans. The Hawksbill Turtle is of commercial importance, as from it is obtained the " tortoiseshell " of commerce.

The Soft Tortoises, or Mud Turtles, are distinguished by the imperfect development of the shell, the upper surface of which is covered by a leathery skin. Their jaws have lips, and the feet are webbed, with five toes, only three of which have nails. All live in fresh water and are carnivorous. A well-known example is the soft-shelled turtle of the United States, about twelve inches in size. A third group are amphibious ; their head and feet cannot be withdrawn within the shell. They are carnivorous with a sharp, hooked beak. The Snapping Turtle of America, which grows to a length of four to five feet, is an example.

The Terrapins may also be included here. They are amphibious in their habits, living mostly in marshes and quiet streams. Whilst many of them are North American, they are very widely distributed, and are both animal and vegetable feeders.

The largest of the Land Tortoises are found in the Galapagos Islands of the Pacific, where they sometimes attain a length of four-and-a-half feet and weigh nearly eight hundred pounds. They are reputed to live two hundred years. It is not difficult to understand why these creatures live so long, as more than half their lives are spent in sleep, and they are so deliberate in their movements that they use up very little energy.

USING THEIR RIBS TO GET ALONG

A SNAKE may well be called a reptile, as the name means literally a " creeper." With snakes the ribs are extremely movable, and it is owing to this construction of body that a snake is able to glide along the ground in the manner typical of the race. The skin of many snakes is very beautifully marked, like a gay pattern of beadwork. Contrary to general belief, a snake is not cold and slimy to touch but in reality is warm and dry. The shedding of the outer skin is a very interesting process and is one that most snakes go through annually, some of them several times during a year. If not renewed, the skin would become too hard and impede growth and breathing. Most snakes lay eggs from which the young are hatched by the heat of the sun, but in the case of the

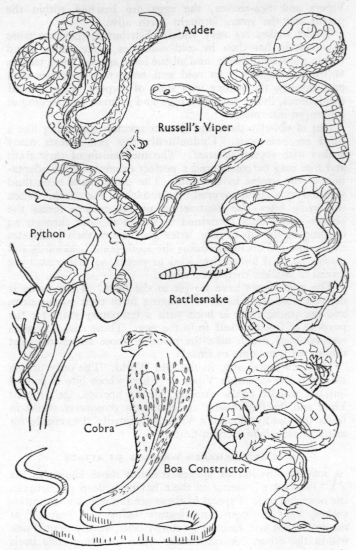

THE SNAKES: KILLERS BY PRESSURE AND KILLERS
BY POISON

Vipers and Sea-snakes, the eggs are hatched within the parent and the young brought forth alive.

Whilst snakes are very widely distributed, they are more abundant in hot than in cold countries, none being found within the Arctic Circle, and all the large species being natives of tropical regions. In cold and temperate countries they pass through the winter in a state of torpor. They are all carnivorous, living on bird's eggs and animals and feeding at prolonged intervals.

Out of about a thousand known species, something like a third are poisonous. Undoubtedly this fact invests many snakes with special interest. The mechanism of their teeth and bite may be considered a perfect example of the adaptation of the means to the end. The poison is a clear fluid secreted by a gland covered by a muscle of the cheek. When the snake bites, the contraction of the muscle forces the poison into a duct contained in the tooth, and through an opening in the tip of the latter the venom then penetrates the wound. With most snakes the teeth point backwards and cannot be used for tearing food to pieces, so that snakes are forced to swallow their prey whole.

The true vipers have no pit in the head. Their name is derived from their habit of bringing forth their young alive, and the young viper is born with a temporary tooth for the purpose of freeing itself from the egg. These snakes possess reserve fangs which take the place of those which may get broken off from time to time.

They are found only in the Old World. The only British species is the Common Viper or Adder whose bite is painful but not usually fatal. Among African species, the Horned Viper and the Puff Adder are extremely poisonous, whilst in India the deadly Russell's Viper is annually responsible for many thousands of human deaths.

THE RATTLESNAKE'S WARNING OF ATTACK

ANOTHER division of snakes contains those known as the " Pit-Vipers " owing to their having a deep pit between the nose and eye. Typical of these are the well-known rattlesnakes, their distinguishing feature being the " rattle " at the end of the tail, formed by horny cells, loosely jointed one within the other. A rattlesnake when attacking coils itself and shakes the rattle, also doing the same when frightened, and this habit has proved fortunate for many persons who have thereby been warned in time of the presence of the snake. It may be said that few snakes habitually attack men intentionally, unless provoked or disturbed.

All the rattlesnakes are confined to the New World, many of them, such as the Copperhead and Water-Moccasin, being North American. The fittingly-named " Bushmaster " of Surinam and Guiana, is said not to avoid man but even to pursue him, and to bite so deeply that a terrible wound is inflicted in which the poison acts at once.

HOODED DEATH : THE COBRAS OF INDIA

THE cobras and keraits of India have good claims to be considered the most venomous of all snakes. The cobras, of course, are celebrated for their power of expanding the neck, usually called the hood, the back of which is marked with a pair of spots joined by a curved stripe, the whole much resembling a pair of spectacles.

In India they have been connected in the popular mind from time immemorial with music and snake-charmers, and in many tales and legends have played a great part, often having been made an object of worship. Most striking of them all is the Hamadryad or King Cobra, which is a tree-dweller and preys on other snakes. It has been known to reach a length of twelve feet.

The pythons are all natives of the Old World, whilst the true boas and anacondas are confined to tropical America. Pythons are among the largest of snakes, sometimes reaching nearly thirty feet, with a body as thick as a man's thigh and weighing several hundred pounds. The anacondas are thought to be sometimes even greater in length. Boas and pythons belong to the most primitive type of snakes and retain traces of hind limbs which other snakes have lost.

All the above are known as " Constrictors " because they coil themselves round their prey, and then by tightening their coils exert tremendous pressure and reduce their victim to a shapeless pulp which they then swallow. They can kill much bigger animals than they could swallow, and cases have been known when the feat has been too difficult and the snake has split itself open by attempting too much.

There are about a thousand living species of lizards, and they are most abundant in warm countries. They are usually carnivorous, but some are largely or entirely vegetable feeders. They differ from the snakes in having movable eyelids. Most of them have long, forked tongues, which they are able to protrude, but with others, such as the iguanas, the tongue is thick and fleshy and not capable of protrusion. Lizards possess neither salivary nor poison glands, the only exception to this rule being the Gila Monster or Heloderm Lizard of Mexico, which is capable of inflicting a poisonous bite. It is a hideous-looking creature, strongly marked with bands of orange, and most people give it a wide berth.

A "SNAKE" WHICH IS REALLY A LIZARD

MANY people in this country are familiar with that small lizard usually called the " Blind Worm," very widely distributed throughout the Old World, and the commonest of British reptiles. Despite a popular habit of regarding this animal as a snake, and consequently dangerous, it is in reality a perfectly harmless creature whose only protection is the production of a rather unpleasant odour when alarmed. Its scientific name (*Anguis fragilis*, literally " brittle worm ") is due to the ease with which the tail can be broken off, owing to the animal stiffening its muscles when handled.

An important group includes the most typical of lizards in which all have a long tail, with four well-developed limbs each terminated by free toes of unequal length. No representatives are found in America, but in Britain the Sand Lizard and the Viviparous Lizard are met with.

The Monitor Lizards are the largest of this family, the Nilotic Monitor of Egypt being about six feet long, whilst an East Indian species from the island of Komodo near Flores is reputed to be nearly twenty feet in length when fully grown and is known as a " Komodo Dragon." Monitors are very fond of eggs of all sorts, and the African variety steals the eggs from crocodiles' nests which he finds buried in the sand.

Geckos, found chiefly in tropical regions, are small lizards with large lidless eyes. Their toes have adhesive discs beneath them, so that they can run with ease over a smooth surface like a wall, or suspend themselves from a ceiling. The curious little Flying Dragon of the East Indies has a membrane on either side, and by expanding this is able to glide through the air.

The iguanas are another notable family, found almost entirely in the New World. They have a crest and pouch with a pendulous fold of skin below the throat. Though very ugly in appearance they are quite harmless, and are much prized by the natives as an article of diet.

THE CHAMELEON: QUICK-TONGUED HUNTER OF INSECT LIFE

CHAMELEONS are distinguished by having the eyelids united and pierced by a central aperture. Also each eye moves independently of the other. Their tails are very long and prehensile; they are well suited for climbing and for a life among trees. Many of them are sluggish in bodily movement, but they catch their insect food by darting out their long tongues so rapidly that they seldom miss their object.

They are proverbially noted for their power of changing colour. This is due to the presence of mobile pigment cells, but though they undoubtedly have this power it must be understood that the process is gradual and not subject to any violent transformation. It is usually governed by their environment and state of health.

Crocodiles have the fourth canine tooth in the lower jaw longer than the others. It is received into a notch in the upper jaw and is visible when the mouth is closed. In the case of alligators this tooth fits into a pit in the upper palate and consequently is hidden when the mouth is shut. With crocodiles the hind-feet are completely webbed, with alligators only partially. Alligators are found only in the warm parts of North and South America, whilst crocodiles are more widely distributed. The Indian crocodile sometimes attains a length of twelve feet, whilst the Nilotic variety, which is very common, has been known to measure as much as fifteen feet. The Caimans of South America are probably the largest of all, having been found so long as twenty feet.

AN ORDER OF INFINITE VARIETY: THE BIRDS

BIRDS constitute the fourth class of vertebrates. They may be defined as warm-blooded creatures, with a double circulation and a covering of feathers, which produce their young from eggs. This definition can be elaborated, but it contains all the essentials and there are no exceptions to it.

Birds breathe more actively and completely than any other vertebrates. They absorb air not only by the lungs but also by some of the bones. All birds, except the Apteryx of New Zealand, possess a number of cavities which form air receptacles. Consequently the aeration of the blood is more complete in their case, and this, together with the perfect construction of their heart and high muscular activity, gives them a higher average temperature than any other living creatures.

HOW A BIRD'S BONES HELP IT TO FLY

THE skeleton of birds is very compact and at the same time exceedingly light. This is partly due to an unusual quantity of phosphate of lime and also in many bones to the absence of marrow and its replacement by air. This lightening of the skeleton is one great aid to flight ; another is the development of a keel-like breast-bone for the attachment of the powerful flying muscles.

There is a great difference in the flying powers of various birds, and many may be termed specialists in some particular branch. Compare for instance the soaring of larks, the swift flight of swallows, the sturdy power of pigeons, wild ducks, and swans ; the mastery of the wind displayed by kestrels, the breath-taking speed and dash of falcons and the glorious strength of condors and eagles on the wing.

Feathers form a unique growth whose evolution is obscure. All birds moult once a year (some twice), generally after the breeding season, and many assume a special mating plumage. Feathers are useful for retaining heat ; they assist greatly in flight and play a great part in courting. Though the theory of protective colouring has often been overworked, there is little doubt that during nesting many female birds are protected by their unobtrusive plumage.

The brains of birds are relatively larger than those of reptiles. Many birds are forced to rely on the alertness of their senses for their sole protection, hence the corresponding increase in brain-power. As regards their physical senses, the eyes are always well developed, and in no bird are they ever rudimentary or absent. Birds have a third eyelid which can be drawn over the surface of the eye in the manner of a curtain, shutting out excessive light.

Most birds have no external ear by which sounds can be transmitted to the internal ear, but in the case of the owls there is an arrangement of feathers which is a forerunner of the external ear of mammals. Taste must always be absent in the majority of birds owing to the horniness of the tongue in most species, whilst their sense of touch cannot be much better. In no living birds are teeth ever present, although in some extinct forms they are known to have existed. The gizzard is a relic of a reptilian ancestry.

Being by virtue of their wings independent of time and place, birds are able to avoid winter and secure the best food all the year round. Whereas some mammals take refuge in a winter sleep when cold weather cuts off the supply of food, the birds simply travel to another region in search of it. The habit of migration is indeed of great service to the race.

It may be noted that when birds migrate northwards it is to find a suitable temperature for breeding, but when they move southwards it is to secure food and warmth. Out of about four hundred recognised British birds, only about one-third remain in this country all the year round; the rest are migrants and summer visitors.

Apart from man, birds are perhaps the only creatures with a sense of beauty. Some species appear to have a natural capacity for selecting certain bright colours. This is well shown by the Bower Birds of New Guinea, small birds related to starlings, which, in the breeding season, not only make elaborate bowers or arbours of sticks in which the males pay court to the hens, but ornament these bowers with bright shells, feathers, etc., and even in some cases change any objects, such as flowers, which have become withered. Curiously enough some of the falcons are known to decorate their nests by the addition of fresh, green branches.

WINGLESS GIANTS OF THE BIRD WORLD

IN the case of birds which do not fly, the breast-bone is flat and the feet and legs have been greatly developed. The African Ostrich is the largest of living birds, the males being six to seven feet high, with extremely strong legs and two-toed feet. The cock-birds are darker than the hens and are kept in semi-domestication for their well-known white tail feathers. In a wild state each male has several wives, and they all lay their eggs in the same nest, which is merely a hole scraped in the ground. In this the huge eggs, each weighing about three pounds, are placed and hatched mostly by the heat of the sun, though both parents watch over the nest and sit on the eggs during the night.

Rheas are natives of South America and are especially plentiful along the river Plata. They are three-toed and not so big as the true ostriches. Like all members of this group they are very swift and wary, but the natives catch them by hurling the " bolas," a cord with heavy balls at each end, which winds round the neck and legs of the bird and brings it to the ground.

The cassowaries of New Guinea and Northern Australia are distinguished by a casque of light bone on the head. Some species have exceedingly brilliantly coloured wattles, the rest of their plumage being dark and hair-like. These birds are often very fierce in temperament and a kick from their horn-covered feet is something to be avoided.

The apteryx or kiwi, of New Zealand, is one of the strangest of living birds. It is about two feet in height, has hardly a trace of wings, is nocturnal in habits, and has a long curved beak with the nostrils at the end. It was preceded by similar extinct forms of a much larger size. Mention may also be made here of the extinct moas of New Zealand, which were enormous wingless birds, at least ten feet in height, with tremendously strong feet and legs. They are believed to have become extinct in recent times.

Penguins are a distinct family. They have webbed feet and scale-like feathers, whilst the somewhat elementary wings are used like fins for swimming under water. They have an upright walk and carry their eggs between their legs, in some cases even hatching them in this position. They are all inhabitants of the Southern Seas and the Emperor Penguin is the largest species, being about three feet high. The King Penguin, with his handsome yellow markings on head and chest, is probably the finest in appearance.

A species which has become extinct within living memory —and that chiefly by man's agency—is the Great Auk, a bird rather like a penguin, once found in millions.

Terns, petrels and gulls are all related. Their general colouring tends to silvery grey with large portions of black and white. They are well known for their voracious appetites and for their keen sight for anything eatable in the water. It is a commonplace sight to see them following a steamer for the sake of any scraps that may be thrown overboard. In winter, when driven by exceptionally cold weather, they often come inland, and in spring also they may be seen along with rooks and jackdaws, following the plough for insects.

Though outwardly resembling a gull the albatross is really not related. The Wandering Albatross, though only sixteen pounds in weight, has a wing spread of twelve feet or more. It rarely comes to land except at the breeding season and then chooses the most remote islands, such as Tristan da Cunha. It is a splendid flyer, almost constantly on the wing, often swooping down just clear of the water, and in the most furious tempests careless alike of wind and wave.

BIRDS THAT ARE PROFESSIONAL FISHERMEN

DARTERS and cormorants are all carnivorous, fish being the food preferred. Their methods of fishing are variable —some thrust their necks down into the water as they swim, others plunge from a height or even pursue their prey under water. The Chinese have long utilised tame cormorants for their skill in fishing. They fix a ring round their necks to prevent them swallowing the fish, and some birds are even trained to work without the collar. They were formerly used in this country in a similar manner, and are still common enough round our rocky coasts.

Next come the pelicans, who constitute a well-marked group. Most of them are large, heavy birds, awkward on land but splendid flyers and swimmers, sometimes spanning ten to fifteen feet across the wings. Found in large colonies, many of them are of snowy white plumage and have a pouch under the bill in which they carry the food they have caught, often giving it to their young in a half-digested state.

The wild duck is one of the best examples of the fresh-water, non-diving ducks, and from this species all our domestic varieties are derived. This bird is a permanent resident in this country and is joined in the colder months of winter by great numbers from the Continent. The Drake, or Mallard (to give him his proper name), is a handsome bird and the rich green of his neck is one of the finest colours in nature.

Though often a by-word for stupidity, geese, at any rate in a wild state, are anything but stupid birds, and their wariness and the way they post sentinels to warn them of approaching danger have often stood them in good stead. Like swans they often assemble in great numbers for migratory flights, when they travel swiftly at a great height in a " V "-shaped formation with the strongest bird leading them.

Flamingoes are midway between swans and herons. They have webbed feet, but much longer slender legs. They are lovely in colour, white above and pink under the wings. One variety is completely rose-coloured. In Africa they are found in vast numbers and the sight of millions in flight is indescribably beautiful.

A FASHION IN MILLINERY WHICH SLAUGHTERED THE YOUNG

HERONS are widely distributed and vary greatly in size, from the Goliath Heron of Africa, standing nearly five feet, to the diminutive Night Herons of Japan, some of which are only a few inches high. The Grey Heron is still fairly common in this country and the large nests of sticks which it builds in trees are a fairly familiar sight. Associating for breeding in colonies, these birds are usually more solitary for the rest of the year, and spend more time by the side of streams, patiently standing immovable to catch their prey by lightning-like thrusts of their sharp bills. In olden times they were a favourite object of pursuit for trained falcons, and often did not come off second best in such encounters.

It may be mentioned that the " osprey " feathers formerly much used in millinery are obtained from a species of heron, namely the Egret, and great numbers of these birds used to be killed to obtain these plumes. Moreover, since these feathers were only obtainable during the breeding season and from the hens, the young ones were left to perish as well as their parents.

THE STORK'S CLAIMS TO HOSPITALITY

THE storks are large birds, common in Europe, Africa and India. They assemble at times in great numbers, flying extremely high, but except for the sound of their wings, they make no noise. The stork has no voice, and is limited in expression to clapping together the mandibles of the beak. On the Continent the Common Stork is a welcome summer visitor, and in several countries it is protected by law on account of the useful work it performs as a scavenger, whilst it is thought lucky to have one nesting on a house.

The Whale-headed Stork, or Shoebill, with his enormous bill shaped like a wooden shoe, is also one of this family, and in Africa and India the Marabou is commonly met with. This bird also acts as a remover of offal.

Typical of Wading Birds are the Coots and the familiar Water Hen. Being aquatic in their habits all wading birds have long legs to enable them to walk in shallow waters. Some of the Rails are also aquatic, with long, slender claws so that they can walk about on the leaves of water plants. The corncrake is an example of a landrail. It is well known in this country from its harsh, monotonous call among the meadow grass.

Snipe are also waders, with long, slender bills, the nostrils being placed at the end. They are usually found near moist and marshy places where they probe in the mud for worms and insects. The flight of the snipe has often saved him from death at the hands of sportsmen. When first flushed, he shoots off in a straight line, and then begins to twist and turn in a bewildering fashion, making it very difficult to aim. In the breeding season the male bird makes a distinctive sound, called " drumming," rather like the bleating of a goat. This is produced by some action of the wings and of the tail feathers.

The lapwing, or green plover, is well known for its constant cry from which it takes its common name of peewit. Like all the plovers, the female, if disturbed on the nest, will try and lure the intruder away by pretending to have broken her wing.

All the cranes are great migrants, changing their abode to find fresh food and climate. They have a loud, trumpet-like note, due to their windpipe which increases the resonance of the voice. Many are very graceful, as for example the Demoiselle Crane, with its delicate mincing walk. The Crowned Cranes of Africa have a beautiful head decoration of twisted, golden filaments of feathers, which appear to shine.

The game birds are mostly grain feeders with large crops and strong gizzards. In many species the males are conspicuous for their brilliant plumage as contrasted with the sober feathers of the hens. This is probably to make the latter less visible to the eye when sitting, as they usually nest on the ground. The young are born fully fledged and able to run about at birth.

The ancestors of most of the breeds of domestic poultry seem to be the Jungle Fowl of Asia, while turkeys are descended from a similar wild species of the New World. The pheasants are a very large family, noted for the magnificence of colouring displayed by many of its members. Of these may be mentioned the Argus Pheasant, which has the tail feathers greatly lengthened and marked with " eyes " like those of a peacock. The Golden Pheasant, gorgeous in crimson and gold, is also among the most beautiful of birds.

Most glorious of all, however, is the peacock, famous for his wonderful display which is caused by his having the tail covert feathers very much elongated. These are erected in the form of a fan, with " eyes " at the end of each feather, whilst the bird's body is a blaze of metallic blues and greens, changing colour according to the angle from which they are viewed.

Pigeons and doves are nearly allied to the preceding group, but the young are born in a helpless state and they take some time before they are able to leave the nest. The males only have one wife, and neither sex possesses any weapons in the shape of spurs or beak. All domestic pigeons are derived from the Rock Pigeon to which many of them still show great resemblance. Some pigeons are ground birds like the Crowned Pigeon of New Guinea, the largest of the group. The Dodo was a still larger non-flying pigeon found in Mauritius. It was stupid and good to eat, reasons which helped considerably towards its extinction.

LOVELY SONGSTERS OF THE PERCHING FAMILY

THE order of perchers contains many of the finest flyers and singers among birds, and the plumage of some of them is hard to surpass. It is the largest order of all and its members are distinct by having, as a rule, three toes in front and one behind. The females are often smaller and less brilliant in colour than the males. They always live in trees and usually build their nests there, frequently showing great skill in their construction. In the early stages the young are very helpless and depend on their parents for food.

One of the largest families of song-birds is the finches, which form a big part of our native British birds. They often add a touch of colour to the hedges by their pretty feathers. They are all small birds with short, stout beaks, particularly well suited for feeding on seeds. The commonest of all birds, the sparrow, belongs to this family, as does also the domestic canary.

The shrikes, or Butcher Birds, may be said to be in a transitional stage between a perching bird and a bird of prey, for while the claws are weak, the bill is hooked and tearing, and some of these birds' characters as regards their neighbours are none too good. The Red-backed Shrike visits Britain in summer and often impales insects and small mammals on thorns near its nest to form a sort of larder. Hence the name Butcher Bird.

THE BLACK CROW AND ITS BRILLIANT BROTHER

THE crow family, of which the raven is chief, contains many birds of strongly marked individuality and intelligence. They are well known for the uniform sombreness of some species, though the jays and pies do much to redeem it by the beauty of their bright colouring. Though apparently not related, the Birds of Paradise are of this family, and surpass all other birds by the range and brilliance of colouring they display, joined to the greatest variety in feather decoration, sometimes bordering on the eccentric.

At first sight, swifts and Humming Birds might not appear similar, but both these wonderful flyers are of the same group. Humming Birds are swift-moving atoms of bright metallic colour, like living jewels. There are over four hundred species, often not more than twenty grains in weight, feeding only on the juices of flowers, which they drink with their long, hollow tongues.

There is no difficulty in recognising members of the parrot tribe, because they are distinguished by their sharply-hooked beaks. They have a thick, fleshy tongue which has helped them in their well-known faculty for imitating all kinds of sounds, including human speech. The macaws and parakeets are amongst the most vividly coloured of all birds, the brightest scarlets, greens, blues and yellows being their most prevalent colours.

The Kea, or owl-parrot of New Zealand, is an almost wingless species with habits different from those of any other parrot. Formerly a vegetarian, it has latterly become obnoxious by killing lambs.

MAGNIFICENT PIRATES OF THE AIR

A SHARP division exists between the majority of the birds already noticed and those known as birds of prey. These have for general characteristics sharp, tearing beaks, short, powerful legs and muscular bodies. Their claws are strong and curved and they have great powers of flight. They may be divided into three groups—the owls; the hawks, falcons and eagles; and thirdly, the ospreys or fish-hawks. The majority of owls are nocturnal, and have large eyes surrounded with circles of feathers, and loose, soft plumage to give them a noiseless flight. The Common Barn Owl in this country has been one of the most persecuted of birds, though its services in destroying rats and mice (its chief source of food) might well have earned it a better fate. This is the owl that is most often found in towns where its hooting note is sometimes quite familiar.

In the second division which includes hawks, falcons and eagles, the type reaches its greatest heights of beauty and efficiency. These birds often have a bold and fearless expression comparable with that of the great Cats, which is not entirely out of keeping with their general character. They are marvels of speed and killing power, differing greatly in method, but always ruthlessly efficient.

Vultures would seem to most people less attractive. Nevertheless all are not repulsive in appearance, and the King Vulture and condor, both South American, are fine birds. The condor has the widest wing span of any flying bird and takes rank as one of the greatest flyers. Vultures undoubtedly find their prey by sight rather than by scent. They are, of course, scavengers by profession and do not use their claws as weapons, relying rather on their strong beaks.

The last group, separate from the rest, contains the ospreys or fish-hawks—beautiful birds found all over the world. They feed only on fish, and their skill and speed when swooping down into the water make them a magnificent sight.

AT THE TOP OF THE SCALE: THE MAMMALS

MAMMALS constitute the highest class of vertebrates and may be defined as warm-blooded creatures in which the outer skin never takes the form of feathers, and in which the young are nourished for a longer or shorter period after birth on their mother's milk. Hair is rightly considered a very characteristic feature of mammals, though it may take several forms such as the spines of a porcupine or hedgehog, or the scales of some of the ant-eaters. In the case of the armadillo a bony-plated armour has been developed. This is the only class of mammal which has adopted this feature.

With a few exceptions all mammals have the same number of joints in the neck—that is, seven, and this number is not affected by the length of the neck. The normal number of limbs is four, hence the common term " quadruped." In the case of the whales the hind limbs are mere rudiments.

The first and lowest order of mammals has only two types, the duck-billed platypus and the echidna, or spiny ant-eater. The first named is a most extraordinary creature ; its body is like that of a mole covered with short brown fur, the feet are webbed, and it has a short, flat tail. The jaws are extended to form a beak like that of a duck. It burrows into the banks of streams and lives chiefly upon insects.

The echidna is rather like a large hedgehog with a snout-like bill, no teeth, and a long, sticky tongue with which it catches insects. Its strong claws enable it to dig very easily. It lays eggs, but suckles its young in true mammalian fashion.

THE KANGAROO'S INCH-LONG BABY

THE marsupials are an ancient order whose distinguishing mark is the pouch in which they carry their young. With very few exceptions all are Australian, the best known of them being, of course, the kangaroos and their numerous allies. All these animals have extremely well-developed hind-legs, with the result that they hop instead of walk. Their tails have grown strong and are used to assist them in balancing when sitting up—their normal position when at rest. All kangaroos live on vegetable food. When they are born they are very small and immature. Even in the case of the Great Red Kangaroo, which attains an adult height of four to five feet, the young are only an inch long at birth. They are transferred by the mother to her pouch, there to live for several months.

The phalangers, some of which are sometimes wrongfully called opossums, take their scientific name from the fact that the second and third digits of their hind feet are joined together. They are small, arboreal animals with a prehensile tail and are omnivorous in their diet. Some of them have a membrane along their side, by extending which they are able to glide through the air for a short distance.

An important division of the marsupials comprises all the carnivorous animals of Australia. These include the dasyures, one of which is the well-known Tasmanian Devil, a small, heavily built, dark-skinned animal with tremendous biting powers.

The next order is that of the edentata, or toothless mammals. This name is not quite accurate as in some cases these animals possess teeth of a sort, but when present the teeth are always rudimentary and are never renewed. First come the sloths, all South American, living in trees and feeding on plants. The feet are either two-toed or three-toed and are furnished with very long claws, which enable them to hang suspended from the branches. In this position they pass their entire lives, and even become covered with minute vegetable growths.

Another family are the Hairy Ant-eaters, also of South

America, among which is included the Great Ant-eater. This animal grows to over four feet and has a long and bushy tail. The jaws are prolonged into a trunk-like snout, from which emerges a long and sticky tongue like a whiplash. All the feet have strong claws, and those on the front limbs, when not used for digging, are bent inwards, and the animal walks on the side of the foot. This ant-eater lives on termites with which the forests of South America abound. It breaks open their nests with its strong claws, thrusts in its long tongue and devours them.

The four-toed Tamandua Ant-eater may also be mentioned. It is in many respects a miniature of its much larger relative. It is strictly arboreal in its habits, usually being found about half-way up the trees it frequents and never descending to the ground.

The aard-vark, or Ground Hog of Africa, is an extremely strange-looking animal, nocturnal in habits, with a long body and tail, in all about four feet. The claws are very strong and curved and the rapidity with which the animal can burrow out of sight must be seen to be believed.

The armadillos, found only in the New World, vary in length from six inches up to three feet, and live on insects, carrion, worms and fruit. They are covered with a bony armour, which in some cases is much divided up into sections, and the animal is able to roll itself up into a ball as a protection against its enemies. All the foregoing mammals are descended from very ancient types, in some cases of great size.

THE COLD TRUTH ABOUT MERMAIDS

THE sirenians are large, aquatic mammals, somewhat fish-like in form, entirely confined to the shores of seas in hot countries. The order owes its name to the fact that it is thought the belief in mermaids may have originated through some traveller seeing some such creatures as these. One family, the manatees, are sluggish, awkward animals of ten feet and over in length, feeding exclusively on seaweed and river plants.

The dugongs are very similar, except for the fact that they are perhaps more strictly marine in their habits and sometimes attain a larger growth. They are found on the coast of the Indian Ocean, extending in range to the north coast of Australia.

HOW THE TOOTHLESS WHALE STRAINS ITS FOOD

UNDER the heading of cetaceans are grouped the whales, dolphins and porpoises. They are all carnivorous creatures living in the sea and are very widely distributed. All the whalebone whales, which are toothless, are placed in one family, and all other groups consist of toothed whales.

In the toothless whales there is a total absence of teeth in the adult, their place being taken by a number of plates of " baleen " or whalebone. The Greenland or " Right " Whale is typical of this family. It is from forty to sixty feet in length, nearly one-third of the length being made up by the head. On account of the absence of teeth and the extremely small size of the gullet, a whale is compelled to live on very small creatures. He swims with his mouth open, and encloses an enormous amount of water containing myriads of diminutive marine animals. He then shuts his mouth and allows the water to strain through the whalebone plates, retaining the food, which he is then able to swallow.

Owing to the fact that many whales are protected against the cold of the water in which they live by a thick coating of fat, known as " blubber," they have long been pursued by man, and in some species the numbers have decreased almost to the point of extinction. Members of this family are the rorquals, the largest of all living creatures, some being known to reach a hundred feet in length.

The sperm whales, or cachalots, are very remarkable. The males are very long, from fifty to seventy feet, but the females are much smaller. The head takes up more than a third of the entire length of the body. The snout forms a broad, truncated mass, with the nostrils placed in the front. These whales live together in numbers, known as " schools," and are found usually in tropical waters. The spermaceti, for which they are specially pursued, is in life a clear, white, oily liquid, contained in certain cavities of the head. On exposure to the air it solidifies. One whale sometimes yields as much as five hundred gallons. From these whales is also obtained the peculiar substance known as ambergris, which is really a secretion of the intestines caused by disease. It is a waxy-looking substance, used as a basis for perfumes, and is very valuable.

A striking member of the dolphin family is the grampus, a large mammal nearly thirty feet long, often spoken of as the " Killer Whale " and noted for its extreme ferocity and the power of its attacks on other cetaceans much larger than itself.

Lastly, the curious narwhal must be mentioned. It is an inhabitant of Arctic Seas, and the body alone measures fifteen feet in length. The dentition of this animal is very remarkable. The lower jaw is devoid of teeth, and in the females no external teeth are present in the upper jaw. In the males, the left canine tooth in the upper jaw grows to an enormous tusk of from eight to ten feet, spirally twisted, and continues to grow throughout life. Cases have been known where two such tusks have been developed. Their use seems undoubtedly to be as weapons, and the traces of their effects on the bodies of other narwhals have been observed.

AN ANIMAL WHOSE " HORN " IS MADE OF HAIR

A VERY large and important order is that of the ungulates, or hoofed mammals. They may be divided into two sections, the odd-toed and the even-toed. The first division includes the rhinoceros and the horse tribes. Though these groups are widely separated from each other by many important characteristics, the intervals between them have been bridged by many forms now extinct.

The Indian rhinoceros has one horn and deeply marked folds in the skin. Like all rhinoceroses, it suggests a type of the very distant past, when such heavy, slow-thinking beasts were very common. In Africa both species, the white and the black, carry two horns. The white rhinoceros is the larger of the two—in fact, after the elephant, it is the largest living land mammal. Another point of difference is the square-shaped muzzle of the white variety, as compared with the finger-like lip possessed by the black rhinoceros.

In speaking of the " horn " of a rhinoceros, it should be stated that this is not the usual structure of horn on a bony core, as in the case of other ungulates, but is a collection of hairs, adhering together, and making a very strong and resilient substance which is, however, only loosely attached to the head.

The tapirs are gentle, inoffensive animals, inhabiting tropical forests, vegetarian in diet, with a short, flexible proboscis used for feeding. There are several South American species, which are dun-coloured, pig-like animals, many of them being aquatic in their mode of life, and usually nocturnal in habits. The Malay tapir is the largest of this family and differs strikingly in colouration, as it has a large, saddle-shaped patch of white on the back. This may be taken as a case of natural colour protection, since it breaks up the outline of the body and makes it difficult to distinguish.

An interesting fact about the pigmentation of this animal is that it is of a free nature, and can easily be rubbed off on the hand if touched. Also the young of both the South American and Malay species do not at birth resemble their parents in marking, but in both cases are striped and spotted, thus pointing to a common ancestry. It does not take them long, however, to lose their spots and become replicas of their respective parents.

HOW THE HORSE LOST ITS FIVE TOES

ZEBRAS, asses and horses are descended from very distant types in which all four legs possessed extremities with five fingers or toes, the whole hand or foot being placed flat on the ground in walking. Gradually the ancestors of the horse came to walk on the ends of the fingers or toes, so that, in the course of a very long time, the middle finger or toe became greatly enlarged, its nail forming the hoof, while the other digits disappeared.

The domestic horse is distinguished from asses, quaggas and zebras by having relatively smaller ears, a more abundant tail, and usually the presence of bare warty patches on the inner side of all four legs. The wild asses of Africa would seem to have been the ancestors of the domestic ass, and one of them, the Somali wild ass, is the finest example of his race. In his case, the stripe on the back and shoulders, so distinctive of all asses, is less noticeable, though the striping on the legs is well marked.

Zebras approach more nearly to asses than to horses. In both, the mane is erect, the upper part of the tail is free from long hairs, and there are warty patches on the fore-legs only. The ears are longer, the head relatively larger and the hoofs narrower than those of horses. Another marked difference is the striping of the head and body. Many hybrids between various members of this family have been produced, thus showing their affinity and common origin at some not very distant period.

The even-toed ungulates make up the larger half of the order. They include the hippopotamus family, which is not far removed from the pigs. They are bulky mammals, with very long, barrel-shaped bodies, short, massive legs, and enormous mouths. The eyes are small, but projecting, and the nostrils are placed on the highest point of the muzzle, so that the animal when in the water can breathe without exposing more than a few inches of the head above the surface. These animals are good swimmers and pass the greater part of their life in the water, feeding exclusively on vegetable matter. The pygmy hippopotamus of Liberia is a much smaller animal, about a quarter the size of the other species and less aquatic in its habits.

Pigs are very nearly related to the foregoing family, and occur in almost every part of the globe except Australia. A special characteristic is the presence of an elongated snout, at the end of which are the nostrils. This is of great use to the animal in grubbing up roots, etc., for food. Pigs have a very keen sense of smell, and are used in some parts of the world to hunt for truffles. They will eat anything. Though not always given credit for it, they are intelligent and courageous animals, and if left to themselves would not be the byword for filth that they are.

Notable species are the wild boars of Europe and Asia, the babirussa of Celebes and Borneo, in which the canine teeth pierce the upper lip and curve backwards ; the wart-hogs of Africa, distinguished by huge, curly upper tusks and warty growths on the face ; and the gigantic black forest hog of the Congo. In the New World, the peccaries are smaller in size, very gregarious, and, in the case of one species at least, credited with a disposition to attack man if molested.

So far all the ungulates considered have been non-ruminants —that is, animals which do not chew the cud. The remainder chew the cud. This means that their stomachs are divided into compartments, into the first of which, known as the paunch, their food passes unchewed. From the paunch it is later returned in small quantities to be chewed while the animal is at rest.

The true camels are found only in Africa and Asia. The Arabian camel has only one hump—the term " dromedary " being applied to the finer breed of this animal, one more suitable for fast travel. The camel may be said to be a first-rate example of fitness to environment, every part of its body being exceedingly well suited to the regions in which it usually lives. It may be questioned, however, if its proverbial capacity for going without water has not been somewhat exaggerated. The Bactrian camel of Central Asia is a heavier, two-humped animal with long shaggy hair, adapted to withstand considerable cold.

The llamas and alpacas of South America are an allied group, which before the Spanish Conquest were the only domesticated animals in Peru. The llama is used in its native country largely as a beast of burden, as is also the alpaca, though the latter is kept more for its wool, which is longer and more abundant than that of its relative.

HOW A DEER GROWS ITS ANTLERS

DEER differ from other ruminants in the nature of their horns, or more properly speaking, " antlers," which with very few exceptions are present in all species. The antlers are confined to the males, except in the case of reindeer which have them in both sexes. Antlers are growths of true bone, covered while growing with a soft, sensitive skin, which contains blood-vessels and is known as " velvet." When the antler is fully grown, the supply of blood ceases, and the " velvet " peels off, leaving the hard bone exposed. Later, by absorption at the base, the antler is shed, leaving a stump on which next year's growth is developed. With most deer the process takes place every year, and when the antlers are many-branched, as in the case of Red Deer, each year's growth is represented by an additional point or " tine," until the antlers begin to lose points, when the stag is said " to go back."

With the exception of one species in the north, Africa has no deer, nor has Australia ; otherwise they are widely distributed throughout the world and the family numbers over a hundred species. To-day the largest living deer is the elk. It is found in Northern Europe and North America, where it is usually known as the moose. The American variety is the larger, and the antlers of the Alaskan race have been known to measure six feet across.

Only one species of deer has been domesticated, namely the reindeer. These animals are confined to Northern Europe and Asia, particularly Lapland, where from time immemorial they have served as beasts of burden and as a source of food. The wild caribou of North America are a closely allied species, and are famous for their annual migration, in which at one time millions of animals took part.

Next to the moose, the Red Deer of North America (which are correctly called " wapiti " not " elk ") and their allied types in Central Asia are probably the finest creatures of their kind. Tremendous animals with great spread of antlers, they make an imposing picture in their wild and native haunts.

SPLENDOURS OF THE HORNED TRIBE

UNDER the heading of bovine animals are grouped the antelopes, oxen, sheep and goats. These include many of the animals man has domesticated and which are of the greatest use to him. Horns are nearly always present, often in both sexes, but they are very different from the antlers of the deer tribe, being a sheath of horn on an inner bony core. None of these animals shed their horns, except only the American pronghorn antelope.

The antelopes are of great variety and number, especially in Africa, where about nine-tenths of the species are found. Many of them are large and splendid creatures with great variety in their horn formation. In the kudu, the horns are spirally twisted ; the sable and oryx have them in a sweeping curve. In the waterbuck, they are lyre-shaped ; while in the gnus, they are bent horizontally.

In sheep and goats both sexes, for the most part, have horns, and they are generally flattened at the edges and turned backwards. The bodies of these animals are heavier and the legs shorter and stouter than those of the antelopes. Both sheep and goats are essentially mountain dwellers and are confined to the northern hemisphere. It is, however, very difficult to draw an exact line between them. Sheep feed on close herbage ; goats browse on leaves and twigs. Sheep have small glands between the feet, while the rams lack the strong smell of male goats. In sheep the horns of the males tend to be twisted in a large curve. In goats the horns are straight, sweeping backwards. Goats usually have a beard.

Oxen are distinguished by having rounded horns instead of twisted ones, and they are usually pointing outwards. Most of them have been more or less domesticated and they form one of man's most useful allies. In Britain the nearest approach to wild cattle are the " Chillingham Cattle," which are white in colour, with a dark muzzle, and have white horns tipped with black. Of this type are the Gaur of India, and their domestic counterpart, the Banteng. The humped cattle of India are marked by a fatty hump on the withers. Representatives of their type are seen in Egyptian monuments, a fact which proves the antiquity of the breed.

Bison are distinguished by having a shaggy mane, a hump on the shoulders, a very large head, and a tufted tail. The American bison, popularly misnamed " buffalo," is the largest of North American hoofed animals. Enormous herds of them once covered the prairies. The story of their near-extinction has often been told, but it was the trade in skins (" buffalo robes " as they were called) which did more than anything to reduce their numbers. They have now been placed under protection and are once more fairly abundant, so that there is not much danger of the species ever becoming extinct. Though formidable in appearance, the bison were never responsible for many human deaths, and there was more risk from a fall from horseback than from their horns.

The European bison is very similar in appearance to the American variety though rather lighter in build. Except for certain individuals in a semi-wild state, the race is much diminished in numbers. The true buffaloes, which in India and Indo-China are commonly domesticated, are heavy, powerful animals, with enormous backward-sweeping horns. In Africa, none of them are domesticated, but they are found in great numbers, ranging in size from the large, black Cape buffalo, to the much smaller, reddish " bush cows " of Western Africa.

Tibet has another member of the family in the yak, a beast of distinctive appearance, with long hair on the body and tail, and a humped shoulder with a heavy, low-carried head. It is known in both semi-wild and domestic states, the domesticated animal being used as a baggage carrier. It is slow but surefooted and capable of enduring the cold of high altitudes.

A LITTLE RELATIVE OF THE ELEPHANT

THOUGH outwardly resembling one of the rodent family, the small mammals called hyraxes have been placed in a separate order. They have, however, certain affinities with the ungulates and are probably of very primitive origin. For the most part they are African, live together in companies, and make their homes in the holes of rocks. The feet have round hoof-like nails, and their owners are good tree-climbers. In Syria a species has been found which has been identified with the " coney " referred to in the Old Testament.

The Indian elephant ranges from India to Sumatra and is smaller than the African species, fully grown males rarely exceeding ten feet at the shoulder, while females are at least a foot less. The forehead is concave, the ears are comparatively small, and there are five toes on the fore-feet and only four on the hind feet. The end of the trunk is formed by a finger-like upper lip and a much shorter lower lip. Both sexes may carry tusks, though the percentage among females is not high. The tusks have been known to reach eight feet in length and their weight over a hundred pounds, though these dimensions are exceptional.

The African elephant is a taller, more leggy animal, of a possible eleven to twelve feet in height, with a sloping fore-head and back, and enormous ears which may measure as much as six feet across. The trunk has a finger-like lip both top and bottom, while the front feet have four nails and the hind feet three. Both sexes usually have tusks, but the tusks of the males much exceed those of the females and have been known to attain the incredible weight of two hundred and seventy pounds, with a length of twelve feet. Such figures are, of course, very exceptional, and the constant pursuit of male elephants for their ivory tusks has rendered the equalling of such records very unlikely in modern times.

The African elephant has been domesticated in the Belgian Congo, but only to a limited extent. Domestication on the scale practised in Indian operations has not been attempted.

MAMMALS BUILT TO SLAY AND REND

IN the order of carnivorous or flesh-eating mammals a very highly developed and specialised type of animal has been evolved. All of the carnivorous mammals are adapted for preying on their fellow creatures, for all must have flesh to live. To enable them to kill and eat meat, important modi-fications of the skull and teeth have taken place, the skull being ridged for the exceedingly strong muscles needed in biting and tearing meat. The canine teeth are very long and tusk-like, while the presence of " carnassials " or sharp, cutting teeth, considerably helps the process.

Not only this, but the possession of claws, long, curved and strong, gives them an added efficiency in killing. The size of the claws is usually in direct proportion to the degree to which the animal is strictly carnivorous. The senses of hearing, sight and smell are usually very keen, the sense of taste perhaps somewhat less so ; but the tongue is often rough and acts like a file in scraping the flesh from bones. Their skins are loose-fitting, as a precaution against being seized by an assailant and to give them greater freedom of bodily movement.

Seals and walruses make up a division of the carnivorous

mammals called Pinnipeds—that is, "with feet shaped like fins." The seals are further divided into true seals and eared seals. The first-named have no external ears. They have short, strong limbs covered with hair. Their hind-limbs are not used in walking but on land are dragged behind. All these animals are true, air-breathing mammals, and come ashore to breed. They spend most of their lives in the water, usually the sea, for which their bodily shape is well suited.

The common seal is frequently seen round British coasts. It is only three to five feet in length, but other species are larger, and the elephant seal of the South Pacific and elsewhere reaches, in the case of the males, twenty feet in length and weighs several tons. This species takes its name from the short, trunk-like appendage of the male ; when the animal is angry or excited, this is capable of being blown out into a miniature trunk.

Sea-lions have small external ears, and are fairly well able to walk on land in a shuffling sort of way. The fur seal of Alaska is a member of this group, and so is the well-known Californian sea-lion. The males of all these animals have short neck-manes, which can be seen when the skin of their bodies is in a dry condition. They all like to live in flocks, are wonderfully fine swimmers and are capable of great bodily dexterity.

Of the walruses there are two known species, the Atlantic and the Pacific walrus. They are remarkable for the immense development of the upper canine teeth into the form of tusks, from twelve to eighteen inches showing outside the jaw. Except for these tusks and the absence of external ears, walruses are most like the eared seals and can move all four limbs freely. They are large animals, attaining ten to fifteen feet in length. They live in communities, feeding for the most part on shell-fish, using their tusks to dig with and to assist them in climbing about the ice floes.

BEARS AND RACOONS ARE ALLIED : THE WEASEL A RELATIVE OF THE BEAR

THE second division of carnivorous mammals are known as Fissipeds, or split-footed animals. They are all terrestrial, the feet being adapted for walking on land, rarely webbed for swimming, and with well-developed claws. First of all come the bears, with which are included the raccoons and weasels. Bears are not truly carnivorous ; they will eat meat when obtainable, but vegetables form the greater part of their food. Consequently their teeth do not conform so strictly to the carnivorous pattern. Their claws are formed for digging, being large, strong and curved.

Bears are widely distributed throughout the world and are found everywhere except in Australia. Africa has few bears, the only well-known species being one found in the Atlas Mountains. The largest species of all is from the Kadiak Islands, Alaska, but the grizzly bear undoubtedly reaches great size. The variation in the colour of the skin makes it very difficult at times to assign any given bear to its correct species. The Polar bear is a very distinct and familiar species. It is exclusively Arctic in habitat and a splendid swimmer ; it feeds entirely on fish, seal and walrus. Its great size, quick movements and snake-like head make it very distinctive. It is quite unlike any other bear.

The raccoons are small American animals, closely related to the bears. They are attractive animals, with bright eyes, banded muzzles and long tails. They have a curious habit of always washing anything before they eat it. They are easily tamed, and their only drawback as pets is their unceasing curiosity, which drives them to turn everything in a house upside down ! The kinkajou is a similar form, bright yellow in colour with close, velvety fur and a prehensile tail. It has a great capacity for climbing.

THE WEASELS: A BEAUTIFUL BUT BLOODTHIRSTY TRIBE

OTTERS, badgers and weasels are all grouped together. Weasels are mostly small, elongated in body with a gliding method of progression. The common weasel and the larger stoat are still plentiful in Britain. The ferret is the domesticated form, the only member of this family to be so tamed. Many of the race, such as minks and martens, are possessed of very beautiful and valuable furs, in consequence of which they have long been closely pursued. They are all of a very fierce disposition, out of all proportion to their size, and their blood-thirstiness is proverbial. They are among the few carnivores which really kill for sport as well as for necessity. The wolverene, or glutton, of Europe and North America is much the largest of the family and is noted for its strength and cunning, some of its feats in defeating the wiles of trappers being unbelievable.

The badgers differ from the typical weasels by walking flat-footed. They are for the most part nocturnal and inoffensive, only wishing to be left alone. A badger, however, is a very courageous beast, and when cornered will give a very good account of himself with his formidable jaws and teeth.

Related to badgers are the skunks, notorious for their power of emitting a most unpleasant odour. As a matter of fact, all the weasel family have this faculty, though not to the same degree.

The ratels, or honey badgers, of Africa and India are queer little beasts, coloured white above and black below. They exist largely on bees and other insects and are reputed to be of unflinching courage.

Otters are land-mammals that have taken to the water in comparatively recent times, as is shown by the fact that the young (as with seals also) do not swim naturally but have to be taught by their parents. In Britain they do not grow to a length of more than a few feet, but there is an American species which is almost five feet long. The sea otter has been so persecuted for its fur, which is reckoned one of the most valuable of all skins, that it is on the verge of extinction and is now only found in the most remote places.

Wolves, foxes and dogs have much in common, and though the ancestry of the domestic dog is in doubt, there is very little difference between some of the larger breeds and wolves. The whole race has been much modified by breeding and is very widely spread. Wolves have at one time been found all over the temperate parts of the world. To-day the finest are probably the timber wolves of North America. Jackals are smaller animals, with a round pupil in the eye and a sharp, pointed muzzle. They hunt in packs and burrow in the ground for shelter.

The foxes differ from all other members of the family in that they have a vertical pupil to the eye. They have pointed muzzles and bushy tails. The common fox, found, of course, in this country, is very widely distributed throughout Europe and Asia, while the silver foxes of the north are much prized for their fur. Mention may also be made of the curious little fennec fox of Africa, with his enormous, erect ears.

ANIMALS WHICH WALK ON THE TIPS OF THEIR TOES

HYÆNAS, civets and cats make up a section of animals which walk on the tips of their toes. Most of them, excepting the hyænas, are able to withdraw their claws when not in use, thus preventing them from getting blunted. Civets are smallish animals, with sharp muzzles and long tails, and are usually conspicuously banded and spotted. Many of them are expert tree climbers and make their living on the various forms of life they encounter in such surroundings.

Half-way between them and the hyænas is the aardwolf of South Africa, which much resembles the hyæna but lacks its power. All the hyænas are natives of the Old World ; they are unattractive-looking creatures, with sloping hindquarters and immensely powerful teeth. But for their usual timidity, they would be formidable indeed. Probably they perform a very useful service to the people in whose country they live, as they are inveterate scavengers and clear away much decaying meat and offal.

The true cats represent a very high form of mammal ; from a physical point of view, some of them may be said to have reached perfection, so well adapted are they for their chosen mode of living, and so perfectly is the balance held between strength and agility, often joined to great beauty of appearance.

The lion is usually placed first in popular estimation, but it may be questioned if the tiger is not a finer animal. Certainly in the Siberian variety he attains a greater size, and his skin is more strikingly marked. The leopard, however, has claims to be considered the perfect cat, for to speed and beauty of movement he joins a very quick mind, capable of acting like a flash.

The beautiful snow leopard of the highlands of Central Asia is a scarce and lovely creature. The cheetah, or hunting leopard, is found in Indian and Africa. In India it has been trained to hunt and is exceedingly swift for a short distance. It is longer in the leg than most cats and its claws are comparatively weak.

The lynxes are the most notable of the smaller types. They are all cold country animals and in winter grow a thick fur. They can always be distinguished by their short tails and tufted ears. There are numerous species of smaller cats, many of them little known. Some of them are of great beauty.

What are known as rodents or gnawing animals make up the most numerous order of all, consisting of over two thousand species. They include mice, rats, squirrels, beavers, porcupines, hares, rabbits, etc., etc. Among so many species only small differences exist in many cases, but for the most part rodents are small, timid mammals, breeding in great numbers.

To this last fact and to their insignificance they owe the firm hold they have taken on life and their presence in every part of the globe.

Their distinguishing feature, from which they take their racial name, is the perpetual growth of their front cutting teeth, which are always worn to a chisel-like edge and thus greatly assist them in their characteristic method of feeding.

THE ONLY ANIMAL THAT CAN FLY

BATS are entirely separated from all other mammals by their ability to fly. This action is made possible by what is really an enormous lengthening of what corresponds to the four outer fingers, which are covered by a delicate and sensitive skin or membrane. All bats come out only at dusk or in the night ; some of them feed on flesh, others on fruit. The senses of touch and hearing are exceedingly acute and at night time they can see quite well. During the day they hang, head downwards, in their chosen retreats, but at night they are very active, though their flight is not so rapid as that of birds. The largest of them all are the fruit bats, some of which are known as flying foxes. In all, about seventy species of them are known, some of them measuring so much as four feet across the wing tips.

There are nearly twenty species of British bats, some quite common. They usually sleep during the winter and put on an extra quantity of fat before doing so. Some families possess very curiously shaped growths on the nose, and the ears are enormously large in proportion to their total size. The so-called vampire bats are confined to the New World. None of them are more than about two feet across and of only a few of them can it be said that they can suck the blood of sleeping men or animals. There seems little doubt however that in some cases they do.

A long-descended order are the insect-eaters, in many respects similar to the rodents but differing from them in dentition. They are mostly small, nocturnal animals, living underground, and in temperate climates usually sleeping through the winter. The order includes about one hundred and fifty species, of which about half are shrew-mice, while moles of many species, hedgehogs, musk-rats, etc., account for most of the others.

The last and highest order, with which man himself is closely associated, is called the Primates. In the first group are what are known as the Lemuroids, about fifty species in all, mostly found in the island of Madagascar. Some of these animals are very unusual in appearance, as for example the curious little aye-aye, which is rather like a squirrel with a hairy body and bushy tail. Some of its fingers have long claws and others short ones. Another member of this family is the spectral tarsier of Malay, which has enormous eyes and a long tail. The small bones of the ankle (or tarsus) are greatly lengthened. The Maholi galago, or "bush baby" may also be mentioned, a gentle little creature easily made into a pet.

More nearly approaching the monkeys are the true lemurs, though their foxy appearance and large nocturnal eyes rather disguise the relationship. The ring-tailed lemur with his long tail is well known, while the largest of the group is the black and white ruffed lemur.

SOME PERSONALITIES OF THE MONKEY TRIBE

MARMOSETS are all South American, small, gentle creatures, often more like squirrels than monkeys. Easily the most distinguished looking of them is the lion marmoset. It is larger than most marmosets and of a bright chestnut colour, with a mane. For the most part the monkeys of the New World are of a lower form and of much less intelligence than those of the Old. They are many of them long and slender in body, with prehensile tails. Some of them, like the spider monkeys, are wonderful gymnasts and fly through the air, like birds, in their leaps from tree to tree.

The howler monkeys are remarkable for the volume of sound which they can produce. This is due to a thickening of a certain bone in the throat, which enables a full-grown male to be heard several miles away. The Old World monkeys include many species too numerous to mention, but attention may be drawn to the baboons, and especially to the West African mandrill. The male is one of the most strikingly coloured of all mammals, which as a class are not given to decoration. Mention may also be made of the colobus or guereza of Africa, which is thumbless and has handsome black and white fur, while the diana monkey is one of the few monkeys with real claims to be considered beautiful.

Last of all is the highest and most important family approaching most nearly to man—the anthropoids. It contains only four members, gibbon, orang-outan, chimpanzee, and gorilla. Gibbons are all Asiatic and tree-dwelling, though curiously enough they are capable of a more upright walk than any of the other apes. Their arms are very long and they are perfectly at home in the trees. They are entirely vegetarian in diet, and mostly possessed of very loud voices. In the case of the largest species, the siamang gibbon, this is added to by the presence of a sac in the throat which when blown out magnifies the sound.

The orang-outans are found in Sumatra and Borneo. They are of a uniform reddish-brown colour, with long hair, and the fully grown males develop great horny growths round the face and neck. Their arms and hands are exceedingly long, and they live mostly in trees, making nests for themselves in which to sleep. Of a languid disposition, they are easily tamed when young.

The chimpanzee is African and approaches more nearly to the human form. The colouring is dark brown, the face is naked, as are the hands and feet. The ears are large, and the brows arched, and these animals are often of a quick, nervous temperament. They are intensely curious and imitative, and in captivity have often been taught to perform many tricks. Individuals would often seem to have very clever brains, though often their efforts seem to lead to no results.

It has been disputed as to whether the gorilla, the last member of the family, should rank higher than the chimpanzee, but, on the whole, scientific opinion tends to place the gorilla first. Certainly in point of size he is a much bigger animal, examples having been known over five and a half feet high, sixty inches round the chest, and six hundred pounds in weight. Such a beast would be a match for most things living, but usually in his chosen haunts the gorilla has few enemies, man always excepted, and leads a peaceful, vegetarian existence, living to a good old age. Man has had very few opportunities of observing gorillas as compared with chimpanzees, but there is little doubt that the intelligence of the gorilla is high and capable of much development.

BOOKS ABOUT THE VERTEBRATES

FROM the foregoing outline of the principal members of the backboned family of animals and their methods of living, the reader may go on to a number of books dealing more fully with the subject, or with specialised aspects of it. Those who desire a general work dealing with the distribution, habits and appearance of vertebrates will find *Wild Life of the World* by R. Lydekker a very comprehensive book. It is admirably illustrated with drawings by Kuhnert. Sooner or later the angle of geographical distribution needs to be approached, and here another book by Lydekker, *Geographical History of Mammals*, deals very lucidly with the subject.

When information regarding particular sections of vertebrates is desired, *The Dictionary of Birds* by C. Black and *The Reptiles of the World* by R. L. Ditmars will be found very helpful. *The Childhood of Animals* by Chalmers Mitchell makes a very good beginning to the study of birds and mammals in their early stages, and is very suggestive of fresh avenues for further reading. *African Nature Notes* by F. C. Selous is also to be recommended, as it contains many items of knowledge obtained at first hand.

THE SOCIAL LIFE OF ANIMALS

by H. St. J. K. DONISTHORPE, F.Z.S., F.R.E.S., of the British Museum (Natural History). Author of " British Ants ", " The Guests of British Ants ", etc.

THE study of the relationship of animals to each other is termed Ecology. Ecology means scientific field natural history. It is the same as natural history, but endeavours to be more accurate and precise. It deals with the law of living things in relation to other living things, and with the relations of animals to their environment, but is connected with a great many other subjects. It seeks to make use of, to give some definite form to, the very large number of observations which have been accumulated during the last few hundred years by field naturalists interested in live animals. Perhaps the greatest number of these observations have been made on insects.

Not much work has been done in animal ecology so far, as during the latter half of the nineteenth century zoologists, entomologists and naturalists generally, took more interest in other aspects of animals, and most of the older work dealt chiefly with attempts to help prove the theory of natural selection. Botanists, however, have developed further the scientific study of the relations between plants and their environment. Ecology is endeavouring to solve some of the urgent practical problems which keep cropping up everywhere as the result of man's interference with the animal and plant life around him.

Different sets of animals are peculiar to different localities, and in the course of evolution the animals become more and more adapted to their surroundings, and are thus specially fitted for the conditions under which they live. They become adapted to climatic and other physical and chemical factors, such as the type of food which is available, the kind of enemies with which they have to deal, and to various communities or associations of plant.

The personnel of every community of animals is constantly changing with the seasons, the weather, and so on, though the changes may be gradual over immense periods, as they were during the advance and retreat of the Ice Age. On the other hand, the changes may be on a small scale.

J. D. Brown observed for several years the inhabitants of a hole in a beech tree, and the succession of the creatures who used it. In the first place, an owl used it for nesting purposes, but as the tissues of the tree grew round the entrance to the hole, it became too small for owls to enter, and their place was then taken by nesting starlings. Later the hole grew so small that no birds could enter, and it was occupied by a colony of wasps. Finally the entrance hole was completely closed up.

The writer also, for ten years, kept under observation a hollow birch tree and noted how soon a new ants' nest became infested with ants' guests. On August 27th, 1915, a fierce battle was witnessed at Woking between workers of the shining black ant and the subterranean yellow ant. The ants were all around the foot of a hollow birch tree in which the yellow ant was nesting ; hundreds of yellow ants lay dead, many dead ones were fastened by their mandibles to the legs and antennæ of live black workers, and some workers of both lay dead, joined inextricably together during their death struggle. A few live yellow ants were still fighting with the black ones, but the colony of the former appeared to have been practically exterminated.

The black ants finally established their colony in the hollow birch tree, building a carton nest at the roots of the tree. As it seemed a good opportunity to note how soon different ant guests came to a new nest, the tree was visited regularly for ten years, and by July 29th, 1925, thirty-eight different species of guests were noted.

The gradual extermination of our British red squirrel by the presence of the introduced American grey squirrel is an example of a change which is now taking place.

WHEN ANIMALS SPREAD DISEASE AND PLAGUE

THERE are many examples of the type of problem which is met with by the ecologist working in the field, some of which may be mentioned here. Epidemics of pneumonia occur regularly in China, killing many people. They are brought about by previous epidemics which have attacked wild marmots living in overcrowded conditions. The danger has been increased by the arrival of numbers of Russian immigrants and Chinese colonists who, ignorant of the danger from the marmots, have taken no precautions so that the infection has rapidly spread. In hotter countries, epidemics take the form of bubonic plague, which is transmitted by the bites of fleas that have been infected with bacilli from rats and other rodents. The sugar-cane leaf-hopper was introduced by accident into the Hawaiian Islands from Australia, with the result that an immense amount of damage was caused to the sugar production. The damage was practically eliminated later by the introduction by Perkins of two Chalcid wasps from Queensland and Fiji, which parasitised the leaf-hopper, and by a Capsid bug which sucks its eggs.

By beating spruce branches in Windsor Forest, the writer recently discovered a sawfly, of which only four examples had previously occurred in Britain. It is a well-known European species, and its caterpillar feeds on the spruce. It has been accidentally introduced into Canada and is doing an immense amount of damage to the spruce forests there. The Canadian government has granted a sum of money to employ an entomologist to study the sawfly on the Continent, and to obtain any parasites which attack it. These are sent to Farnham Royal, where they are bred and thoroughly tested to see that nothing is sent which could become a pest in itself. They are then despatched to Canada to be used to eliminate the spruce sawfly danger.

As an instance of how the intentional introduction of an animal into a strange country to compete with a pest there may be too hasty and the animal may become a pest in itself, mention may be made of the mongoose in Jamaica. It was originally introduced to kill the snakes, but rapidly increased, and when it had exterminated all the snakes, it took to killing all the birds, poultry, etc., and thus became as bad a pest as the snakes.

WHY PLENTY OF CATS MEANS PLENTY OF CLOVER

DARWIN has shown how the extermination of cats could affect the growth of clover. He writes : " I find from experience that humble-bees are almost indispensable to the fertilisation of the heartsease (*Viola tricolor*), for other bees do not visit this flower. I have also found that the visits of bees are necessary for the fertilisation of some kinds of clover ; for instance, twenty heads of Dutch clover (*Trifolium repens*) yielded 2,290 seeds, but twenty other heads protected from bees produced not one. Again, a hundred heads of red clover (*Trifolium pratense*) produced 2,700 seeds, but the same number of protected heads produced not a single seed. Humble-bees alone visit red clover, as other bees cannot reach the nectar. . . . Hence we may infer as highly probable that if the whole genus of humble-bees became extinct or very rare in England, the heartsease and red clover would become very rare, or wholly disappear. The number of humble-bees in any district depends in a great measure upon the number of field-mice, which destroy their combs and nests, and Newman, who has long attended to the habits of humble-bees, believes that ' more than two-thirds of them are thus destroyed all over England.' Now the number of mice is largely dependent, as everyone knows, on the number of cats, and Newman says : ' Near villages and small towns, I have found the nests of humble-bees more numerous than elsewhere, which I attribute to the number of cats that destroy mice.' Hence it is quite credible that the presence of a feline animal in large numbers in a district might determine through the intervention first of mice and then of bees, the frequency of certain flowers in that district."

Other aspects and problems of field natural history, of the kind mentioned above are malaria infection carried by the bites of mosquitoes and sleeping sickness spread by the bites of the tsetse flies ;   the activities of earthworms in the soil ; the activities of animals and insects that are enemies of crops, timber and other resources ;   the conservation of game and of marine fisheries ;   and the control of numerous insect pests.

Among the social insects many excellent examples of animal behaviour may be found, and there are also many observations and experiments which have been carried out and put on record by numerous students working on these creatures. The communities of the social insects, especially of the ants, termites, bees and wasps, also show similarities in various respects to the society of mankind.

HOW THE INSECT BUILDS UP ITS SOCIETY

THERE are, of course, examples of social life, or a tendency towards it, in other animals besides man, such as in wolves, for instance, hunting in packs ;   in beavers living in communities ;   and in the baboon community on the Rock of Gibraltar. There are also other social, or partly social, insects besides the four families before - mentioned.   Examples are the bark-beetles, lady-birds in hibernation, and also some tropical spiders.   It is evident that evolution has taken a very long time to produce the insects who lead a permanent social life and it is also clear that they are descended from solitary forms.

Wheeler has given a series of seven stages by which social life may have been built up, and the series may be quoted with advantage here:

1. The insect mother merely scatters her eggs in the general environment in which the individuals of her species normally live. In some cases the eggs are placed near the larval food.

2. She places her eggs on some portion of the environment (leaves, etc.) which will serve as food for the hatching larvæ.

3. She supplies her eggs with a protective covering. This stage may be combined with (1) or (2).

4. She remains with her eggs and young larvæ and protects them.

5. She deposits her eggs in a safe or specially prepared situation (nest) with a supply of food easily accessible to the hatching young (mass provisioning).

6. She remains with the eggs and young and protects and continuously feeds the latter with prepared food (progressive provisioning).

7. The progeny are not only protected and fed by the mother, but eventually co-operate with her in rearing additional broods of young, so that parent and offspring live together in an annual or perennial society.

Having reached this stage, let us consider some of the many interesting problems to be found among the social insects. For this purpose we will take the wasps first; next, the ants, about which, perhaps, the most is known, and on which the most work has been accomplished; and then we will consider the termites.

THE WASP COLONY AND ITS GUESTS

THE social wasps themselves have been evolved from various primitive solitary wasps. One of the most striking phenomena which wasps possess in common with ants is the mutual exchange of food between the mature wasps and their grubs. This can be more easily observed in wasps kept in captivity than in other social insects.

After a worker wasp has given chewed-up pieces of insects to the grubs, she then imbibes drops of a saccharine liquid which the grubs let fall from their mouths. Sometimes, however, she demands this secretion when the grubs have not been fed, and should the latter not respond at once, she will gently bite their heads to force them to produce this salivary fluid.

Both male and queen wasps are very fond of this secretion ; in fact, the larvæ appear to be rather exploited, often having to give more nutriment than they receive, and this has been said to help to produce the worker caste, that is, imperfectly developed females.

THE WASP AND THE HONEY-POT: AN EPIC OF PERSEVERANCE

WASPS devour a quantity of insects, but are also fond of sweets, nectar from flowers and honey. They can be seen to eat a little meat in butchers' shops, but they are useful to the butchers, as they catch " blue-bottles," cutting off their heads and wings and flying away with their spoils back to their nest. They have a very good memory and will fly long distances from the nest in search of food and chewed wood which they scrape off posts and trees, to make the paper with which they construct the nest. The present writer made observations on a wasp which visited his study for ten days to obtain honey from a pot kept on his table for the benefit of his ants.

Whilst writing at the study table, he noticed a worker wasp, which had come in at the window, hovering over and flying down into the small jug containing the honey. Only a small quantity of honey was left at the bottom of the jug, and the wasp had to go right down to the bottom to get at it. It was found that the wasp came back on and off to the honey, so the writer determined to put down the times of its arrivals and departures. It was found to come regularly from August 22nd to September 9th, after which date it was seen no more.

It started coming as soon as the study window was opened in the morning. Seven thirty a.m. was the earliest time noted, and seven-thirty-six p.m. was the latest departure before the window was shut. The time the wasp spent at the honey varied considerably, but the time between its departures and its return was mostly about seven minutes. It was very nervous at first, and the least jar of the table, or a shadow cast over the honey-pot, caused it to fly off ; but eventually it got quite tame and did not fly away even when the honey-pot was moved about.

When it left the honey, it flew straight out of the window across the garden, and over some trees at the bottom of the garden, but when returning, it was more deliberate, entering the window with a " buzz " and circling over the honey-pot before dropping into it. In the morning it was generally waiting outside for the window to be opened, when it entered at once ; and on several occasions it continued to come during heavy rains. The following is the time-table kept for one day, which shows the wonderful industry and the perseverance of the brave little creature.

Arrival	Departure	Arrival	Departure
7.43 a.m.	7.55 a.m.	2.26 p.m.	2.37 p.m.
8.8	8.20	2.46	2.54
9.25	9.33	3.1	3.10
9.41	9 55	3.19	3.28
10.5	10.16	3.35	3.44
10.21	10.30	3 51	4 0
10.35	10.43	4.4	4.20
10.50	11.0	4.28	4.35
11.7	11.20	5 0	5.9
11.35	11.45	5.15	5 26
11.52	12.3 p.m.	5.36	5.45
12.11 p.m.	12.22	5 53	6.5
12.35	12 44	6.12	6.24
12.49	1.0	6.31	6.42
1.9	1.19	6.49	6.59
1.30	———	7.9	7.16
2.5	2.17	7.25	7.36

Where there is a long interval in the records, the observer was either out of the room or at meals.

Colonies of the chief social wasps are each started by one fertile female which has passed the winter in hibernation. In the spring she starts a small nest of a few cells made from the paper mentioned above and lays eggs in them. The nests may be built in the ground, in hollow trees, or hanging on branches. When the workers hatch, they help to increase the size of the nest and to bring up the brood. Later in the summer, males and females are brought up, and, after mating has taken place, which is generally late in the year (we have noticed it as late as November), the whole colony perishes, except for the fecundated females which go into hibernation.

WASPS WHICH TAKE IN YOUNG BOARDERS

DURING their journeys after food, wasps must come in contact with many different organisms and surroundings ; but in their nests, they also become associated with other creatures which seek out these nests and live with their inmates as scavengers, messmates, or parasites. There are two parasitic species among the social wasps which have lost the worker caste, and their males and fertile females live in the nests of wasps which possess workers. The latter feed them, and bring up their brood, treating them in the same way as they do their own. Some small beetles which live in wasps' nests and feed upon the paper and débris in them are confined to special types of nests. Thus one species only occurs in nests in the ground ; another in the nests of wasps and hornets built in trees.

The large rove beetle, which bears a superficial resemblance to the well-known " Devil's coach-horse," lives in hornets' nests, where it lays its eggs and where its larvæ are bred. It is not harmful to the hornets, as its larvæ feed on rejectmenta, dead hornet grubs and other refuse in the nest. It is nocturnal in its habits, and, with the aid of a dark lantern, the writer has seen it at night fly to and enter a hole in a hollow birch tree inhabited by a colony of hornets.

There is a bright metallic blue tropical species which lives a similar life in the nests of a small but populous species of bee. One of the parasites lays its eggs in wasp grubs, and its larva hatches in the grub's body. It is careful not to destroy the wasp grub until the latter has assumed the pupal state. Then it devours the hind body of the pupa completely, and makes a cocoon in its place at the bottom of the cell which contained the wasp grub. It leaves the head and thorax of the grub, which retain their shape but present a rather ghostly appearance as a lump of colourless jelly.

There are certain fly larvæ, some of which are covered with spines, which act as scavengers in wasps' nests. The perfect fly of one of these, which is not unlike a honey-bee superficially, boldly enters its hosts' nest to lay its eggs. Its larvæ are bred in the débris at the bottom of the nest.

"A CUCKOO IN THE NEST": THE BEETLE'S SUBTLE PLAN OF LIFE

FINALLY mention may be made of *the* wasps' nest beetle *par excellence*, whose interesting life-history is briefly as follows. The eggs are laid by the parent beetle in the autumn in cracks of bark and crevices of rotten wood in places where it is likely wasps will come to collect their wood-pulp. The only point that is not quite cleared up is whether the eggs hatch in the autumn and the larvæ hibernate in suitable hiding places, or whether they pass the winter in the egg state and hatch in the spring. The beetle has been induced to lay eggs in captivity, but the eggs never hatched ; also it often happens with experiments that males and females are not caught or bred at the same time, and thus the fertility of the eggs is not assured.

The young larvæ when first hatched are little active black mites with six legs. As soon as the wasp approaches the hiding place of the little larvæ to obtain the paper for its nest, which it does by scraping the surface of the wood with its jaws, the beetle larva attaches itself to it and is carried by the unconscious wasp to its nest. It will thus be seen that there must be an enormous amount of mortality among the larvæ in the cases where no wasps come to the tree, post, or fence where they lie hidden. But no doubt the female beetles lay a great number of eggs to counterbalance this, as do the oil beetles ; the larvæ of the oil beetles mount flowers and wait for a bee to come and carry them away to its nest.

On reaching the wasps' nest our little larva at once bores into a wasp grub, and there lies bathed in its body fluids. The wasp grub is generally half-grown when the larva enters it. The larva should be looked for in the flank of the third or fourth abdominal segments, and as it is of a black colour it can be seen through the transparent skin of the wasp grub. It remains in the body of the grub until the wasp grub has closed the entrance to its cell with the usual silken cap. It now bores its way out of the wasp grub, changing its skin as it does so, and leaving the old skin as a plug to the hole through which it made its escape.

At this stage it is a fleshy, worm-shaped larva without any legs, and lies like a collar round the neck of the wasp grub. For a time it only sucks the juices of its victim, but eventually devours it altogether and changes to a pupa in the cell intended for the unfortunate wasp. When the silken cap of the cell is removed, the beetle is often found ready to emerge, and several beetles are often discovered occupying cells close to each other. When it has emerged from the cell, the beetle immediately leaves the nest, and probably dies as soon as the duties of paternity or maternity have been performed, since it is very rarely found outside the nest. It has, however, been taken on flowers and from under bark.

The writer has seen it leaving a nest, and also running across the root of a tree. Lacordaire recorded it at the sap of trees ; but in this case it was probably a female beetle laying eggs, and as the mouth-parts are more or less rudimentary, it is doubtful if the beetle does much, if any, feeding in the perfect state. There is a larger race of this beetle which feeds on the larvæ of the queen wasps, but the majority only feed on the worker larvæ.

THE AMAZING SOCIETY OF THE ANTS

IT may be convenient to consider briefly what ants are before dealing with their habits and their association with their surroundings and with other animals. Ants are all social insects and are polymorphic, that is, each species consists of several quite distinct castes. Except in certain parasitic species they are generally trimorphic, that is, they consist of three castes : (1) the male, usually winged ; (2) the fertile female, or queen, usually winged until after fertilisation, when the wings are shed ; (3) the more or less sterile wingless female, or worker, quite different from the queen. In many species the worker caste is divided into (a) soldiers, (b) workers, differing much in form, the soldiers often having the head and jaws disproportionately developed ; and these sub-castes may be further subdivided.

Ants have complete metamorphosis, that is, the egg, larval, pupal and adult stages are quite distinct. The larvæ are legless maggots. The pupæ are either naked or enclosed in a cocoon. The objects popularly spoken of as " ants' eggs " are really the cocoons. Ants occur everywhere, from the outskirts of the Arctic regions to the Tropics ; from the timber line of the highest mountains to the plains and deserts ; in forests, nesting up in the highest trees, and in swamps ; underground and in caverns ; in cultivated places, fields and gardens ; in towns ; in hot-houses and even in houses.

ANTS THAT HUNT AND TEND THEIR FLOCKS

THEIR habits are very varied, and it has been suggested that they present a curious analogy to the hunting, pastoral, and agricultural stages in the history of human development. Some of them, for example, live chiefly on the produce of the chase, probably retaining the habits formerly common to all ants. They live the lives of the lower races of man, subsisting mainly by hunting. Dwelling in small communities, collective action is little developed, and they hunt and conduct their battles singly. Others live a higher social life ; they are skilful in agriculture and have domesticated certain plant lice and beetles. They are thus comparable to the pastoral peoples

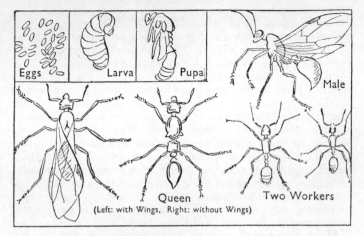

Eggs   Larva   Pupa   Male

Queen
(Left: with Wings. Right: without Wings)

Two Workers

QUEEN ANT AND HER OFFSPRING

*There are four distinct stages in the life of the ant—egg, larval,
pupal and adult. Of the adults, only the male retains wings
throughout life. The fertile female or queen normally sheds
them when she has laid her eggs ; the workers or sterile females
are wingless.*

who live on the produce of their flocks and herds. They live
in large communities and they know how to act in combination both in war and peace. Finally the harvesting ants
and mushroom growers are comparable to the agricultural
nations.

There are now no solitary ants, though the social ants are
descended from solitary ones. The stages of the racial development of ants are as follows:

1. A pre-social stage with a single kind of male and female.

2. A social stage with a single kind of male and female, but
the nesting and nursing instincts have developed.

3. A social stage with one kind of male and two or more
kinds of female, all fertile, but those that build and hunt for
food are becoming less fertile.

4. The present stage with usually one kind of male, a fertile
form of female, and one or more so-called " sterile " females or
workers. These workers, however, are fertile with sufficient
frequency to maintain (principally through the male) a representation of their characters in the germ plasm of the species.

HOW AN ANT COLONY BEGINS

THE colony-founding of ants presents a number of problems. The subject has occupied the attention of many observers over a long period, but it has only comparatively recently been possible to give a connected account of the origin of the ant colony. Various experiments on colony-founding were carried out by the older writers on ants, but Lord Avebury was the first to prove that after their marriage-flight female ants were capable of bringing up their brood without assistance from workers, or from any other ants. It was subsequently assumed that all species of ants founded their colonies in this way. More recent experiments and observations have proved that although very many species found their colonies in this manner, other species adopt other methods.

The following list gives all the known methods by which a colony may be founded:

I. (a) The female ant, after the marriage-flight, removes her wings, seeks a suitable situation where she constructs a cell and brings up her colony alone. (b) Several females voluntarily associate and found a colony in a similar manner.

II. The female seeks a nest of another species of ant, and is adopted willingly or otherwise by the workers who bring up her brood. In some manner, the host queen, if present, is eliminated. Then either (a), in course of time, the host colony dies out and a pure colony of the female species remains, or (b) the mixed character of the colony is kept up by means of slave-raids on nests of the host species by the female's offspring.

III. The female is adopted into the colony of another species and lives side by side with the rightful queen. The intruder's offspring of all castes, but only workers of the host species, are reared together in the nests.

IV. Differs from II(a) only by the fact that the species of the alien queen having no worker caste, the colony only lasts for the lifetime of the host workers. Group I represents the normal method, and Groups II, III, and IV represent the abnormal methods.

Wheeler has recently carried Group I a stage further back, by observations made in Australia on rather primitive ants. He found that the female, after she has constructed her cell and laid her eggs, occasionally leaves the cell to forage for food, returning and closing up the cell again. It is a remarkable fact that an old queen, if removed from her nest, will carry out once

THE HOME OF AN ANT COLONY

A nest of the ant Formica rufa *is here drawn in section to show the arrangement of the galleries and egg-chambers*

more all the necessary labours for the founding of a new colony, although she may have lived for years in her old nest, doing little except laying eggs and being fed and cleaned by the workers. In the case of Group I, an old queen will construct a new cell, lay eggs, and bring up her first brood as before ; and one belonging to Group II will, if introduced into a nest of the host species, act in the same manner as she did when she was a young fertilised female.

Having given this general account of what ants are, and how they found their colonies, we will consider more closely a few of the very many striking facts in connection with their association with other animals, and with their environment.

ANTS THAT ARE FOOD STORES FOR THEIR FELLOWS

THE true honey-ants live in Mexico and in the south-west of the United States and have long been esteemed as an article of food by the Indians. The best-known species is " The Honey-ant of the Garden of the Gods "—the Garden of the Gods being a place near Manitou, in Colorado. It may be as well before dealing with its dwelling-place and habits to consider what a honey-ant is and why it is so called. Many ants are in the habit of collecting honey-dew and storing it in their crops, which become distended. When they reach home, they feed their brood and the rest of the colony by disgorging the sweet liquid. Ordinary ants may often be seen returning home with the abdomen much distended.

Now in the honey-ants this habit has been developed until a class of workers has been produced which are called " repletes." Their bodies are enormously swollen ; in fact, they are literally honey-pots. The size and rotundity of the abdomen are due to the crop, and not to the stomach. The former, being filled with honey, forces back all the other organs against the walls of the abdomen, which are stretched to their utmost capacity.

The ordinary worker is a quick and graceful creature, but the " repletes " or " honey-pots " are only able to waddle along. The replete form is confined to certain workers, and these are only formed when they are callows, that is to say, when they are newly hatched from the pupa into which an ant grub changes before it becomes a perfect insect. At this stage, the covering of the body is soft, but when the ants get older it becomes hard and they are unable to be formed into " honey-pots." This has been proved in observation nests in captivity, the callow being fed with maple sugar and other sweet liquids. The callows greedily devour these foods, and some of them become semi-repletes, whilst others acquire the complete rotundity of genuine honey-pots.

It is chiefly the larger workers that act as honey-pots, but the smaller ones sometimes play this part. The " honey-pots " never leave the nest but store the sweet liquid fed to them by the other workers which go out to forage for food. In return they disgorge some of their store when the other workers wish to be fed. They are thus the living casks, or barrels, of sweet stuff, kept by the ant colony as a store in time of want. They live a quiescent life, hanging to the roofs of the subterranean chambers of the nest. They can move about a little, but should they fall from the ceiling, they are unable to return to their former position without assistance.

There are often as many as three hundred " honey-pots " in the chambers of a large colony. The nests are found on the top of the stony ridges in the Garden of the Gods and in other suitable localities. The large circular entrance to the nest is in the centre of a cone-shaped crater composed of small pebbles. A gallery goes down into the ground and is divided into smaller ones. These lead to underground chambers which have smooth, flattened floors and rough vaulted ceilings. The " honey-pots " hang from these ceilings side by side, and the irregularity of the roof enables them to hold on by their claws.

The workers are nocturnal in their habits, and do not go out during the day. A guard, however, is set at the doors of the nest to prevent other ants, or spiders, etc., from forcing an entrance. About half-past seven in the evening, the workers leave the nest and visit the thickets of slim oaks which are in the neighbourhood. The twigs of these oaks are covered by roundish galls caused by a small four-winged insect, and at night these galls exude drops of a sweet, watery fluid. These drops are eagerly sucked up by the foraging ants, and when they return home they feed the repletes with the contents of their crops. The galls probably provide only a portion of the ants' food, and no doubt a large quantity of their honey is obtained from the scale insects and plant lice which occur on the oaks and on other plants in the neighbourhood.

INSECTS THAT SELL THEIR SERVICES TO ANTS

THE relationship between ants and other creatures with which they associate, or which associate with them, is of two kinds—active and passive. In the first instance, the ants actively seek out their guests ; in the second, the ants are themselves passive, and are sought out by their guests. As instances of the former, one may mention the relationship between ants and plant lice, scale insects, the caterpillars of the blue butterflies, etc. The ants milk and obtain a sweet and nutritious secretion from these creatures, and in return the latter obtain protection from enemies and often shelter as well.

The ants seek out these guests on their food plants, and some they bring back, keep and rear in their nests. One of the most important items in the menu of many kinds of ants is obtained from plant lice. They are insects which possess a long, delicate rostrum with which they pierce the integument of plants and suck up their juices. They are well called " ant cows," as ants both milk and breed them, keeping them in herds and building sheds for them, and walls to protect them. The liquid which the ants obtain from these " cows " is voided in colourless drops, and contains a fair proportion of sugar. When voided on to the leaves of plants, it is called " honey-dew." Some species of ants lick it off the leaves, but others actually milk the plant lice. They stroke them with their antennæ, when a droplet is exuded, which the ants suck up.

Many of the plant lice possess two tubes which are situated on the top of the back near the end of the body. It has been incorrectly stated that it is from these tubes that the droplet is obtained, and indeed many textbooks on entomology repeat this error. It is, however, from the extremity of the body that the sweet secretion is supplied. The tubes contain a thicker and more sticky substance, and this is used by the " cows " to protect themselves from the " aphis-lion," the larvæ of the lady-birds, and other insects which prey on them.

HOW THE ANTS BRING UP THEIR "COWS"

SOME ants collect the eggs of plant lice when laid and keep them in their nests during the winter. When the eggs hatch, the ants carry the young plant lice out of the nest and place them on their proper food plants. These eggs, which are covered with a thick, black membrane, may often be found in large numbers in ants' nests. Of the underground species which live on roots, many are only found in ants' nests, and some of the yellow subterranean ants live exclusively on the excreta of root aphides. When winged forms of these species are hatched in the nests, the ants clear a way for them to allow them to escape into the open.

When an ant's nest which contains subterranean aphides is disturbed, the hosts will be seen to pick up the " cows " and carry them down the galleries into safety. A large grey species with a long rostrum lives under bark in company with a brown tree-ant. It generally has the end of its very long proboscis buried in the wood of the tree, and it is with considerable difficulty that it can be removed without breaking the proboscis. However large they may be, when there is danger, the ants drag and jerk at them unmercifully to make them leave go so that they can be carried off into safety. Plant lice produce vast quantities of " honey-dew," and it is not surprising that ants should have found out their value, and utilised them as cows.

Let us now consider the case of the " Honey Caterpillars," the caterpillars of the " Blues " (Blue butterflies) which are attended by ants all over the world. The ants milk the caterpillars as they do plant lice, attending them on flowers or leaves where they may be feeding. The caterpillars possess an unpaired gland in the middle of the back of the eleventh segment, which can be protruded through a transverse slit. The ants caress the posterior end of the caterpillar with their antennæ until it emits from the gland a droplet of colourless sweet liquid which is eagerly imbibed by the ants.

The benefit gained by the relations between the larvæ and the ants is marked, for the latter obtain a sweet secretion, of which they are very fond, and the caterpillars are protected by the ants against their natural enemies. Some of the caterpillars are carnivorous and feed on the ants' aphides and scale-insects, and even in some cases on the ants' brood. An Indian species, when it is in the butterfly stage, attends aphides, stroking them with its long front feet, and sucking up the secretion emitted with its proboscis. These observations suggest the existence of three-cornered relations between ants, the " Blues " and plant lice.

The caterpillar of the " Large Blue " is an instance of the caterpillar feeding on the brood of its hosts. The caterpillar feeds on the wild thyme, and when it leaves its food plant, it wanders about until it meets, or is met by, an ant. The ant will then probably milk it, or perhaps other ants may come up and do so. But it is always the ant that finds the larva first which carries it into the nest.

After milking the caterpillar, the ant walks round about it, and eventually some sort of signal is given by the ant, or by the larva, when the latter hunches itself up into an extraordinary shape—the head is much retracted, the middle of the back swells up, and the posterior part becomes very narrow in consequence—and the ant seizes it about the middle and carries it into her nest. There the caterpillar does not appear to attract much attention ; it seeks the chamber where the ants' brood is thickest and rests among them. It devours very many of the ants' larvæ and grows very rapidly. When full grown it spins up, pupates in the galleries of the nest, and the perfect butterfly emerges in June.

THE MENACE OF THE UNINVITED GUEST

A RELATIONSHIP wherein the guest is uninvited and merely tolerated by the host is the truer form of insect hospitality, and is more in the nature of parasitism, often being harmful to the hosts. When the guests seek out the ants, they may be friendly, indifferent, or actually hostile to them. They live in the nests for many different reasons ; for protection, shelter, warmth, or food. Some feed on the ants themselves, or on their brood ; others live on the excreta, food or prey of their hosts. They are always seeking their own advantage, although at the same time they may supply a sweet secretion of which the ants are fond, or they may act as scavengers in the nests. The following biological division of the regular ants' guests may be noted:

1. The True Guests: these receive true hospitality from their hosts, being fed or licked, or both fed and licked, by the ants.

2. Indifferently Tolerated Lodgers, which are tolerated for various reasons, and stand in many kinds of different relationships to their hosts.

3. Hostile Persecutor Lodgers, living as beasts of prey and murderers in and near the nests, and devouring their hosts or their brood.

4. Outer and Inner Parasites living and feeding on, or in the ants, their brood, or their guests.

As an example of a " true guest," we can select a beetle which passes its whole life in the home of its hosts, the blood-red, slave-making ant. The beetle is fed by the ants and supplies them with a sweet secretion which exudes from small orifices in the segments of the hind body. It is reddish brown in colour, with tufts of golden hair covering the places from which the sweet fluid springs. When it wishes to be fed, it taps an ant with its antennæ in the same way that one ant does to another when asking for food, and the latter feeds it from its crop.

A near relation of this beetle, also a true guest, has gone a step further. It not only uses its antennæ when supplicating its host, but also strokes the ant's cheek with one of its front legs, which is what an ant would do under these circumstances. The beetle can also feed itself, for when kept in captivity in observation nests it has been seen to bite at dead ants and to suck caterpillars and other creatures given to the ants as food.

This beetle is not very ant-like in appearance when examined by itself, but when it sits among a lot of its hosts—and it is always found where the ants are thickest—it becomes practically invisible. The reason for this is that the light which is reflected from the concave sides of the thorax of the beetle appears to the eye like the narrow back of an ant, and the rolled-up hind body of the beetle reflects the light in the same way as the rounded hind body of a fat ant.

When their hosts change their nest or move from place to place, these beetles move with them. They can also fly, as they possess ample wings, wrapped up under their short wing-cases. The courtship takes place in May, and the female, who is viviparous (i.e. brings young larvæ direct into the world), deposits her offspring on the egg-masses of the ants. The young grub proceeds to feed on the brood of its hosts. The ants not only feed it by mouth (this can be proved by feeding the ants with honey coloured red or blue, when the colour can be traced in the intestinal canal of the little larva through its transparent skin), but they place it on their own larvæ.

The beetle larva is very like that of the ant, and though it possesses six short legs, it does not use them, but imitates the behaviour of an ant larva. The ants pay it the greatest attention and when danger threatens the nest they carry it first into safety. It is extremely voracious and devours large quantities of the ants' grubs. The larvæ change to pupæ in the galleries of the nest, and they are often killed by the ants carrying them about as they do their own cocoons. This serves to keep the beetles in check.

THE INDIFFERENTLY TREATED LODGERS

THERE are very many species of indifferently treated lodgers, with many different habits ; many act as scavengers ; some pass their whole lives in the nests of their hosts ; others pass

only the earlier stages there. A certain beetle, which is superficially like a lady-bird in appearance, is an example of the
latter case. The perfect insect is found on trees and shrubs
overhanging and near the nests of the " Wood-ant " which
builds its hillocks of pine needles, etc., in pine and other
woods. It also occurs on the wing in the neighbourhood,
often in company with a large lady-bird, both species resembling each other.

Its life-history is briefly as follows. The beetle seeks a
tree or shrub above or close to the wood-ants' nest and drops
her eggs on to the ground beneath. Each egg is covered by a
case, or capsule, which is formed around it by the female
and consists of her own excreta. This covering is placed in
position with the hind feet, the egg being held in a depression
of the abdomen. The covered egg exactly resembles a small
bract, and is also exceedingly like the end of a birch catkin.

The ants pick up the covered egg and carry it into the
nest. The larva, which hatches in about twenty-one days,
uses the egg-covering as a nucleus on which to build the
larval case, and while very young carries it about fixed to the
posterior end of the case. The egg-case has a threefold *raison
d'être*—to protect the egg and newly hatched larva, to attract
the ants by its resemblance to a bit of useful vegetable refuse,
and to give the larva a foundation on which to start the larval
case. When the larval case grows larger the egg-case may be
found embedded in it ; or it may be broken off. If this should
happen the larva fills up the hole with the same material as
that with which it builds the rest of the case. This material,
which it prepares with its jaws, consists of its own excreta
mixed with earth.

To enlarge the case the larva removes particles from the
inside and plasters them on to the outside. The object of the
case is, of course, to protect the larva from the ants. The larva
feeds partly on vegetable refuse in the nest, but also on the
droppings and pellets of the ants. During its moults the larva
fastens the case to some object in the nest. When full grown
it fixes the case to a piece of wood, or twig, and turning
completely round changes to a pupa with its head facing the
broader end of the case. The perfect beetle emerges from
the case by biting a circle inside it and thus forming a de-
tachable cap, which it forces off. After this, it escapes from
the nest. It then seeks a mate and the courtship takes place
on trees, etc., near the " wood-ants' " nest.

SINISTER GUESTS THAT ROB AND KILL

THE Hostile Persecutor Lodgers are mostly beetles with short wing cases ; some are very like their host ant, and are confined to one host ; some have two hosts and live with one species in the winter and early spring, and with the other in the summer. All these beetles prey upon ants, lurking in the " runs " of their hosts, and in corners of the nests, and falling upon and murdering solitary individuals. When disturbed they curl up and pretend to be dead, remaining motionless for some time. They are also protected by well-developed repugnatorial glands, which emit a gas or vapour possessing a strong, pungent smell. If a beetle is attacked by an ant it pokes its tail in the ant's face and gives off this vapour, when the ant falls back and the beetle is unhurt.

As an example of an Outer Parasite the larva of a little fly which lives in the colonies of an ant in Texas may be mentioned. Its small larva clings to the neck of an ant larva by means of a sucker, and encircles its host like a collar. Whenever the ant larva is fed by the workers the fly's larva uncoils its body and partakes of the feast. Sometimes, when there is no food in reach, the larva will tweak with its sharp little jaws the sensitive hide of a neighbouring ant larva, or even its own host, till the ant larva squirms, and by wriggling incites the worker-ants to bring a fresh supply of food. When the ant larva spins its cocoon it encloses the fly larva within its web. The fly larva pupates beneath the host, but the host hatches first, and the apparently empty cocoon is thrown on the refuse heap. The fly emerges from its puparium and escapes from the cocoon by the opening made by its host.

There are also a number of curious mites which attach themselves to different kinds of ants' bodies. In connection with this it is very interesting to note that two specimens of an ant, closely related to a living species, have been found in the Baltic amber, each of which bears a large mite attached to the ventral side of the base of the left hind shank. The close similarity in the position of the two specimens suggests that these mites had already acquired the habit, so remarkably developed in some of the recent species, of attaching themselves to very definite regions of the hosts' bodies.

The mites called " antennæ bearers " are very good examples of this. They exhibit most interesting parasitic relations with their hosts. They are partly true guests as they are fed by the ants, and partly outer parasites as they are always attached to the ants' bodies. The feet of the three pairs of hind-legs are provided with suckers, with which the mites can hold very tightly to the ant, and are not easily dislodged. They wave about their long pair of legs, which are directed forwards, and look like antennæ.

The usual position for these creatures is on the chin of the ant. Sometimes, however, two or more will be found resting on a single ant. The positions taken up are either on the chin and forehead, or on each side of the head, or on the hind body. They are always arranged symmetrically in order not to upset the ant's centre of gravity. Six specimens may, very rarely, be found attached to one ant, when they fix themselves as follows : one on each side of the head, one on the chin, one on each side of the hind body, and one on its upper side.

When a mite resting on the ant's chin wishes to be fed it scrapes the mouth of the ant with its front legs, and the ant disgorges a drop of fluid, which the mite sucks up. These mites are often fed by other ants besides the one on which they happen to be. They will solicit another ant for food and the ant immediately feeds them. When an ant which bears a mite is fed by one of its fellows the mite leans forward and shares in the meal. These mites often transfer themselves to the young callow ants soon after they have emerged from their cocoons. The callows often try to get rid of them, falling on their backs, rolling on the ground, and rubbing their chins against anything handy. The mites, however, dodge about on the ant's body out of harm's way, and eventually the callow becomes reconciled to its fate.

Besides the four-winged parasites, and certain flies (two-winged creatures) which lay eggs in an ant's body where their young are reared, the nematode worms are the best examples of inner parasites. Some of these worms live in the glands in the head of ants, others in the abdomen. Those worms which live in the crops of the larval, pupal, and adult workers of certain foreign ants, produce a great distension of the host's abdomen in the adult stage. They enter the larvæ and by unduly stimulating their appetites cause them to be fed to excess so that they grow very large and a gigantic worker form is produced, having various female characters.

It is a larval form of the worm which enters the ants' larvæ. Sometimes the worms emerge from the host after death, when they bore out through the lower part or end of the hind body. They cannot emerge and live on dry ground, but on very wet ground they quickly emerge and bore into the earth. This accounts for the presence of parasitic colonies living on or near damp places. As many as two worms will sometimes be found in the abdomen of a single ant. When the worms become adults, which takes place some time after leaving the host's body, very many eggs are formed—some twelve thousand for each worm—and are laid in the larval skin of the worm.

ANTS THAT USE THEIR YOUNG AS SEWING-MACHINES

ANTS in four different genera have developed the habit of using their larvæ, literally, as sewing-machines, to construct their nests. The first mention of these nests in literature is to be found in *Captain Cook's Voyages*. He observed the nests of one of these ants in the branches of the mangroves in Northern Queensland, Australia. The passage, of course, only refers to the nests and not to how they were constructed.

Nests are made in the following way. The ants select a cluster of leaves, and pull them together in a very ingenious manner. Ants stretch across the gap between two leaves, and catching the edge of one with their jaws and of the other with their back legs, they pull them together until they meet. Whilst some of the ants hold them together, other ants appear with their larvæ in their jaws and apply them to the edges of the meeting leaves. Whenever the larva touches the leaves it deposits a thread of silk. The ant moves it from side to side, touching it against first one leaf and then the other, and thus the leaves are stitched together. The process is repeated with other leaves until the nest is completed.

Small nests occur, but the largest may be nearly as big as a football. Inside, the nest is divided into compartments made with leaves and silk, and contains the ants' brood, workers, sexes and prey. These ants also construct " cattle-sheds " of a few leaves to house their scale insects, etc. When a queen founds a colony she lays her eggs in a curled-up leaf and uses the larvæ, when they hatch, to spin together a few leaves and thus start a nest. They kill and devour large quantities of other insects, stretching them to death.

These ants possess long waists and hold on to each other by them to form chains to stretch over large gaps. It has been suggested that their long waists have developed as a result of their habit of stretching across gaps. This theory is strengthened by the fact that the species found in the Baltic

amber have a considerably shorter waist than the species
existing at the present time. The writer also found this to
be the case in the fossil specimens from the Gurnet Bay
deposits on the Isle of Wight.

ANTS THAT GROW MUSHROOMS AND CARRY "SUNSHADES"

THERE are a certain number of ants which are mushroom
growers, and use cut-up leaves as a substratum on which
to grow the fungus. Some are called " parasol ants " on
account of the habit they have of carrying the large round
pieces of the leaves they have cut off trees over their heads,
when they return with them to the nests. The excavations
for these nests are very extensive. Chambers are constructed
deep down in the ground, one above the other but with some
little distance between them, and they are connected by tunnels
and galleries.

The mushroom gardens are usually grown on the ground
of the chambers, but in some cases they are hung from the
roofs. The fungus garden consists of a mass of chewed-up
leaves covered with a white fungus. It looks like a number of
tufts of wool. The ants do not allow the hyphæ of the fungus
to grow to mushrooms, though if left alone, the fungus will
become an ordinary-looking common mushroom. The hyphæ
are only allowed to produce small, round, white growths
called bromatia, and on these the ants feed exclusively.

All the different species of mushroom growers cultivate a
different species of fungus ; no other species is allowed to
grow. It is only the smaller workers who cut up the leaves
in the nests and cultivate the bromatia. The larger workers
go out along regular paths to shrubs and bushes which they
mount, and snip out with their sharp and powerful jaws
large circular pieces from the leaves, often entirely defoliating
a tree. For a long time it was uncertain what use the ants
made of the leaves. It was suggested that they were used to
thatch the roofs of the underground nests, or even as food.
Belt, in Nicaragua, was the first to discover that their real
use was as manure on which to grow the fungus gardens.

FOUNDING A COLONY: HOW THE VEGETABLE GARDEN IS SOWN

THE colonies of these ants often consist of very large
numbers of individuals. A colony is founded by a young
fertile female in this way. After the marriage-flight she

removes her wings and constructs a small underground cell. She then spits out the pellet from her infra-buccal pocket. This pocket is a spherical cavity situated below the pharynx, and forms a receptacle for the solid and semi-solid parts of the food rasped off by the ant's tongue, and also for foreign matter scraped off the ant's body by its tongue and strigils (the spurs on the front legs). Any juices that remain in these substances are extracted and sucked into the pharynx, the residue being ejected in the form of a solid body, the pellet, which retains the shape of the infra-buccal chamber.

After this pellet has been ejected it must still contain a considerable amount of nutritious matter, for it forms the chief, if not the only food of the larvæ of a genus of flies and also part of that of some beetle larvæ. Moreover, Wheeler discovered that in the larvæ of all four genera of one of the sub-families of ants the swollen front or ventral portion of the first abdominal segment, just behind the mouth, forms a pocket in which the workers place the pellet from their own infra-buccal chambers. No other ants have been observed to feed their larvæ in this way, but eventually spit the pellet out.

The pellet in this instance contains hyphæ of the fungus, some of the substratum of chewed-up leaves, the scrapings from the female's body, etc., and with it she proceeds to cultivate a small fungus garden, manuring it with her fæces. She lays eggs, some of which she breaks up and plasters over the mass ; others are allowed to hatch in it. The young larvæ, when hatched, feed on the fungus growth, and eventually pupate. When the young workers emerge they tunnel through the earth of the cell to the open air, and collect pieces of leaves which they bring back to add to the fungus garden. The latter is now only attended to by the workers, and the queen devotes herself to egg-laying. The colony increases in size, other fungus gardens are started, and eventually a very large colony, occupying a large extent of ground, is formed.

THE GRANARIES OF THE ANT CITIES: PROVIDING FOR A "RAINY DAY"

IT was originally recorded by the ancients that ants stored seeds in granaries to serve as food in time of scarcity. This was doubted in the early part of the last century, being regarded as a fable, or myth. Later, however, the fact was thoroughly re-established, and it is now well known that a variety of ants of many different and distantly related genera do harvest seeds for food. It can be readily understood that in hot, arid countries where insect food may be lacking, or very scarce for many months in the year, and where competition with other insect-eaters may also be very keen, it would be of great advantage to ants to become, in part, vegetarians. Moreover, carnivorous ants possessing powerful jaws for crushing the hard integuments of their prey are well fitted to deal with seeds.

In many of the harvesting ants the larger workers, or soldiers, have enormously developed heads to support the powerful muscles by means of which their large jaws are worked. These workers are literally living " nut-crackers " for the rest of the community, and they crush up the hard seeds when required for food. At the time when these large workers are of no further use to the colony the other ants cut off their heads and throw them on the refuse heap—a very drastic, but effective, method of getting rid of a superfluous working-class.

As stated above, it is now established without doubt that many ants do collect grain and store it. When damp, they bring up the seeds to dry, in order to prevent them from germinating, and if any seeds sprout they gnaw that part away. Moreover, ants play no small part in the distribution of plants, as even in England several ants collect seeds which they carry home. Many seeds get dropped by the way, and thus give rise to plants at some distance from their original spot. The agricultural ant of Texas has been stated, however, not only to collect seeds of a plant called " Ant-rice " but actually to plant and cultivate them, and gather the seed next year. The seed resembles the grain of oats, and tastes like rice.

The ant itself is of a rusty red colour and possesses, in common with many species that live in deserts and dry ground, a beard of long curved hairs. It is able to endure prolonged droughts. The nests of this ant are variable in construction according to the nature of the ground on which they occur, but they are always fully exposed to the sun. They generally occur among the herbage, and all plants growing on or around the nest are cut down and a flat area or disc is cleared for ten or twelve feet round. Should a growing tree be near they move the nest, or else strip all the leaves off the tree.

WHERE ANTS MAKE ROADS AND WEED THEM

ROADS five inches broad near the nest but narrower farther from it are made through the herbage for hundreds of feet in different directions, and these roads are weeded and kept as bare as the disc. If the soil be of a gravelly nature the ants use the gravel to build a cone or crater in the centre of the disc about three feet high, which is sometimes surrounded by a low mound, two or three feet in diameter.

There may be from one to five entrances to the nest. The nests are perforated beneath with flat chambers, some of which form the granaries and are connected by galleries. The granaries never occur deeper than two and a half feet, but the galleries may reach a depth of fifteen feet. Some of the bits of gravel which form the cone are of immense size and weight as compared with the ants. Although they also feed on insects and on other seeds, the " ant-rice " is the only plant allowed to grow in a circle round the nest, and all other plants are cut down as soon as they appear. This rice is regularly sown before the wet season, and about November 1st the young green shoots spring up ; the seeds ripen in June of the next year. The ants carefully weed and attend to these plantations, and gather the seeds. When the seeds have been harvested, the stubble is cut down and removed. The ants throw away the chaff and refuse and, if damp, the seeds are brought up to dry.

A colony is founded in the following manner. The marriage-flight of the bright red females and darker males takes place at the end of June or the beginning of July, after which the female, having removed her wings, digs down into the earth and closes up the opening. She gradually brings up her first brood of some twelve very small, timid workers. In the spring the workers open up the nest, but are careful to conceal the entrance with small pebbles and bits of stick which look as if they might have been brought together by the wind. It is not until the second year when the large workers are produced that the ants begin to cut down the vegetation around the nest and establish the circular discs. These discs increase in size as more workers are produced.

The discs are evidently for the purpose of ensuring as much dryness as possible, to help to prevent the germination of the seeds. The grubs of the ants are fed with portions of crushed seeds, which the workers first coat with saliva to ensure that the starch contained in the seeds is converted into sugar. The sting of this ant is exceedingly painful.

THE BIG COMPANY OF WOOD-EATERS: THE TERMITES

TERMITES possess a social life parallel in many ways to that of the ants. They cultivate mushrooms, for instance, and keep many different species of guests. The males and females fly away into the air together, but they do not mate in the air as many ants do, but descend again to the ground to do so. As with ants, the colonies of the more primitive species consist of a few, or very few, individuals, living a more primitive life, whereas the more highly specialised ones may consist of enormous numbers of individuals, living a much more elaborate and specialised life. But the termites are much more primitive creatures than ants, and have a more primitive structure.

They possess some characters similar to those of cockroaches, and are considered to be descended from an ancestor common also to those creatures. In the tropics where termites are most plentiful they are extremely destructive to all woodwork, books, or anything which contains cellulose, of which they are very fond ; but wherever they are they destroy woodwork. They consist of males, females, and workers, as with ants ; but they are divided up into many more castes. Wheeler gives five castes which he classifies as follows :

1. First form adults, called kings and queens. They are very similar, deeply pigmented insects with large compound eyes, large brain and frontal gland, well-developed reproductive organs and at first with well-developed wings. The wings, however, later break off at pre-formed joints at their bases and are discarded. Old individuals of this caste, therefore, can always be recognised by their short wing-stumps.

2. Second form adults, complemental and substitutional kings and queens, only less pigmented, with wing pads or imperfectly-formed wings with which they cannot fly ; brain, compound eyes, frontal gland and reproductive organs somewhat smaller than in the first form.

3. Third form adults called worker-like, substitutional, or complemental kings and queens. Scarcely pigmented, entirely wingless. Brain small ; eyes and frontal gland vestigial ; mature reproductive organs smaller than in the second form.

4. Workers. Wingless, unpigmented ; brain, small ; compound eyes and frontal gland extremely small, or absent ; reproductive organs rudimentary, as the workers do not reproduce. Head broader than in the first and second adult forms.

5. Soldiers. Wingless ; head large and more or less pigmented ; brain very small ; compound eyes vestigial ; frontal gland, and in very many species the jaws and jaw muscles large. In a few genera the soldier caste is represented by a different form, usually smaller than the worker, with a retort-shaped head, produced in front in the shape of a long, tubular snout, with the opening of a large frontal gland at the tip.

THE TERMITES' CASTE SYSTEM

THE castes vary in the different species, and there may be two or three different forms of soldiers and workers present in one colony. Thus there could be sixteen different kinds of individuals present, though it is probable not all occur at once in one colony. Five or six, however, of the following are often to be met with in a single colony :

1. First form males and females
   (true kings and queens).
2. Second form males and females.
3. Third form males and females.
4. Large male and female workers.
5. Small male and female workers.
6. Large male and female soldiers.
7. Medium-sized male and female soldiers.
8. Small male and female soldiers.

It has recently been shown that the castes appear to be determined in the egg, and not by special feeding alone. The first form males and females can reproduce themselves, and all the castes beneath them ; but the second and third forms can only reproduce themselves and soldiers and workers.

A termite colony is founded as follows. The winged kings and queens rise into the air for a short flight, and then descend to the ground and get rid of their wings. The male termite then runs after a female and when she has found a suitable spot they both dig together to excavate a cell. When the cell is completed, mating takes place ; the queen lays eggs and a small colony is started.

THE TERMITE THAT LAYS A HUNDRED MILLION EGGS

IN some species the king and queen are kept in a special cell, when they are fed and attended to by the workers. The queen is fed very freely, and her body becomes enormous in size, being distended with fat and eggs. She lays eggs every few seconds, and it has been estimated that the number of eggs laid by her in one day is 30,000 and a hundred millions during her lifetime. Should the king and queen happen to die, the second or third form adults are substituted for them. The workers spend most of their time in feeding and cleaning their fellows and in repairing the nest. The soldiers protect the nest with their jaws, and those with snouts do so by ejecting a paralysing secretion.

Termites eat large quantities of wood, but also are fed by their fellows with saliva, with half-digested food, and with excreta. Further, fatty substances exude from parts of the body and these are licked up by other individuals. The queen produces most of this substance and the workers are continually licking her and even bite tiny bits out of her skin to make it flow.

It is a curious fact, which has been thoroughly demonstrated by experiment, that termites are unable by themselves to digest the cellulose obtained from wood, and are only enabled to do so by the presence of a number of protozoa in their intestines. In different species of termites, different species of protozoa occur. The protozoa in the intestines of a termite can be killed off by keeping the host in a temperature of 36° C. for twenty-four hours. If the termite is then fed with a diet of wood it will die in about fifteen days, but if given digested wood or fungus-digested cellulose, it will live indefinitely.

Some species only bore galleries in wood or in the soil, but others build elaborate dwellings, using nest materials which are very hard and strong to resist the attacks of ants and other enemies. The nest materials consist of wood or soil, fastened together by saliva, or of foods which have passed through their bodies, and also of food partly digested and then brought up again. These materials, when dry, form a substance as hard as cement. There are very many different forms of nests, but the termites do not leave entrances and exits as do ants. The nests are entirely closed in, as darkness and no draughts are essential to the well-being of termites.

The fungus gardens in a termite's nest are somewhat similar to those of ants, but the substratum on which the fungi are grown consists of vegetable matter, cut up, eaten, and passed through their bodies. The newly hatched young are kept in the fungus gardens where they devour the food portions of the fungus. Only the first three adult forms are fed with the fungus; the soldiers and workers do not feed on it. Many other creatures live in termites' nests, including a certain number of species of ants, and termites of other genera. They steal from their hosts, living apart in the galleries of the nests, and are hostile lodgers.

There are also many other guests which fall under similar categories to those of ants. The most interesting point in connection with many of these guests is that they possess enormously developed hind bodies, with extraordinary finger-shaped processes which exude fatty substances. Various two-winged flies, and beetles with short wing-cases may be mentioned among others that produce these exudations which are greedily devoured by their hosts.

WHAT TO READ NEXT ABOUT ANIMAL SOCIETIES

ANIMAL ECOLOGY by Charles Elton (Sidgwick) is a very useful text book and can be thoroughly recommended to anyone who wishes to learn something more about the social life of animals. It is clearly written and not too long. For anyone who is anxious to learn all about the social lives of insects *The Social Insects* by W. M. Wheeler (Routledge) is essential. It is written in a most interesting as well as lucid style and likewise deals with everything on the subject. *Animal Ecology* by Roy Chapman (McGraw) is a very large book and is recommended to the more advanced students; *Laboratory and Field Ecology* by V. E. Shelford (Baillière) is also a large work which will repay very careful study. It contains a very complete Bibliography.

WHEN LIFE BEGAN: THE PIONEERS OF THE LIVING WORLD

by W. E. SWINTON, Ph.D., B.Sc., F.R.S.E., F.G.S.,
of the British Museum (Natural History)

PERHAPS there can be no more absorbing themes than the inquiry into, and the discussion of, the history of Life. We talk glibly of the æons of the past, of the queer forms of life, now so dead and buried, that flourished unchecked in so-called " prehistoric " days, of missing links, and of " the Descent of Man." How is it that we can record the history of prehistoric times ? How are we so confident of the life and habits of forms we only know as dead remains and which have left no descendants to these present days ? By what devious and obscure paths do we follow the rambling pioneers of the world of Life, discern their footprints, feel the ashes of their long-abandoned camp-fires, and finally discover the ruins of their ancient dwelling-places ?

This study and the elaborations of these themes are no time-laden branches of a mediæval alchemy ; indeed, the science, or if you like, the art, is scarcely two centuries old, at least in its purer and more informative aspect. Yet already it is established. Its legionaries are indeed legion ; its truths no less than scientifically attested truths.

GOING BACK ALONG THE PATH OF TIME

HOW then shall we, the humble followers of a science that is new to us, approach the task ? There are three main ways, but none is a carriage way, and certainly there is no royal road. Let us follow each at least a little distance and in a simple style, and see what we can make of it.

First, there is no one of us so poor in experience or intellect but can know a little of at least a few animals and plants, and for this purpose we can include Man (a term so used that it includes woman) among the animals. The most superficial observation will have convinced us that a great variety of forms exists. We can, for example, distinguish males and females, parents and offspring, and cousins of near or distant degree. We know that each has some sort of traceable ancestry or lineage, that some forms will interbreed and have offspring like themselves, and that others cannot, or, at least, do not appear to have this habit or ability.

We see also that animals and plants do not interbreed and have no familiar relationship, though both are obviously living things, as living, and certainly as capable of death, as we ourselves are. We see, also, that every new-born animal or plant, however or in whatever form it may be produced, is directly related to some form of similar character or appearance. Search as we may we do not see that Life is of spontaneous occurrence, that it comes from inanimate nature, or that it flowers without some stem or root.

If we search more closely we find that superficial resemblance in animals and plants is often, though by no means always, correlated with an underlying structural similarity. We find, for example, that birds always have feathers and always lay eggs, while mammals never have feathers but always have hair and very seldom lay eggs. Reptiles, on the other hand, never have hair or feathers and may lay eggs or produce living young. Thus even a superficial examination is sufficient to show us that there are broad lines of demarcation between different groups of animals and plants, or, as we may say, we see the rough outlines of classification. We find later that these broad groups are divisible in other sub-groups, into orders, families, genera and species.

FLEETING GLIMPSES OF THE DIM AGES: THE EMBRYOLOGIST'S VIEW

EXAMINING all such groups or sub-groups or even individuals in great detail we see that there is sometimes very great disparity between them, and if we further study the similarities and disparities we can work out a certain relationship between living things. This does not give us, of course, the family tree, but it does give us the outline of its branches and the pattern of its foliage, leaving us to fill in the more solid and woody details of the trunk and inner branches. This method of approach, the easier and more obvious, is called, if we consider only animal life, Zoology and Comparative Anatomy.

The zoologist or anatomist is aware that when he studies the new-born young he is seeing the simplest form of the particular living animal. But if he can examine it before it is born, in what is called the embryonic or fœtal stage, he sees some remarkable things. At certain stages in the development or embryology of the little animal it bears resemblances to forms very little akin to its ultimate condition. For instance, in the human embryo's development, at one period it has gill clefts in the neck like those of a fish, and in another stage it has a well-developed tail. Examples of this sort could be multiplied a hundred-fold.

Embryology has now come to be almost an exact science, well documented and with a wide range of discovery. It is now known, perhaps widely, that the young individual in its pre-natal condition runs through the whole developmental history of its kind, though it does it very quickly, just like a cinematograph film that is speeded up. Thus we can learn that the ancestors of the human race once possessed tails, and before that belonged to a race with gills. It may not be a flattering observation, but it is interesting and, as we shall see, there is confirmatory evidence.

The second avenue of approach is, therefore, through Embryology, which gives us in the developmental stages of the embryo a fleeting glimpse of the past, like the leaves of the family album slipped through the fingers.

A SLOW-MOTION FILM OF THE PAST: THE FOSSIL HUNTER'S STORY

THE third and last avenue of approach is through the study of fossils, and it is in some ways a supplement to the method of comparative anatomy, and in others a reversal of the method of embryology. It is a slow-motion film, not, unfortunately, a complete film, and one much the worse for wear ; but we have full liberty and plenty of time in it to examine each piece of the evidence. This study of fossils, which we shall see is called Palæontology, gives us direct confirmation of the observed embryological facts, it amplifies the structure and findings of comparative anatomy, and gives, above all, actual facts and details of the history of the things that have lived in the past, which are the relatives and ancestors of all the living things we know now.

EARLY MISTAKES ABOUT THE FOSSILS

IT is this third method of approach that we must examine more closely now. What are fossils ? What is this science of Palæontology ? How can we proceed to investigate it ?

The term Palæontology is derived from three Greek words meaning " the science of ancient life " (palaios, ancient ;

ontos, life or being ; *logos*, science). It is concerned with the evidences of animals and plants that existed in former times and which are found occurring naturally in geological deposits. Fossils are so called from the Latin word *fossilia*, meaning " things dug up," because most of them have to be excavated from their rocky, sandy, or clay covering.

Fossils have been known for centuries, but the early observers did not attach any great importance to them. Some regarded them merely as curiosities, others recognised that they had once lived but had become petrified or had been left derelict by the retreat of the waters. At the time of Aristotle it was commonly believed that living things could be generated from mud and slime and their subsequent petrifaction was, therefore, not surprising. General opinion, therefore, was content to regard them merely as curiosities, a belief that persisted for many centuries. But a small number of more scientifically-minded persons, including Leonardo da Vinci the painter, in later days came to realise that they were the preserved remains of once living creatures, and ultimately, at the beginning of the eighteenth century, this was the accepted view. To-day the study of fossils is the whole-time occupation of quite a number of persons in universities, museums, and other educational and even commercial institutions, besides being the hobby of hundreds of people. We will now proceed to examine the subject and see what it can tell us.

THE MYSTERY OF HOW LIFE BEGAN

MOST people to-day realise that the world is a very old structure, so old that the approximate figure of two thousand million years which may be given as its age is beyond the comprehension of most of us who are not mathematicians and astronomers. For at least half of this immense period the record is so inscrutable that we have absolutely no knowledge of the forms of life that were flourishing then. How life itself originated is a complete mystery. It has been suggested that the original " germ " of living substance was conveyed to this earth by a meteorite which came from another world. This theory seems, however, rather to beg the question. Another suggestion is that the germ or spore of life might be borne from some planet to this world without a meteoric conveyance merely by the action of light and its pressure. Demonstration of this " light pressure " is easy, but neither of these theories helps us very much for they both simply transfer the problem from our door to that of another world.

Perhaps the most satisfactory theory so far advanced is that known as the Protobion (Greek, *protos*, first ; *bios*, life). We may assume that in the earlier days the atmospheric and climatic conditions of the world were rather different from now. Temperatures may have been more or less stable ; night and day much alike. The humid atmosphere charged with carbon dioxide lay heavily on the land where the muds and oozes of the waters' edge may have been rich in such elements as carbon, nitrogen, and phosphorus. These substances are relatively unstable, and it is not impossible that under these conditions and in the presence of some additional substance which could work a change in them while remaining unaffected itself, the combination of these chemicals may have taken place and the first life-jelly may have been formed. This simple chemical compound, endowed with the purely physical power of absorbing food chemicals (i.e. endowed with the power of eating), and able to reject waste products, with limited powers of jelly-like movement, may have formed the first life, the Protobion, the first link of a chain whose last segment we ourselves shall never see.

LIFE A THOUSAND MILLION YEARS AGO

HOWEVER this primitive germ may have arisen we have no possible means of learning its composition or characters. The earliest of the rocks [1] are grouped together as pre-Cambrian, a grouping which includes the oldest and most diversified rock deposits in geological history. So crushed and worn are those rocks that no definite knowledge can be obtained of any forms of life that may have then existed. Their record is truly inscrutable and perhaps irretrievably lost. We know that masses of phosphatic material occasionally occur and these probably indicate the ultimate remains of once living things, but beyond that we know nothing of pre-Cambrian life.

In the succeeding period, known as the Cambrian, however, we find that fossils are widely scattered and that diverse and complicated forms are not unplentiful. Down through the long corridor of time, over one thousand million years long, there comes this evidence of the flowering of life. Many of these fossils are beautifully preserved and capable of the

[1] For table showing the Geological Epochs of the Earth, see p. 120.

most minute examination. So here is evidence that during that first half of the world's history, of which we can catch no satisfying glimpse, the simple original " germ " must have been developing in complexity and giving rise to a great series of very different sorts of animals, as if the tiny seed had produced at last a great tree with many branches but with each of the leaves of different appearance.

At any rate, one of the most striking features in the geological history of the world is that, first, we have this great pre-Cambrian period like an unillumined stage, and then, suddenly, as if the floodlights had been switched on, we see a new scene with many well-developed types of life, set to play their part as the opening chorus of this great drama of living things.

On the other hand, complex as the developing forms undoubtedly were, they must also have been without shells or any hard skeleton and they were certainly water-living forms. This helps to explain the absence of fossils in the pre-Cambrian rocks, for fossilisation is difficult where there are only soft structures in the body. For this reason the pre-Cambrian period is occasionally known as Collozoic (Greek, *kolla*, glue ; *zöon*, an animal).

HOW TIME'S DEEPEST ARCHIVES WERE FORMED

IT should be explained here that for an organism to be preserved certain definite conditions must be fulfilled, and their fulfilment is largely a matter of chance. The animal dies on land or in the water, and if it is a soft-bodied and shell-less form, as the earliest were, decay is usually so speedy a process that no trace is ever left. Occasionally, however, where the " body " is left in comparatively fine mud in quiet waters, a faint impression may be made and the subsequent consolidation of the material may preserve for ever this trace of the long-vanished form.

Naturally, shelled or bony animals are by far the more common among fossils. This is due to the resistant nature of the material which will withstand the transportation of the dead creature by river or flood, and will also endure the geological or physical changes to which the containing deposit is later subjected.

The animal dies, and its body may lie at the place of death or may be carried by some agency to new surroundings, so that the position in which a fossil is found is not always the place of death. If the body or specimen lies on land it may disintegrate and leave no particular trace, though it may be covered by wind-blown sand or volcanic ash or have preservation aided by chemical means, such as percolating waters. Where the dead animal is left or borne into water the chances of fossilisation are much greater. Silt, mud, and sand may be gently laid upon it, and as the years roll by the deposit may harden and become the rock we see to-day. Thus, so very many years afterwards, and again by chance, we may break into that rock and discover its long-hidden history.

These processes of fossilisation and this building up of sedimentary deposits has always been going on so that really the historically blank core is surrounded by layer after layer of younger and younger age, most of the deposits bearing within them the secrets of their life.

Thus there might be a continuous record from the first preservable things up to the present day, if it were not that geological processes are always going on. Rivers, rain, snow, frost and ice all do their work of breaking down the tardily-built cliffs and of rotting hills. Earthquake and flood, volcanic action and the slower hand of time exert their influence so that the record becomes discontinuous and jumbled. Thus, nowhere do we have revealed the unbroken sequence of geological events. The complete story is obtained only by collating and adding up the fragments that are visible in cliffs and quarries, in river-banks, canyons, and railway cuttings. With this evidence from the very numerous fossils that have there been obtained, have been marshalled the groups of facts that have gone to make the story of Palæontology.

WHERE THE STORY BEGINS: THE EARLIEST FOSSILS

THE oldest forms of life that we have so far been able to trace through fossils in this way are those of the Cambrian period. These fossils appear suddenly and in great variety, but all are the remains of marine forms. All the chief kinds of invertebrate animals (i.e. those without backbones) now recognised in zoology are already represented by well-developed groups—a fact which not only indicates how old their history is but what a lamentable blank there is in the earlier history of the development of life.

The simplest forms of this assemblage are those belonging

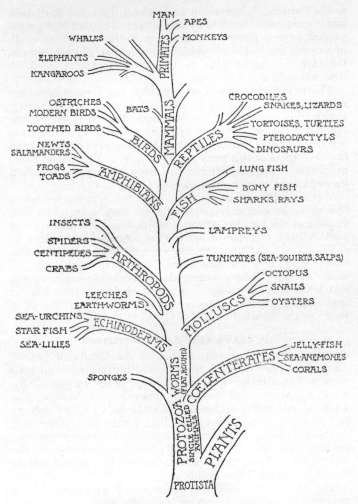

MAN
APES
MONKEYS
WHALES
PRIMATES
ELEPHANTS
KANGAROOS
CROCODILES
OSTRICHES
SNAKES, LIZARDS
MODERN BIRDS
BATS
MAMMALS
TORTOISES, TURTLES
TOOTHED BIRDS
BIRDS
REPTILES
PTERODACTYLS
NEWTS
DINOSAURS
SALAMANDERS
FROGS
LUNG FISH
AMPHIBIANS
TOADS
BONY FISH
FISH
SHARKS, RAYS
INSECTS
LAMPREYS
SPIDERS
CENTIPEDES
TUNICATES (SEA-SQUIRTS, SALPS)
ARTHROPODS
CRABS
OCTOPUS
SNAILS
LEECHES
EARTH-WORMS
OYSTERS
SEA-URCHINS
MOLLUSCS
STAR FISH
ECHINODERMS
SEA-LILIES
JELLY-FISH
PROTOZOA WORMS (FLAT, ROUND)
COELENTERATES
SEA-ANEMONES
CORALS
SPONGES
SINGLE CELLED ANIMALS
PLANTS
PROTISTA

THE TREE OF EVOLUTION

*This reconstruction of the tree of evolution shows the probable
interrelationships of the great families of animals. It is possible,
but more difficult, to reconstruct a similar evolution tree for
plants as well.*

to the Protozoa.[1] Numerous genera and species of Radiolaria and Foraminifera have been described. They all had proto-plasmic bodies generally possessing a fine " test," or shell, of variable composition. Although common and widespread they are sufficiently akin to the living forms to need no description here.

The next higher group of creatures, the Cœlenterates, are represented by quite a numerous company comprising Porifera, or sponges, in which both the six-rayed spicule types and the stony-walled sponges occur. The corals are represented, too, and the remains of jelly-fish have also been found in rocks of this early age in Sweden. The Sea-urchins, or Echinoderms, are represented only by the small stalked variety known to palæontologists as Cystids.

Worms, which seem to have been specially numerous at this time, are curiously important, for they were tube-living forms and the remains of these worm-tubes and casts are so plentiful that in certain districts they actually form rocks.

The three main kinds of molluscs, or shell-fish, were also in existence, and the Cambrian rocks have yielded the re-mains of limpet-like gasteropods, *Nautilus*-like cephalopods, and small lamellibranchs. The first of the brachiopoda, or lamp-shells, were apparently numerous even in the early stages of the period.

THE CRAB'S VERY EARLY ANCESTORS

THE most characteristic fossils of the Cambrian period, however, are none of these kinds, but are more compli-cated and of a higher zoological order. They are the Trilo-bites, which are now extinct. They are crustaceans, dis-tantly related to the crabs, and characterised by very definite and constant features such as their rather oval shape and segmented body, with two longitudinal lines or furrows running backwards along the body from the head, so that the body is divided into three parts or lobes. It is to this feature that they owe the name trilobite.

The back of the body was protected by a strong and hard covering or carapace of chitin, usually strengthened by car-bonate of lime. On the underside of the body there were numerous jointed limbs. An interesting feature of the group is the structure of their eyes. Although many of the Cambrian forms were blind, many others had very complex visual

[1] See pp. 194–5.

organs usually with a number of lenses. In one form of a later geological formation, the eyes are said to contain 15,000 lenses. The Trilobites were usually small in size, an inch or two long, although some forms exceed this figure, and they were all marine.

WHY ANIMALS STARTED TO GROW SHELLS

LOOKING at this Cambrian period of geological history and its well-developed and varied forms of life, we see that it includes all the groups that have given rise to our living invertebrate contemporaries and that, so far, they were all sea-living things. They have been preserved because most of them had hard structures such as shells, and this sudden appearance of shelly structure, whether of chitin or lime, has long been a knotty problem. By some it has been suggested that in the pre-Cambrian times there was insufficient lime in the waters to allow the animals to manufacture shells or " skeletons " for themselves, but there is much evidence to counter this theory.

The more acceptable idea is that all the pre-Cambrian forms were vegetarians and lived happily on the simple plant-forms, without interfering with one another. Then perhaps one group of animals by chance developed a taste for animal food and, given an ample supply, this kind would rapidly increase and develop until the other forms of animal were almost extinguished. To protect themselves in this primeval struggle for existence the others may have developed armour, in the only way they could, which was by the absorption of lime and the manufacture of shells and limy skeletons.

It may be that the trilobites themselves were the villains of the piece, but villains or not, it was this struggle which would help to develop and diversify the forms of living things, and the adoption of armour led to the possibility of preservation as fossils and so to our knowledge of the story of life.

From the evidence of the rocks themselves we know that in Cambrian times the land was more extensive than now and that the seas were somewhat restricted, so that though the living forms were well distributed there was little mingling of the different faunas. It was a long period, this Cambrian with its teeming seas, and so far as we can ascertain the world-wide climatic conditions varied from cool to moderate, but were less differentiated perhaps and less genial than now.

In the succeeding period, right up to modern times, various

developments of the different invertebrate groups have taken place, forms have come into being, have flourished, and finally died away, some without descendants and others leaving their characteristics to be transmitted more or less faithfully by some related form. None, at any rate, has carried on from these early days until the present.

Of the groups we have named, the Foraminifera and Radiolaria have had great development since Cambrian times. Foraminifera were especially abundant in the long Carboniferous period and, because they were widespread in certain localities during the formation of the oil-bearing strata, they are of great interest to oil-field prospectors. Indeed, some hundreds of persons in America devote their time to the study of these little fossils which help them to unravel the history of the oil-bearing deposits, and thus serve to indicate the presence and extent of oil.

THE ONE-ROOMED TENEMENTS OF THE GRAPTOLITES

A SERIES of animals important in the earlier days were the graptolites, which are now long extinct. Their soft parts are quite unknown and we can only guess by analogy at the meaning of the structure. We know them from the abundant remnants of their skeleton of chitin, though that substance itself has generally been carbonised or replaced by iron compounds in the long course of time.

They appear to have consisted essentially of a long hollow chitinous rod from which many little cups projected on one or more sides, so that the whole animal was a sort of tenement of one-roomed cuplets each of which was occupied by a single living polyp, while the whole communicated by means of the central cavity. There are many different varieties of dissimilar appearance, some with several polyp-bearing branches. Others, with only one set of tiny cups, look in the fossil state like tiny saws. Their remains are to be found particularly in the slates of Wales and Shropshire, and they range in antiquity from the Cambrian to the close of the Silurian periods.

The animals known as the corals, which were in some ways related to the graptolites, continued to be important and to grow great reefs in the warmer seas just as they do to-day, and the remains of many of these reefs have been examined. The Sea-Lilies, or crinoids, were common enough too at some periods to be what are known as rock-formers, for we know of several places where beds of limestone have been built from the remains of these graceful animals. Sea-Lilies, which were so common in the Silurian age that this period has been called " The Age of Sea-Lilies," are like slender-fingered starfish, but with numerous fingers. They are attached to the ground by a flexible stalk of varying length.

THE AMMONITE AT HOME: ONE ROOM IN A GAS-FILLED HOUSE

PERHAPS the most enduring and abundant of the animals without backbones have been the Mollusca, or shell-fish, which include not only the common forms familiar to us all to-day but also some extraordinary forms in the past which call at least for mention here.

The most important of them were the ammonites whose serpent-like coiled shells are so common in our Dorset and Yorkshire coasts. These coil-like shells, when sectioned, show that the interiors consisted of a number of communicating chambers similar to those in the shell of a modern nautilus (or one-valved animal). The occupant, a kind of cuttlefish, lived in the last chamber, and it is very probable that the other chambers were filled with gas so that the whole served as a float.

Closely related to the ammonites are the fossils known as belemnites. The narrow cone-shaped fossils of that name are really the same sort of thing as the " pen " of the modern squid, although they are more solidly built. This cone is, of course, merely the horny and internal skeleton of a cuttlefish, and though the belemnites are common and well known, only in a few instances have we any knowledge of the soft-bodied creature itself.

Perhaps one of the most astonishing fossil molluscs, if indeed it is a shell at all, is the gigantic spiral form whose remains were discovered in Alexandra Park, Hastings, some years ago. Actually indications of two individuals were obtained, one with a right-handed, and one with a left-handed, spiral. From the clues as to size, which the fragments of one of these gave, the whole structure was completed in plaster, and a great but moderately thin spiral shell, over seven feet high, resulted. It is now exhibited in the geological department of the British Museum. This was described as a fossil under the name of *Dinocochlea*, or " huge-shell," but it has been the subject of much controversy, as many people maintain it to be merely some curiously shaped mass of materials which had grown together. This diagnosis is very probably correct, although how such a concretion could be formed is a problem likely to be perpetually debated by geologists.

Along with these molluscs the somewhat similar Brachiopoda, or lamp-shells, continued to exist. Occasionally they were very numerous, but like the molluscs they have succeeded in coming down through the æons of geological time and have living representatives, so that no special attention need be paid to them here. It may be pointed out, however, that their popular name of " lamp-shell " is derived from the similarity between the shell and a Roman lamp.

THE ARRIVAL OF THE INSECTS

THE Arthropods, the highest of the invertebrate group, to which belong the trilobites already mentioned, continued to flourish and to produce new and complex forms. The insects, for example, first came upon the scene definitely in the Carboniferous period.[1] They must have been in existence before then, and are probably contemporaneous with the earliest land plants, but it is interesting to see that in the Carboniferous period, with its prolific plant life and perhaps dense atmosphere, the marine arthropods like the trilobites and the eurypterids were dying out, while on land the new arthropods of the air, unhampered by competition as there were yet no birds, were making a conquest that they have not yet relinquished. Remains have been found of dragon-flies of this age whose wings are two and a half feet in span. At this time, too, were the swamps, the luxuriant vegetation, and the generally warm temperature which, combined together, have given us our seams of coal.

THE BACKBONED ANIMALS APPEAR

HOWEVER important these animals without backbones and plant fossils may be, scientifically or commercially, they have not the hold on the public imagination that the backboned creatures, or vertebrates, constantly exercise. The term " prehistoric animals," popular and loose though it is, is almost always synonymous with backboned animals, with the larger of the ancient fish, with giant amphibians, and especially with the enormous and grotesque extinct reptilian creatures and with their successors, the almost equally bizarre

[1] See table, p. 120.

mammals and the forerunners of man. Let us turn then to
the study of these more important creatures.

The earliest of the backboned animals are known only from
fragments contained in the Upper Ordovician rocks of the
Western States of North America and of Russia. While the
great developments of the invertebrate fauna were essentially
marine, it would appear that these earliest known vertebrates
developed and lived in fresh-water lakes and in the rivers,
and that their excursion into wider habitats was not accomplished until probably the Devonian period, which is much
later.

THE FISH ARM THEMSELVES FOR THE BATTLE OF LIFE

IT is also of great interest to speculate upon the mode of life
of these ancestral forms, the foundation of all succeeding
backboned animals. It is very probable that at first they were
speedy creatures, already well adapted in many ways, but like
the earliest of the invertebrates, they were also unarmoured.
Similarly, subject to some kind of attack, probably from a
crustacean enemy, these primitive fish adopted armour and
came to be smallish, broadened creatures, groping their way
and feeding at the bottom of the water. Their descendants
were, so far as we know, completely armed from the front of
the head to the end of the tail in plates and scales. Curiously
enough, it is known that, in some of the forms, this casing
was of bone, and that therefore apparently the primitive fish
were bony fish. In the development of the so-called primitive
or lower fish living to-day, a cartilaginous stage precedes the
bony, and for long it was considered that this was a primitive
condition. Now, however, it may prove to be a secondary or
degenerate state of affairs.

There were comparatively small fish, seldom more than a foot
or two long, with a fish-like body with one or two fins on the
back and perhaps the elements of a pair of pectoral fins behind
the head. The head itself was a flattened, oval-shaped structure, completely covered above by a bony shield. In the
middle of this shield, close together, were the eyes, which
looked upwards. Between them was the tiny opening for the
third, or pineal eye, of which we shall hear again later. The
opening of the nostril was a single, unpaired slit. The mouth
was without jaws and there were numerous gill-pouches.
Strange as such creatures were, they bore many resemblances
to such modern fish as the lampreys and the hag-fish, and it is

possible that these last are descendants of the armoured types but modified for a parasitic life.

Cephalaspis (head-shield) was typical of the primitive type of fish. Its slit-like mouth and its position on the head suggest that the fish was something of a scavenger, seeking its food on the bottom. The skull had a pair of bony horns, and it is believed that, as in certain eels, some of the bony plates were connected to the nervous system and may have served as protective electrical organs.

There were many allied forms of fish, but all were armoured. Their successors, too, were armed, and sometimes were of gigantic size, so much as thirty feet long. However, as has commonly been the fate of these heavily burdened forms of life, they did not survive. Among the primitive forms were the sharks, and they have become modified and have persisted ; but few of their bone-protected contemporaries survived the Devonian period, leaving the field to other kinds of fish which were now fast developing and which were to leave their influence on both land and sea.

THE FISH THAT LEARNED TO LIVE ON LAND

THE Devonian period is one of the great milestones in the study of fossils. As we have seen, in its deposits is the first definite mingling of the hitherto fresh-water fish and the marine forms of life. The primitive armed types of fish were dying out, giving way to freer swimming and faster types. The age was a time of comparative warmth, and in Old Red Sandstone days, many of the river pools were drying up, trapping yet preserving for all time the fish within them. This time has been well named the " The Age of Fishes," for many of its deposits are crowded with the remains from these dried fish pools.

While this was the end of life to many forms, it was a stimulus to others. Certain kinds living in pools which were drying up circumvented the oxygen deficiency of their element by a new device—the gulping of air. Very gradually this habit produced lung-breathing types of which we have direct descendants to-day. More than that, these lung fish produced two very important lines of development. They founded two groups, the first of which produced in time the majority of the fish we know to-day and thus secured the mastery of the seas ; while the second group gave rise, though indirectly, to the partial conquerors of another element, the land, for they produced eventually the amphibians, creatures living partly on land and partly in water. Thus, in the Devonian period, for the first time in the earth's chequered history, a four-footed backboned creature made its bow upon the land.

This transition was responsible for many fundamental changes in the skeleton and external ornamentation of the creatures we have so far considered. In the water, a backbone composed of cartilage was quite satisfactory, and gill breathing was a necessity. For ease in swimming, it was an advantage to have the skull and shoulder girdle intimately connected. On land, however, things were very different. More solid support was necessary, and so a bony backbone came into being, while the skull and the shoulder bones ceased to be so intimately related in order to give more freedom of movement. Fins gave way to a long but somewhat compressed tail and to four simple limbs, each with five fingers or toes. Then, of course, gills disappeared in the adult, and some of the structures were absorbed into a more compli-. cated blood circulation system, while other parts helped to form an ear capable of catching the more elusive sounds in the thinner medium of air.

The covering of scales and plates characteristic of many of the fish gave way to the moist skin we associate with modern frogs, but some of the earlier forms kept the conspicuous scales on the front or ventral side of their bodies.

GLORIES OF THE FROG'S GREAT ANCESTORS

MODERN amphibia, the frogs, toads, newts and so on, do not make a very impressive show in the pageant of living things ; no living amphibian approaches in size or interest the rather diverse forms of the Carboniferous and Permian times. The first forms must have lived along with their not so distant fishy relatives in the rivers and ponds, occasionally venturing on the muddy banks, but having of necessity to return to the water in the breeding season.

In the beginning they were not so unlike the fish in feeding habits and in sense organisation, but they were probably less able to defend themselves from attack and so had to leave the water for the land. On the other hand, from the safety of the shores, they could snatch a plenteous food supply from their contemporaries swimming in the water or stranded in the mud of drying pools. In size, in habit, and in general appearance some of these amphibians were not unlike crocodiles.

We have the evidence of bones from the Permian period [1] found in Texas, that some amphibians (such as *Cacops*) were to all intents and purposes terrestrial, having to return to the water only to lay eggs. Though this particular animal (the *Cacops*) was only about two feet long, others of a similar kind grew to five and six feet.

By this time the amphibians had lost one of their five fingers, the hands having now only four of them well developed. Some forms, too, had developed a certain amount of armour on their backs as a protection against flesh-eating contemporaries. While most of the amphibians were probably still flesh-eaters at this time (the Permian period), it is possible that some may have eaten insects, which we know to have been plentiful, while yet others may have become vegetarians. The amphibians can hardly have been beautiful creatures. With their large triangular skulls, broad and low bodies, and sprawling limbs stuck well out from the body, they must have walked slowly and awkwardly over the land.

THE AMPHIBIANS' STRATEGY TO PRESERVE THEIR RACE

HAPPILY placed in some circumstances, they were not however free from troubles. The reptiles were now beginning to roam the land and harass their amphibian progenitors, and they were a more advanced type without the amphibian limitations. To avoid this new complication, some of the amphibians delayed their water-living and gill-breathing larval state (like the modern axolotl) and eventually became entirely water-living. Indeed we have evidence that some were actually marine, which seems strange if we remember how deadly the salt waters are to the larval forms of the modern amphibian.

These secondarily aquatic and degenerate amphibians are common in the Triassic deposits of Germany, where remains of the large *Mastodonsaurus*, whose skull was four feet long, and the smaller but well-known *Capitosaurus* have been found. These forms are often grouped together under the name of Labyrinthodonts (" labyrinth-toothed "), a name which has reference to the remarkable pleating of the wall of the conical and hollow teeth. The marine kinds were long and narrow-headed, and are known from deposits in Spitsbergen.

[1] See table, p. 120.

HOW THE LITTLE "LIZARDS" DISAPPEARED

NOT all the amphibians were large, for many very interesting kinds, of Carboniferous and Permian age, have been grouped under the name of Microsauria, or "little lizards." The name is not altogether misleading, because they were certainly small, and in some characters were intermediate between the reptiles and the amphibians. Their remains were first discovered in fossilised tree trunks in Nova Scotia, and apparently in Coal Measure times the little animals had been trapped there accidentally. Numerous other examples have been obtained from Bohemia, Ireland and England.

Despite the great number and variety of all these preceding kinds, they did not survive the Trias, but gave way in the struggle with the more highly-equipped reptiles. Fossil examples of the ancestors of living amphibians, frogs, toads, newts and salamanders, are, however, known although they do not date back later than the Jurassic period.[1] In the Eocene and Oligocene ages they are especially well known, and many beautifully preserved specimens have been found which show them to have been very closely similar to the living forms.

One salamander of especial interest must be mentioned. It is a form closely allied to a salamander now living in Japan, and one specimen, now in a Dutch museum, was described in 1726 under the name of *Homo diluvii testis*, " man a witness of the deluge," as the physician who originally identified it believed it to be the remains of a man who had perished in the Flood.

The amphibians now living have only a fraction of the importance of the group as it was in the early days, and the disappearance of the more varied and the larger forms must be attributed to the rise of the higher forms, to which the amphibia themselves gave birth, known as the reptiles. The transition from some amphibian (probably related to the Permian Labyrinthodont *Seymouria*) to reptile was apparently accomplished in Carboniferous times, as a result of the genial conditions and abundant food supply, perhaps reacting favourably on one of the more successful land-living forms. At any rate in the Carboniferous period we have the first remains of this new class of animals, and by the Permian age they are widespread and greatly diversified.

[1] See table, p. 120.

THE FANTASTIC COMPANY OF THE REPTILES

THE early forms of reptiles, whose remains are chiefly known from Pennsylvania, gave rise to a diversity of crude-looking creatures which in the course of time led to an assemblage as powerful and important as any the world has ever seen. In the air, in the waters of lakes and rivers, in the sea, and on land, reptiles were to become rulers at least until the end of the Cretaceous period.[1] During the hundred million years occupied by the Triassic, Jurassic and Cretaceous periods, they were without question the dominant animals in every domain, hence this long time, commonly known as the Mesozoic, or " period of middle life," is also known as " The Age of Reptiles." Here were produced the most fantastic of nature's creations, the most interesting forms, and the great company whose living descendants give but little indication of their former glory.

The name reptile means " creeping," but we shall see that these great reptiles were by no means merely creeping things. The simple amphibian ancestor which produced some unknown reptile started a stem that quickly sprouted to give the Ichthyosaurs, Plesiosaurs and Mosasaurs as monsters of the sea ; the pterodactyls in the air ; crocodiles, turtles and tortoises, snakes and lizards, and the remarkable giants of the earth, the Dinosaurs.

Though little is known of the Carboniferous reptilian fauna, in the succeeding period, the Permian, there was quite a diversified representation, both of land-living and water-living forms. Amongst these, one or two will serve for description.

A HELMET-CLAD LIZARD WITH THREE EYES

THE first of them comes from South Africa and is known by many specimens, the best of which is on public view at the Natural History Museum, South Kensington. Its name is *Pareiasaurus*, which can be translated as the " helmet-cheeked lizard." It may be pointed out here that the suffix " saurus " means in Greek " lizard," though " reptile " must generally be understood. This African form derives its name from the fact that the whole of the head is completely roofed by bone, except for the eye openings and for the comparatively large orifice (foramen) for the pineal, or third eye.

This last-named organ, which we have already mentioned,

[1] See table, p. 120.

occurs in some fish, in the amphibians, and in many reptiles, chiefly the swimming kinds. The structure so far as we can judge it from living animals, was a primitive eye, with nervous connections, lens, and retina, but whether it had visual powers or not we do not know. In the living Sphenodon, a reptile with a very long history, this organ persists, but experiments have failed to reveal its function. In the purely aquatic forms it may have served as an eye, sensitive to movements and to light above the creature. At any rate, in the higher kinds of animals, the optical arrangement of the eye is lost and the opening in the bones of the skull is closed up. The structure is identifiable only as the pineal gland (a gland situated in the brain) which, in man, was considered by the early anatomists to be the seat of the soul.

THE REAL ADAM: A REPTILE THAT WAS FATHER OF HIS AGE

THE teeth in *Pareiasaurus*, like those in the amphibia we have already mentioned, were not confined to the margins of the jaws as in mammals, but extended over the palate as well. The animal was large and unwieldy, sometimes so much as ten feet long, and is thought to have been a vegetarian. Its heavy and awkward limbs had the elbows and knees stuck out from the body, so it must have walked with a wide but slow and ungainly stride. The feet were adapted for digging like a mole, so probably this animal dug about for its vegetable food.

Pareiasaurus belongs to the most primitive reptilian order, and is at the base of the whole family tree that produced various other reptiles, the birds, mammals, and man, so that in a way, we may regard it as a reptilian Adam, the remote father of us all. Although it is known from South Africa, other animals closely similar to it have been found in deposits in northern Russia and Scotland, while smaller related forms of a later date are known from Scotland, Switzerland and the United States of America.

The other interesting Permian reptile we must mention comes from Texas in the United States, and is known as *Dimetrodon*. It belongs to a different order of reptiles from *Pareiasaurus*, although in general build and size they were somewhat alike. *Dimetrodon* was a flesh-eater, however, as its conical and compressed teeth indicate, and had an alligator-like head and a body like a monitor.

The most remarkable feature in its make-up was the astonishing length to which the neural or dorsal spines of the vertebræ grew. One spine was often a straight rod, three feet long, while sometimes this rod had cross-pieces like the yards on a mast. These neural spines extending along the body must have been covered by a thin web of skin during life, and the purpose of this awkward structure is not clear. It is possible that it was a sexual characteristic, and that only the males were thus adorned.

Living at this same time and till the Upper Trias [1] in South Africa, Russia, Scotland, and North America were many varied animals related to *Dimetrodon* but rather different in structure. They are all grouped under the names of Anomodontia or "irregular toothed," or Theromorpha, "beast shaped," and consist of forms varying in size from that of a little lizard to a large dog. Some were purely land-living, others were aquatic. It is noticeable that in nearly all groups of animals, some forms persist in returning to the ancestral habitat of the waters.

While there is considerable variation in the teeth of these animals, as is indicated by the name Anomodont given above, one group with a head like a dog had remarkably mammal-like teeth. Instead of being constructed all on the same pattern as in most reptiles, the teeth of these creatures were differentiated into incisors, canines or eye-teeth, and the chewing teeth, pre-molars and molars. The only real difference, indeed, between these teeth and those of a mammal lay in the manner of their replacement, though it is possible that these reptiles had also only two sets of teeth during life. Like the mammals also, the skull had two condyles at the back for movement upon the neck. Many of the bones of the skeleton, too, were mammal-like.

We thus reach the conclusion that during the Trias age, when conditions were arid—always a stimulus to evolution—and the advantage was with the more adaptive and fast-moving types of animals, the mammals were evolved from the slower-moving, less efficient creatures. At a comparatively early stage in the development of the reptiles, therefore, the most significant feature of their history was accomplished.

This does not mean that the importance of the group dwindled in the immediately succeeding period, because, from the Trias [1] onwards till the close of the Cretaceous [1]

<hr>

[1] See table, p. 120.

some of the most remarkable creatures were evolved, per-fected, and lost again to flourish no more.

In Triassic times these forms were already well indicated. Already many had given up the struggle for existence on land and had returned to, and adapted themselves with great success in, the seas.

One such group was the Plesiosaurs, whose first forms we know from the Trias, and which became dominant during the Jurassic and the Cretaceous periods. In one of the early accounts of them, they were aptly described as being like " a snake threaded through the shell of a turtle." In type they were small-headed animals with a very long neck, a flattened, barrel-shaped body and a long tail with a small fin at its end. In size they varied from a few feet to thirty feet in length. Their remains have been found in England, America, Germany, Australia, and Africa—indeed, all over the world.

The small head had the margins of the jaws lined with sharp, conical teeth fixed in deep sockets. The eyes were large and, again, a pineal eye was present on top of the head. The long and slender neck was composed of many vertebræ, but appears to have been almost inflexible ; while the body was probably covered by smooth skin without any trace of armour.

For its swimming abilities, the animal did not depend on the sinuous movement of the fish or on the strength of the fins, but on the propulsion of its modified paddle-like limbs. Both the front and the hind limbs were of about equal size, and their construction bears ample testimony to the land-living habit of their ancestral form. All the ordinary limb and toe bones were present, though the joints of the toes had increased in number. The whole structure was strengthened by cartilage and covered with skin to form a powerful paddle.

While the soft structures of the body were protected above by the backbone and ribs, the flattened front or ventral sur-face was strengthened by the expanded plates of bone which supported the paddles, and by numerous rows of secondarily-developed abdominal ribs, the whole protective structure being not unlike the lower shell, or plastron, of a turtle.

MONSTERS OF THE SHALLOW WATERS

So far as we can gather, these grotesque sea-monsters roamed the shallower seas, feeding upon fish and especially upon cuttle fish, whose remains we actually find in the fossil-ised stomach-region. As the neck was comparatively immovable, we can only imagine that the prey was obtained through speed and the quick snapping movement of the jaws. From a few fossilised stomach contents that we have, we know that the plesiosaurs swallowed pebbles, consequently known as gastroliths or stomach-stones, whose function was to grind up the hard ingested matter and thus aid digestion. It would seem that like most other reptiles the plesiosaurs laid eggs, and that, though well enough adapted for life in the water, they had to return to land to lay their eggs, the inverse process to that we saw in the amphibians.

The fossilised remains are especially common in some geological horizons, and some of the specimens are truly enormous, with skulls six feet long. Thus we can clearly visualise these ancient monsters ploughing their way through the seas near land, playing havoc among the lesser kinds of creatures and probably occasionally attacking their own kind.

Living in the seas at the same time, but better adapted for marine life, were the " fish-lizards," or Ichthyosaurs. These equally well-known and numerous animals rivalled their contemporaries in size, but were of strikingly different appearance and habit. They were similar to porpoises or large fish. They had a long skull with narrow jaws containing sharp and ribbed conical teeth. The narrow skull had prominent eyes and a small third eye. The neck, in contrast to that of the plesiosaurs, was short, while the body was quite porpoise-like. It had a single, triangular, fleshy dorsal fin, and a tail with a large triangular tail fin, which was supported by the downwardly bent tail vertebræ. It is interesting to note that in fish with a similarly shaped tail the supporting vertebræ are turned sharply upwards.

As a modification for life in the sea, the nostrils were placed far back on the head and just in front of the eyes ; the latter, too, were protected by a ring of hard plates which were also of assistance in focussing. Whereas the sections of the plesiosaurian backbone were moderately long and tended towards inflexibility, the ichthyosaurs had very short centra and consequently considerable flexibility of body.

Swimming was still accomplished by paddles, but here the front limbs greatly exceeded the hind in size, and the paddles consisted of a mosaic of modified bones in a cartilage setting. The skin was smooth and unarmoured. The ichthyosaurs were therefore much more highly adapted for life in the seas, and must have been powerful swimmers and ferocious enemies.

THE CLUE OF THE UNBORN SKELETONS

FOR many years it has been known that the stomach cavities of these animals frequently contain the remains of little skeletons. At first it was naturally assumed that they were the remains of food, but a more complete and detailed examination of many specimens has proved that the species to which the little remains belong is always the same species as the " devouring " animal. Such reptiles can hardly be credited with preferring only their own very limited species as food, and the inevitable conclusion is that these little forms are not the remains of food but are the skeletons of embryos or unborn young. This conclusion has been greatly strengthened by recent discoveries and may, in fact, be taken as proved.

As the ichthyosaurs were thus not obliged to return to land to lay eggs, they enjoyed a much greater measure of freedom than the plesiosaurs, and are amongst the most successful of all the creations for water-living.

Towards the close of the Cretaceous [1] period, there came into being a group of marine reptiles which had a short geological history but were world-wide in distribution. Although confined to the period when the chalk was being deposited, remains have been found in Kent, Belgium, Holland, New Zealand, Nigeria, Canada, and in the United States. This group is known as the Mosasaurs, or " Meuse-reptiles," since the first specimens were found at Maastricht in the valley of the Meuse.

In appearance they were like lengthened ichthyosaurs or porpoises, with a reduced skeletal structure adapted to their marine habitat. Their somewhat fragile skull bore strong, recurved teeth not only on the margins of the jaws but on some of the palatal bones as well. Further, the connections between the jaw bones were loose, like those of snakes, so that bulky prey could be swallowed. Propulsion was effected by means of flattened lizard-like limbs used as paddles, but some forms may also have had the assistance of a long but narrow tail fin. The skin was probably smooth, but may have had a thin covering of scales.

Some mosasaurs grew to fifty feet or more in length. Their thin bodies, capable of high speed in the water, and their cruel teeth made them the most rapacious animals that have ever lived in the sea. They were, indeed, the sea-serpents *par excellence*, but have been long extinct for reasons we cannot guess.

[1] See table, p. 120.

A STRANGE AND SUDDEN DISAPPEARANCE

ALL these marine reptiles which lived so long and with such conspicuous success suddenly fade out of the picture at the close of the Cretaceous period. No new forms of any importance had been introduced to alter the tenor of their lives. For the whole of their time, they had suffered the competition of the fish without the least discomfort. Suddenly and for no explicable reason, except that they had had their day, they vanished from the world of living things merely to become a portion of geological history.

During their time, the crocodiles had also been developing and becoming comparatively abundant. The earlier crocodiles were more adapted for a marine life than the later and living forms. One important difference is that they lacked the secondary bony palate which enables the present-day crocodiles to drown their prey and yet breathe comfortably themselves. Unless, therefore, these earlier types were provided with some compensating fleshy structure of which all trace is lost in the fossils, their mode of life and feeding habits must have been different from those of their representatives to-day.

The later crocodiles are so closely akin to living forms that no mention need be made of them here, beyond pointing out that certain Indian forms of the Pliocene age grew to the enormous length of fifty feet.

While these swimming reptiles sported in the seas, the shadows of others of their relatives in another element no doubt fell upon them ; for at this time, reptiles, like many other vertebrate groups, attempted the conquest of the air. These flying reptiles are generally known as Pterodactyls (" wing fingers "), because the thin skin that served as a wing was attached to the greatly lengthened fifth finger.

The early pterodactyls were small, about the size of sparrows ; some had short tails, others had long ones. They are especially well known from the Lithographic Stone of Bavaria, where slabs of rock often reproduce with great clarity the delicate impressions of complete individuals.

Pterodactylus itself was a small animal like a thrush, with a long, bird-like skull set at right angles to the neck. The slender jaws were toothed. The arms were strongly developed compared with the legs, and the latter could not have been of much value for movement. The breast bone was keeled for the insertion of muscles, as in birds.

The wing-membrane consisted essentially of three parts : a little flap of skin between the forearm and the neck, a large area of this skin between the disproportionately strengthened " little " finger and the hind-leg, and a small area between the hind-legs. In some forms at least there are indications of bird-like habits, and a certain amount of flying in the strict sense may have been accomplished.   Others, it seems, only glided on wind currents.

A GIANT REPTILE THAT COULD NOT USE ITS FEET

LIVING at the same time as *Pterodactylus* was another genus of very similar nature known as *Rhamphorhynchus*.   It had, however, a long tail with a sort of little fin at the end. In its mouth were many slender teeth, but the front of the mouth was toothless and beaked.   Impressions of the wing-membrane have been found which show that it was smooth, and the body appears to have been quite smooth and un-armoured also.

The later pterodactyls, those of the Cretaceous period, were much larger than their predecessors.   The most notable form was *Pteranodon*, whose remains have been found in the Chalk of Kansas, U.S.A.   This animal had a large skull with long but toothless jaws.   The fore-limbs were enormously developed and the span from wing-tip to wing-tip was no less than eighteen feet.   The long beak in the head was counterbalanced by a strong bony process on the back of the skull, and to this process it is thought the muscles actuating the wing-fingers were attached.   Apart from the great fifth finger, the hand had three little fingers with claws.   The hind-legs were absurdly small when contrasted with the front limbs, and must have been too weak to support the creature.   Certainly these pterodactyls could not have walked about like modern flying birds.

The bones are remarkably light in weight and construction, but when we try to arrange the mental picture of the life of these larger flying reptiles, we come up against some pretty problems.   How and where did they live, and how did they catch their food ?   We have seen that most of them seem to have been poor fliers and to have been mainly wind-gliders : we see, too, that the hind-legs could hardly have served for walking ; so that obviously the life of pterodactyls was not at all like that of most birds.

We can only assume that forms like *Pteranodon* launched themselves off from a cliff in a favourable wind and glided over the water where they caught fish. What happened when they landed on the water, as they must occasionally have done, and were becalmed, we do not know. The fragile wing-tip, too, would easily be broken in contact with the choppy seas.

But at any rate that is how they must have lived ; floating on the air streams, perching on the rocks, finding food in the seas or amongst their flying fellows, the insects. Like so many of the other reptilian groups, they disappeared without descendants or survivors at the end of the Cretaceous period.

MONARCHS FOR A HUNDRED MILLION YEARS: THE DINOSAURS

AT the same time as the flying reptiles, the ichthyosaurs and the plesiosaurs, there lived, mainly on land but occasionally in the rivers and lagoons, some of the most remarkable animals the world has ever seen. These were the Dinosaurs, who dominated the world for something like a hundred million years. When we remember that man has been dominant for a mere million or so, we can realize something of the kingship that the dinosaurs enjoyed.

The earliest dinosaurs, evolved from a stem which gave rise both to the crocodiles and to the birds, made their bow in the early Trias.[1] Originally they were probably small and leaping creatures, and the most primitive walked habitually upon the hind-legs, using the front merely for feeding or while resting. The bipedal forms are divisible into two kinds, those that lived upon flesh and those that were vegetarians. It is interesting to note that the first dinosaurs ever discovered and described were these bipedal kinds and that the discoveries were made in England by Englishmen just over a hundred years ago.

The earliest of the bipeds were smallish, hopping or jumping creatures, and while some remained comparatively small throughout the history of the whole group, others became large. *Iguanodon*, well known from the Wealden rocks of the South of England and from Belgium, was herb-eating, subsisting on the tree fronds. It was about fourteen feet high and over twenty feet long, measured along the backbone.

The fore-limbs were less stout than the hind and were adapted for grasping, while the thumb was a bony spike, useful for digging off branches from trees as well as in defence or attack. The strong hind-legs supported the body, and the three-toed feet, formed rather like those of birds, have

[1] See table, p. 120.

Dinosaurus
(Styracosaurus)

Iguanodon

Diplodocus

THE "TERRIBLE REPTILES" OF THE REMOTE PAST

The enormous size of these pre-human Dinosaurs can be gauged from the six-foot man drawn to scale beside them.

left footprints which are not uncommonly found. The tail was flattened from side to side and may have been used in swimming, an advantage when rapacious carnivores had often to be avoided.

A CREATURE WITH TWO THOUSAND TEETH

AMONG the American grass-eating bipeds one of the most notable is *Trachodon*, a dinosaur similar in general build and appearance to *Iguanodon*, but having a duck-billed skull and webbed fingers. There is no doubt that *Trachodon* was adapted as a swimmer. From a mummified skeleton found in the United States, we know the impression of the skin and that it consisted of tuberculated areas[1] in a definitely arranged pattern which seems to indicate that the back was darker than the belly.

The jaws of *Trachodon* are remarkable for the number of teeth, which approached two thousand. All these teeth could not be used at once, but the tooth rows consisted of several lines of compactly arranged teeth which gradually became worn and discarded, while by an imperceptible escalator-like movement the new teeth grew up into position. Apparently these animals lived on horsetails and coarse grass with a high content of silica.

Many forms closely related to *Trachodon* became very curiously modified in the skull. The growth of the nasal bones seem to have run riot, and bony structures like spikes, helmets, and cockscombs developed, but all were hollow and communicated with the nostrils so that they were perhaps adaptations or consequences of living a good deal in the water.

HOW THE "TERRIBLE REPTILE" LIVED UP TO ITS NAME

THE flesh-eating dinosaurs do not appear to have been at all aquatic and contented themselves with life on land. Many of them attained huge size, and with their cruel teeth and rapacious habits justified the name of " terrible-reptile " which the word dinosaur signifies.

The commonest English and the oldest-known form is *Megalosaurus* (" large-reptile ") whose remains, generally only fragmentary, have been found in many parts of England as well as abroad. In size these creatures were from ten to about

---

[1] Tuberculated areas are areas covered with little tubercles of thick skin. We assume that these carry pigment and indicate a colour pattern.

twenty feet long, with a skull measuring just about twelve inches. The teeth were sharp, flattened from side to side, and the fore and back edges were notched like a saw. The strong hind-legs and three-toed feet suggest a nimble habit on the track of prey. The skin was probably quite unarmoured.

In America a form closely similar to *Megalosaurus* was living at the same time, but it differed in having a large horn on the nose, from which it has been given the name *Ceratosaurus*, " horned reptile."

The two-footed flesh-eating forms attained their maximum in the Cretaceous period, in the guise of the truly terrifying *Tyrannosaurus* (" tyrant-reptile "). This enormous creature, forty feet from nose to tail end, had a skull four feet long and a mouth full of sabre-like teeth six inches high. The strong hind-legs contrasted markedly with the feeble front limbs with their small but specialised hands. Although this is the largest animal of prey that has ever existed, it must have been an awkward even though a powerful creature. However richly endowed it was physically, it was of low brain power, both quantitatively and qualitatively. Immense and dreadful as it was, it could no doubt easily be defeated by the much smaller mammals of to-day.

FOUR-FOOTED VEGETARIANS, GIGANTIC AND GROTESQUE

IT is curious that some time in the Trias, both the grass-eating and the flesh-eating bipeds gave rise to quadrupedal or four-footed forms. These flourished particularly in the Jurassic and Cretaceous periods, and many were gigantic and grotesque. The carnivorous bipeds' four-footed relatives were huge, unarmoured, water-living vegetarians. In the quiet waters of rivers and estuaries, they lived and moved, feeding upon the floating water-weed. In this environment, safety from enemies was assured, and the placid life was one suited to the encouragement of great size. From all over the world, we know the remains of these amphibious dinosaurs, or Sauropods, which prove them to have attained truly gigantic dimensions. *Diplodocus*, a well-known American amphibious dinosaur, attained a length of eighty-five feet.

The head of *Diplodocus* was small and the nostrils were joined in a common opening *on top* of the head. The teeth were pencil-like and confined to the front of the jaws, so that they formed a kind of rake to pull in the water-weed. The whole skull was only about the size of that of a horse and looks very inadequate for the long neck, the great elephantine body, and the very long tail.

There is no doubt that, immersed in the waters of lakes, lagoons, and estuaries, these creatures would stand with heads erect, perhaps thirty feet or more from the bottom, and so long as the nostril opening was over the surface of the water, they were not only safe but comfortable, because their burden of flesh was eased by the water's buoyancy. They probably did not require an immense amount of food, as they were cold-blooded and without the energy requirements of present-day forms. They laid eggs, too, apparently, and laid them on land. For this purpose, therefore, and to change from lagoon to lagoon, they would occasionally leave the water and lumber awkwardly over the land.

In North and South America, in Africa, Australia, India, and in England, other remains have been found. Some forms were taller than, but not quite so long as, *Diplodocus*, others were somewhat smaller, but all were the nightmarish creations of a " lost world," creatures of a mechanical complexity that we shall not be likely to see again.

One point of great interest is the fact that these quadruped dinosaurs, both amphibious and armoured, possessed unusual developments in the arrangement of their nerves. While the brain in most of them was ridiculously small and lowly organised, the spinal column in the region of the hip girdle was greatly swollen and formed a kind of second brain. While the brain proper was concerned with sight, smell, hearing, etc., this second brain controlled the movements of the heavy limbs and tail. Despite their complexity in this direction, they were not intelligent creatures, and were totally unfitted for change of environment and alteration of habit. When, therefore, uplift movement of the land, and a consequent draining of lakes, etc., occurred towards the close of the Jurassic period, all the sauropods of the northern hemisphere died out.

The four-footed relatives of the grass-eating bipeds were also vegetarians but sought protection from their enemies in armour. The early forms, such as *Stegosaurus* from America and *Scelidosaurus* in England, had merely rows of plates or scutes upon the back. Some specimens of *Stegosaurus* (plated-reptile) were over twenty feet long and over five feet high at the hips. Here again there is evidence of slender cerebral organisation, but accessory brains were developed strongly in the spinal cord at the hips and slightly in the shoulder region.

LIVING "TANKS": THE IMPREGNABLE "THORNY" REPTILES

OTHER and later forms became armoured like armadillos; they became, in fact, mobile "tanks" armoured with bone instead of steel. The thick skull, the neck with its protective collar of bone, and the segmented cuirass of bony plates and spikes on the body suggest that when attacked the animal merely lay close to the ground and became an impregnable armoured citadel. Such a specimen, called the "thorny reptile" or *Scolosaurus*, is excellently preserved in the British Museum (Natural History). It is about eighteen feet long and walked with bent elbows and knees, keeping the body close to the ground.

There was another kind of armoured dinosaur which, instead of having a plated body, had a bony skull with horns. These Ceratopsia ("horned-faces") were remarkably rhinoceros-like but were sometimes larger, as much as twenty-five feet long. The earliest dinosaurs of this sort that we know came from the Lower Cretaceous deposits of Mongolia, where nests of eggs and skeletons of young were also discovered. These creatures were small, with a beaked skull and a simple scaffolding of bone from the back of the skull over the neck, to hold the muscles for the heavy jaws.

Gradually, in different geological deposits in North America, we can trace the development of larger types where the simple structure over the neck has become a great bony and protective shield. The climax was obtained in the great *Triceratops*, with its three-horned head, a horn over each eye and one on the nose. Here the skull alone was six feet long, but it was controlled by a brain smaller than a man's clenched fist. A bird-like toothless beak was in front of the mouth, and with this the animal cropped the vegetation on the leafy glades near the Cretaceous streams. When attacked, it had only to stand fast with lowered head, so that the attacker was in danger of being impaled on the three-feet long horns.

These then were some of the dinosaurs, kings of all the continents for a hundred million years; yet at the close of the Cretaceous period they were gone, with most of their fellow reptiles of the sea and air, charmed away by an unknown Pied Piper, to lie in their rocky fastness till Man could come and unravel their long story. When they were gone, the world was given over to the few groups of reptiles whose survivors constitute the reptiles of to-day, and to the birds and mammals which, now unchecked, flourished and evolved to give the dominant faunas of the present.

THE COMING OF THE BIRDS

Fossils of birds are rare until comparatively recent times, when we see them to be closely related to the living forms. We have a few examples in the fossil record, however, from the long time that elapsed between their first appearance in the Jurassic and the appearance of the modernised kinds. The earliest and most interesting one we know is called *Archæopteryx*, and is known by skeletons in London and Berlin and by a tail in Munich. Fortunately these were preserved in a limestone of such fine grain that we know many details of their structure. At first sight, it seems that this was a flying reptile rather than a bird, for it has teeth in the jaws, three-clawed fingers in the wings, and a long but not tufty tail. It differed from the reptiles however by the quality of its brain and by having feathers. The tail was formed of a series of twenty vertebræ each bearing a pair of feathers.

Of the later flying birds, those of the Cretaceous period, we have occasional evidence. From the Cretaceous deposits of Kansas, we know of a little bird called *Ichthyornis*, while from the Eocene remains of Nigeria we have the breastbone of a bird that must have had a wing span of twenty feet—the largest known to us. A large swimming bird of the Cretaceous, named *Hesperornis*, was probably three or four feet long. The Cretaceous birds still had teeth, and some of their London Clay (Eocene) successors had tooth-like serrations on the jaws.

NATURE RUNS RIOT: THE HUGE AND GROTESQUE MAMMALS

At the closing stages of the Age of Reptiles and the time of primitive, toothed birds, the mammals were slowly but surely evolving. During that time they must have been numerous but unobtrusive, for though we have seen that they came from their ancestral reptilian stock during the aridity of the Trias, it is not until much later, in the Jurassic period, and then only rarely, that we find their remains in any number. Examination of these early forms shows that many of them were marsupials—that is, animals that carry their young in their pouches—whose protected and isolated descendants constitute the animal population peculiar to Australia to-day.

The great era of the mammals is the Tertiary, comprising the Eocene, Oligocene, Miocene, Pliocene, and Pleistocene, but as the last two of these are concerned essentially with Man, we may concentrate on the earlier times. However scarce or unenterprising the Cretaceous mammals may have been, the same cannot by any means be said of their successors in the Eocene, for here we have numerous large forms of grotesque appearance and herbivorous habits which strongly remind us of the dinosaurs. Here again the constructive powers of Nature ran riot and produced great horny skulls and other modifications which seem to be the death warrant of the creatures they adorn.

"TERRIBLE-HORN": A GIANT WITH ITS WEAPONS ON ITS FACE

ONE of these mammals was called *Dinoceras* ("terrible-horn"). It had a body larger than a rhinoceros and almost as big as an elephant, supported on pillar-like legs with five-toed stumpy feet. The large skull was very curiously ornamented with three pairs of horns. The first pair was on the nose, the second pair stood in front of the eyes, while the third was on top of the brain-case. The last two pairs were connected by bony ridges and formed a basin-shaped depression on top of the skull. In life these horns would be covered with skin something like those of a giraffe. The teeth were small and adapted for the succulent vegetation of the well-watered lowlands, but the males possessed long, dagger-like fangs which must have been for fighting and which were protected by flanges on the lower jaw.

Dinoceras comes from the Middle Eocene deposits found at Wyoming, and a very similar but larger form called *Tinoceras* is known from the same locality. These and related animals are placed in a group called the Amblypoda, or "blunt-feet" and were hoofed, or ungulate. Although specialised and large, they had very small brains. They paralleled many of the dinosaurs, and, like them, soon became extinct. Brain is always more important than brawn, and they were inadaptive creatures.

A curiously-skulled mammal of the Oligocene times was the great, horned *Arsinoitherium* of Egypt. This animal was in some ways related to the Amblypoda, but it had a larger brain and teeth adapted to a less juicy diet, and had no great incisors. The skull had two pairs of horns ; one small pair over the eyes, and an enormous pair developed from the nose bones in front of the eyes. Both these horn structures were really hollow horn-cores and were sheathed during life with true horn which probably increased their size. *Arsinoitherium* played the part in that ancient world that the rhinoceros plays now, and there is little doubt that it had the same sort of habits.

Other curious forms of somewhat later date were also rhinoceros mimics and were confined to South America. Large in size, about nine feet long, they had heavy bodies, feet modified for living on and travelling over the pampas, and heavy skulls with extraordinary ever-growing and powerful teeth adapted for cutting and grinding up the plant food. *Toxodon* is a typical example which is exhibited in the British Museum (Natural History).

Another interesting group, also Miocene and later in age, is the Chalicotheres, whose remains have been found in Africa, America, and Asia. They are related in some degree to the horses, and are quite well known in such forms as *Moropus*. This peculiar animal shared the features of the ground sloth and the horse. It had clawed feet, suitable for digging up such plants and roots as it fed upon ; its head was like that of a horse and its front legs were distinctly longer than the hind ones.

ANIMALS THAT HAVE DESCENDED TO THE FARMYARD: PIGS AND HORSES

AT the same time there were living a great number of mammals, grass-eating and flesh-eating, whose descendants are the kinds we know to-day. The grass-eating ones were pigs, some of which grew to a considerable size, rhinoceroses, antelopes, okapis, and smallish three-toed horses, of which we must write later. The carnivorous mammals that preyed upon them were wolves, hyænas, bears, and the sabre-toothed cats. Most of these forms were so much like those we know to-day that there is no need to discuss them. The sabre-toothed cats, however, are not so well known, and their common name is rather misleading.

They were not true cats, but only related to them, and they were certainly not tigers, the name often applied to them. Equal to a lion in size, but of slightly heavier build and with shorter and stouter limbs, *Machærodus*, a typical representative, possessed an unusually powerful neck and two tremendous fangs in the upper jaw. These fangs were like sabres, wide and thin, and had faint saw-like markings on the hinder margin. Their use is something of a mystery, for although we know that the jaws opened very widely, they cannot have opened so widely as to allow these fangs to be used like ordinary teeth. Most probably they were used to tear the flesh and cut the blood-vessels of the victim—to kill, and to reduce the food to the proper size.

This fauna, diverse in characters and widespread over Europe and Asia, continued to flourish greatly until the close of the Pliocene. Then it passed slowly southwards into Africa, where much of it, a little modified, remains. Its place in the North was occupied by true horses and true elephants, and by many kinds of deer, about which something must now be said.

THE HORSE'S LITTLE FIVE-TOED ANCESTORS

THE evolution of both the horses and the elephants makes fascinating stories which have often been told. It is hardly correct to call them evolutionary stories because, though we know most of the stages, a great many links are not in our possession.

The horses of to-day have specialised teeth and hoofed feet which are composed of only one toe. If we go right back in the records of the Tertiary age, we can gradually see a series in which progressive alteration of the tooth structure and reduction of the number of toes has taken place. In the Eocene, for example, the first-recognised horse forms appear to have been little animals the size of foxes. Like most of the other Eocene hoofed-creatures, they were five-toed, and their appearance and structure would make it difficult to think of them as being related to the horses at all were it not for the fact that we know of intervening, later forms.

In the related forms of the Upper Eocene and later ages, we see that not only are the animals becoming larger in size but that they are changing the form and shape of the teeth, which are becoming suited to a less succulent diet. The toes are only three in number, and the side ones are gradually seen losing their connection with the ground.

In the Pliocene age, a genus named *Hipparion* was widely established, for fossilised remains are known from England,

France, Germany, Spain, Italy, India, Greece and Persia. *Hipparion*, though not quite so large as the typical modern species, was in all essentials a true horse, but it had a toe on each side of the main, or middle, toe. Gradually these side-toes disappeared, becoming the mere splints of bone we know in the living horse.

The true, one-toed, horse is of Lower Pleistocene age, and first appears in such widely separated places as Norfolk, Central France, and North America. To-day the wild horses are found only in Africa and Asia, while the North American ones are extinct. The distribution of horses is now man-made, the result of domestication, and the American horses now living have been transported there.

HOW THE ELEPHANT BEGAN: AN ANCIENT EGYPTIAN FOREBEAR

THE elephants now to be found in Africa and India are similarly the results of a long Tertiary evolution. They appear to be descended from an animal like a tapir, which lived in the Fayum in Egypt during the earlier Oligocene times, one of the primitive hoofed animals not so distantly related to the original ancestor of the horses. This animal is named *Mœritherium* and, although in general features there is no similarity between its skull and that of the elephant, the position of the nostrils suggests that a short proboscis was already developed. In both the upper and lower jaws, the second incisor teeth are very strongly developed, forming little tusks which stretch forwards and so prolong the jaws.

The next stage is seen in an animal known as *Palæomastodon*, which is larger than *Mœritherium* and already approaches the bulk of a small elephant. The skull and jaws show a similar advancement, the main features being the reduction of the nasal bones and retreat of the nostril opening, the lengthening of the incisors or tusks, and the presence of spongy bone in the back of the skull. The incisors of the lower jaw come together to form a shovel-like extension, and the molar teeth in the jaws have three transverse ridges. The next advance is to be found in *Trilophodon*, from the Miocene and Pliocene deposits of the northern hemisphere. Here the appearance and structure are much more like those of the true elephant. The air cells in the skull have become greatly increased, so that the skull is flat and somewhat domed. The upper and lower tusks are enormous and the great lower jaw projects far in front of

[After Lull]

THE EVOLUTION OF THE HORSE

the upper. The teeth in the jaws have also become modified, for the skull of the adult has no pre-molars as the two molars completely fill the available room. Sometimes indeed there is only one molar. These molars are large, and the last has often so many as five ridges. The shovel tusk arrangement of the lower jaw was no doubt used for digging up vegetable food.

The next stage is *Tetralophodon*, found in Germany. The skull is much like that of the preceding form, but the teeth are more complicated in structure, and the lower jaw does not project so far in front of the upper. The lower tusks, too, are not close together and the fleshy proboscis would therefore hang down and probably was a real trunk, able to reach the ground, a feat the lower jaw was no longer able to perform. Then in *Stegodon* we reach the true elephants, for the lower incisors are lost and only the upper ones, the tusks, remain. The lower jaw is quite short, but the teeth are complex with many ridges.

Since the Pliocene period, many kinds of true elephants have lived and are known quite fully. The famous mammoth, of which complete specimens have been found in the frozen soil of Siberia, was a gigantic form with enormous curved tusks. Its teeth are commonly found and are really a series of compressed plates, the development of the ridges referred to in the earlier genera. Of all these elephantine forms only two, the African and the Indian, are present-day representatives.

The latest animals found in fossil form are mostly allied to, if not identical with, the living ones, and only the geographical distribution is changed.

In all these animals, we see that reaction to environment has been an outstanding factor, and only when we come to the highest of the mammals, Man, do we find one capable of altering conditions to suit his own limitations. So, the advent of Man, probably in Pliocene times, not only profoundly affected the contemporary and later faunas and flora, but modified some of the age-long natural laws as well.

WHAT TO READ NEXT

THERE are some fascinating and instructive books about animal life in prehistoric times and its remains, both for recreational reading and for practical assistance to the fossil hunter. Those who wish to follow up this article would do well to begin with Professor J. W. Gregory's *Geology* (one of

Dent's *Scientific Primers*), which is a simple and general introduction to Geology and the study of fossils for the beginner. *An Introduction to Palæontology* by A. Morley Davies (Murby) is an excellent general survey suitable for the amateur and specialist. A more specialised and entirely systematic work, very useful to the student, is *Palæontology* by E. Woods (Cambridge University Press). These three books deal principally with fossils of the invertebrate animals, although *An Introduction to Palæontology* includes a chapter on those with backbones.

Among the books that deal with the vertebrate fossils, the reader would do well to study the Natural History Museum's *Guide to the Fossil Mammals* which, although essentially a guide book, is written in general terms to suit the visitor. It gives a clear idea of the relationships between the different fossil mammals. *Vertebrate Palæontology* by A. S. Romer (University of Chicago Press) is perhaps the best general book on the subject. It is suitable both for the interested amateur and the serious student.

Another of the Natural History Museum's guide books, W. E. Swinton's *Guide to Fossil Birds, Reptiles and Amphibians*, can be used as an elementary text-book. *Monsters of Primeval Days*, by the same author, contains a series of twenty-four half-tone plates, illustrating fossil reptiles and mammals as they lived. Each plate is faced by a page of simple explanatory notes, and a short general account of the subject is given in the preface. W. E. Swinton's *The Dinosaurs* (Murby) is the only book on this subject, and is intended for both the layman and the student. It deals with every aspect of this great group of fossil animals.

NATURE'S SUPREME TRIUMPH:
THE HUMAN MACHINE

by THOMAS ARMSTRONG, M.A. (Cantab.)

*T*HE study of Anatomy is the study of the architecture of
the human body. It is the study of how the house is built
and what its walls are made of. It does not tell us how
it works, or any of the intimate details of the family circle that
lives inside it. This is left to Physiology. However, when an
architect builds a house, he must be certain that it will not
collapse on its inmates, and for this he must know many things
about the materials he is using, and how best they can be put
together in order that each may be used to the best advantage.

Anatomy by itself is only the study of the geography of the
body, but we shall find it much more interesting if we do not
confine ourselves strictly to this, but always keep in mind the
use and "team work" of each organ that we study. The intimate
family affairs, however, we will leave to the next section on
Physiology.

LET us start with the bones or skeleton, without which we
should collapse into an indeterminate mass of jelly. The
bones serve several purposes, for they are not only used to
keep us rigid and to support our weight, but also as levers
upon which the muscles can work so that we can move about
and do all that we want to do. The two essentials that an
engineer would require in a support and a lever would be
lightness and strength, and it will be found that this holds
good in the body, for most of our bones are hollow tubes,
the outside of which is hard like ivory while the inside contains a substance which is used for making blood. Nature is
never wasteful of space. Lightness and strength are combined, therefore, for everyone knows that it is almost as
difficult to bend a hollow steel tube as to bend a solid rod of
steel which would weigh perhaps six times as much, while
it would certainly not be six times as strong.

Each bone must be movable and must be moved with the
least possible amount of difficulty. To accomplish this, the
ends of the bones that are jointed are covered with a very
smooth substance called cartilage, while between the two

380

cartilage-covered ends of the bones lies a small space which is filled by fluid that serves the purpose of " oiling the bearings." Sometimes when the joint is damaged, this fluid collects and distends the joint and the familiar condition of " water on the knee " is found.

A joint must not only be freely movable but it must also be strong and must not be easily dislocated. Therefore between the two bone ends are strong bands of ligaments which prevent the bone ends being separated, because they are made of tissue which will not stretch unless subjected to enormous force. The ligaments are collected together so that they form a sort of sleeve for the joint, which is thus converted into a closed cavity from which the joint fluid cannot escape.

Each joint is made specially for some particular purpose. Some, like the shoulder where free movement is necessary, have had to increase their power of movement at the expense of their strength, whereas others, like the joints in the spine where only the smallest movement is allowable, have become immensely strong.

Movement between the bones is effected by the muscles. Each muscle is firmly attached to the bone on each side of a joint. If the muscle contracts or becomes shorter, its two points of attachment will be brought closer together and therefore the joint will be moved. The muscles are used for two purposes, one of which is to move the joints and the other to keep them still and rigid and to prevent movement when the limb is being used as a support.

Let us take for example the knee joint, which is used chiefly for supporting the body when we are standing. If the muscles at the back of the knee contract, the knee will be bent, while if those in front contract, the knee will be straightened. If, however, both contract at the same time, not only will no movement take place but the knee will be made into a perfectly rigid support, just as if the knee joint did not exist and the two bones were continuous.

THE LEG: A TRIUMPH OF ENGINEERING

THE legs must be capable of sufficient strength to support the body, they must be movable to allow walking and running, and they must have some " spring " in them to prevent jarring of the delicate mechanisms of the body when, for example, a jump is made. Let us start at the foot and work upwards.

If the skeleton of the human foot is examined, it will be found to consist of a large number of small bones closely held together by very strong ligaments. These bones are so arranged that they form a series of arches, all of which are capable of being slightly flattened out if weight is put upon them, by virtue of the slight amount of movement allowed at each joint. It is this power of being slightly flattened out and then returning to their original shape that gives our feet the " spring " that protects our nervous systems from excessive jolting.

There is an arch which runs along the inner border of the foot from the heel to the big toe, another on the other side of the foot from the heel to the little toe, and a third which runs across the middle of the foot transversely. This last is only half an arch and is made into a complete arch by the other foot when both are placed together side by side.

In order to prevent the arch from falling in and its good effects being abolished, Nature has been most ingenious in her provisions and has worked according to the best engineering principles. First, she has so arranged the shape of the bones that they fit closely one into the other like the bricks on the lower surface of a bridge. Secondly, she has fixed very strong ligaments, incapable of stretching, between the bones forming the arch. The important thing is that these are situated on the *under* surface of the arch where they are most useful in preventing its collapse, and not on the upper surface where they could do no useful work.

Thirdly, a "tie," composed of muscles and ligaments, has been fixed to the pillars of the arch, preventing their separation and the collapse of the superstructure. Fourthly, and last, two straps composed of the tendons of two muscles have been passed under the keystone of the arch in order to hold it up. These two muscles come down to the foot from the back of the leg so that they work to the best possible mechanical advantage.

It will be noted that much of the power of the arches to withstand strain depends on the muscles which are always exerting a slight pull upon them. This continual action of the muscles is known as " tone." If by any chance the muscles become weak or exhausted by a bad attitude in standing (as, for example, when the toes are turned out), they may be incapable of holding the arch up, when the ligaments, after a time, will stretch and the condition known as flat foot will develop. Of course, the proper way to cure such a condition is not by wearing specially built shoes, but by making the muscles more efficient by exercise.

THE HINGE THAT ALLOWS US TO BEND OUR LEGS

THE only movement that is necessary, or indeed desirable, at the knee joint is one in which the lower part of the leg moves forward and backward on the thigh like a hinge. Sideways movement must be avoided at all costs and the joint must be very strong. Sideways movement is prevented by the shape of the bones and by very strong ligaments which lie on each side of the joint. The ligament in front has a large, flat circular bone developed in it, upon which we kneel. The ligament behind is not so strong, for it has little strain to bear.

Inside the joints there are two very strong ligamentous bands which cross one another at right angles, and they are specially adapted so that, although they prevent dislocation under almost all circumstances, they still allow the hinge movement to take place. The upper surface of the tibia, which is the lower bone, is almost flat, and in order to make this more cup-shaped and the joint more stable, two flat, circular rings of cartilage with a hole in the centre and with their outer edges thicker than their inner edges have been placed between the bone ends. Sometimes, as in a "missed kick" at football, a little piece of one of these cartilages becomes broken off and sticks in an awkward place inside the joint, preventing all movement. This is the torn cartilage that is such a common accident of the football field.

WHY MAN CAN WALK ON TWO LEGS

THE upper end of the thigh bone is formed into an almost completely circular globe, covered with smooth, shining cartilage. This globe fits exactly into a perfect cup, which is situated on the outer side of the hip bone or pelvis. This joint is one of the most important in the body, for it is by means of this very strong but yet movable joint that the erect attitude has been made possible in man, as opposed to walking on all fours as most of the animals do. This has been achieved by fitting the ball into a very deep socket and by placing a very strong ligament which is nearly a quarter of an inch thick on the front of the joint between the hip and thigh bones. This prevents the thigh being bent backwards. If, therefore, the muscles at the back of the hip contract, they will have to work in opposition to this ligament and, when balance between them has been made, the hip joint will be immovable and the body weight will be carried with the least amount of difficulty.

In the work she requires of us in standing, Nature has again been most economical. The ability to stand has indeed been man's great salvation, for it enabled him to use and develop his hands for other things besides being walked upon. The original use which was made of his hands was for climbing trees, but once this was accomplished, many other uses were readily found, and it has been said that it was this that led to the enormous development of the human brain as compared with that of the lower animals.

The hip bone or pelvis is in two halves, which when fitted together form a basin. In front the two halves meet one another in a joint, but behind the lower part the spine comes between, and between each hip bone and the spine there is a joint. Here the requirements of the joints are quite different from those in the limbs, for great strength is required while movement, except to a minimum degree, is most undesirable. What is wanted is stability. To suit these principles, the joints have been modified and the ligaments are enormously strong, while the cartilaginous surfaces of the bones which were smooth in the limb to diminish friction, are here roughened to increase it. The joints between the lower part of the spine and the pelvic bones are very neatly contrived, for the spine, which transmits the body weight, is wedge-shaped in its lower part and fits into the wedge-shaped socket formed by the two pelvic bones. The weight of the body will, therefore, tend to drive the wedge further into the socket.

Within reasonable limits, therefore, the greater the weight to be borne the more stable does the joint become. The pelvis is one of man's great difficulties, for through it his head must pass during birth. Owing to the large size of the human head, which results from the growth of the brain, birth is made very difficult, and in some rare cases impossible, because the pelvis is too small to allow the head to pass. Nature allows for this, however, for she softens the ligaments at the joints we have mentioned and allows the surfaces to separate before the birth of the child takes place.

The muscles lying in the pelvis are of extreme interest, for when man was a four-footed animal, his body lay horizontally and certain muscles in his pelvis were used for moving the lower part of his spine, which was, of course, his tail. When he learnt to stand, however, he was in extreme danger, for he possessed nothing in his pelvis which was capable of preventing his intestines falling through it. He soon learnt, however, to control them with the muscles that originally wagged his tail, and these have now been formed into a complete diaphragm which closes the outlet of the pelvis and holds up the viscera.

THE SPINAL COLUMN: A SHOCK ABSORBER FOR THE BRAIN

THE main function of the spine is to support the head and to act as a shock absorber to prevent jarring of the brain and the spinal cord. It also forms a tube which protects the delicate nervous elements of the spinal cord from injury. In the child the vertebral column is composed of thirty-three separate bones, but in the adult, the lowest four vertebræ, which were originally the tail, have become fused together to form the coccyx and the next five have joined together to form the sacrum.

In the adult, therefore, there are twenty-six separate bones. Each bone is joined to the one above and below it by a thick disc composed of gristle, which acts as a shock absorber. The discs are so thick that altogether they form nearly one-quarter of the whole length of the spinal column. Each vertebra is connected with its neighbour by ligaments so that very little movement is allowed at each joint, although when all the movements are added together, the possible movement of the spine as a whole is very considerable.

When viewed as a whole, the spine will be found to have several curves in its different regions. The neck has a convexity forwards, the chest is concave forwards, the region of the abdomen has a convexity forwards and the sacrum is hollowed out towards the front. Again the reason for this is to prevent jarring, for it enables the vertebral column to coil and uncoil like a spring in bearing the weight of the head and shoulders.

Each vertebra is shaped like a ring, the front of the ring being much larger than the back and forming a body which articulates (i.e. is connected by a joint) with the one above and below it. There are also small joints between the back of the rings. All these rings together form a tube in which is contained a continuation of the brain known as the spinal cord. Between each vertebra there is a small hole through which nerves leave or enter the cord. Delicate ligaments stretch from the side of the cord and connect it with the insides of the vertebral tube, while the cavity is filled with a fluid called the cerebro-spinal fluid. Both these mechanisms act as a buffer and prevent jarring.

BONES WHICH FORM A CLOSED BOX

As can be seen from a glance at a picture of the skeleton, the ribs are long, flat, curved bones which are connected by joints with the vertebral column behind and in front with the sternum or breast bone. Only the upper seven ribs are articulated (or jointed) directly with the sternum, for the lowest two have their front ends free and are known as " floating " ribs, while the remaining three have their front ends attached to one another and to the sternum by long pieces of cartilage.

It is important to notice the direction of the ribs, which is downwards and forwards, for this gives the whole clue as to how they work. Taken as a whole the ribs, sternum and spine form a closed box which is called the thorax. The intervals between the ribs are filled with muscles which are capable of varying the capacity of the chest and thus make breathing possible. The interior of the thorax is filled with the heart and great vessels and with the lungs, which may be compared to a sponge filled with air. If the capacity of the chest is increased by the action of the muscles, the lungs must also expand and increase in size to fill the now greater thoracic cavity. In so doing they suck air in through the nose and down the windpipe or trachea.

It will be seen, therefore, that the essential thing in breathing is to make the capacity of the chest greater. This is done by the muscles which lie between the ribs, for their action is to raise the ribs and especially their front ends, together with the sternum. If the front ends of the ribs, which lie normally lower than their posterior ends, are raised, the distance from the front of the chest to the back is increased and so the size of the chest cavity is also increased. At the same time the muscles turn the lower edges of the ribs outwards so that again the capacity of the chest is increased.

The rising of the ribs is not the only way in which the capacity of the chest is increased, for there is a great sheet of muscle, called the diaphragm, which is fixed in a circle all the way round the lower part of the thorax and separates it from the abdomen. When this muscle contracts it pulls itself downwards out of the thorax into the abdomen, thus increasing the depth of the chest from top to bottom. This is the whole mechanism of respiration reduced to its simplest terms.

HOW OUR SHOULDERS ARE KEPT APART

THE collar bone or clavicle is long and nearly straight and acts as a strut, preventing the shoulders from passing inwards towards the midline. In some of the very rare cases where these bones are absent the two shoulders, if pulled forwards, can be made to meet together in the front of the chest. The inner end of the clavicle articulates with the upper end of the breast bone which has already been mentioned, while its outer end is in contact with the shoulder blade or scapula. This bone is flat and lies on the back of the upper part of the thorax. Although there is no joint between it and the chest wall, it is capable of moving upwards or downwards and it can slide forwards, thus enormously increasing the mobility of the shoulder. At the outer end of the scapula is a shallow cup-shaped depression covered with cartilage, which forms a joint with the humerus (the bone which forms the upper part of the arm).

The shoulder joint is of the ball-and-socket variety, but unlike the hip joint, where great stability is desirable and the cup is exceedingly deep, here the cup is shallow in order to increase the possible movement. Of course this means that the joint is relatively weak and in practice it is the joint which is most frequently dislocated. However, Nature has been very careful, for above the joint are two strong, bony processes bridged by a thick ligament which prevents the arm being raised from the side of the body to more than a right angle, for it is this movement that causes dislocation.

We all know, however, that we can raise our arms above our heads, so this movement must come from somewhere else besides the joint. Actually it is possible because the shoulder blade can rotate on the chest wall. Here again, therefore, Nature has so contrived matters that a maximum amount of movement can take place with the least possibility of damage being done.

THE DELICATE ADJUSTMENTS OF HAND AND ARM

LIKE the knee joint, the elbow is a hinge and though less complicated than the knee it presents some difficulties, as three bones enter into its formation. These are the humerus above, and the radius and ulna below. The two latter form the bones of the forearm and the radius is on the thumb side and the ulna on the side of the little finger. The object of this joint is not only to allow the forearm to be bent but also to allow it to rotate on itself so that the palm of the hand may be turned up or down. This is accomplished by making the bone on the thumb side of the forearm (the radius) articulate both with the humerus and with the ulna.

The upper end of the radius is a thick, circular disc, saucer-shaped on top and with both its top and sides covered with smooth cartilage. The saucer fits exactly on to a round knob on the lower end of the humerus, and the rim is surrounded by a sleeve of thick ligament with a very smooth inner surface, thus enabling rotation to occur very easily. This sleeve of ligament binds the radius to the ulna and helps to prevent damage to the joint.

The main function of the elbow, however, is to allow the arm to be bent so that we can feed ourselves. It must also be a strong joint so that we can carry things. These two necessities have been fulfilled by making the upper end of the ulna into a hook that looks like the curve on the top of a question mark. The more or less cylindrical lower end of the humerus fits into the hook horizontally and there is a very strong muscle holding it down into the hook and preventing its dislocation forwards. This arrangement allows the arm to be bent forwards but prevents bending backwards and in addition the hook prevents the elbow from being " pulled out " of joint when, for example, a heavy weight is carried.

HOW THE HANDS OF MAN AND ANIMAL DIFFER

THE hand, as we have said already, was originally used for walking upon when we were four-footed animals. In the course of evolution it started to be used for climbing trees. The great difference between the hand of man and the apes and that of the lower animals like the dog is that the thumb is " opposable " to the other fingers. This means that the front surface of the thumb can be brought to meet the front of any of the other fingers so that we can pick objects up and grasp them. This action was used first for grasping the branches of trees in climbing but it soon came to be used for picking things up.

In this connection the activities of a monkey are interesting, for this animal is notoriously one of the most curious of beasts and will pick up and inspect anything it can lay its hands on. Climbing trees came first and then came curiosity and the ability to pick up and inspect. As movement depends on the action of the muscles, which are themselves told to move by the brain, all these new movements necessitated that the brain should become bigger and more efficient. The brain of the monkeys and apes is much bigger in proportion to their size than the brain of other animals, but the brain of man is much bigger still, and, of course, much more useful.

Only a few points in the anatomy of the hand can be given, for the subject is very long, although it is absorbingly interesting. If we look at the skeleton of a hand we shall see that beyond the two bones of the forearm are a collection—actually two rows—of small, irregular bones closely bound together by ligaments. These bones articulate at the wrist joint with the lower ends of the radius and ulna. Articulated with these bones are five small, long bones radiating like the spokes of a wheel and known as metacarpals. These together form the palm of the hand. With each metacarpal articulates a finger, each of which is composed of three bones, one beyond the other.

At the wrist joint the movements possible are those of bending the hand forwards and backwards, and to a slight degree from side to side. Rotation, or twisting of the hand, if incorporated in the same joint, would have made it weak, so it has been relegated, as we have seen, to the joints between the radius and the ulna.

The muscles which work the fingers are nearly all situated in the forearm where their fleshy bellies arise from the radius and ulna, both on the front and on the back of the two bones. As these muscles pass downwards to the hand, they become thinner and smaller to economise space and form long inelastic bands or tendons. They cross the wrist joint on its front and back and eventually are fixed to various points on the front and back of the fingers. When these muscles contract they have two actions, one on the fingers and one on the wrist. Those in front bend the wrist forwards and make the fingers curl up ; those on the back bend the wrist backwards and straighten out the fingers.

THE MECHANISM THAT ENABLES US TO GRASP THINGS

IF an object (such as a pencil) is grasped tightly with the fingers (not with the thumb), or if " a fist is made " as in boxing, it will be found that the wrist is bent backwards.

This is an essential of a good grasp and well illustrates the team work which the muscles must accomplish before they can act in a useful way. First the extensor muscles on the back of the forearm extend—that is, bend backwards the wrist so that the flexors on the front of the forearm can get a better pull on the fingers. This is the reason why the grasp is weakened when a broken wrist heals badly so that the extensors cannot do their work properly.

Flexion of the fingers and extension of the wrist are only one aspect of the mechanism of grasping and are done mainly by muscles lying in the forearm. The other activity which is so essential is opposition of the thumb, and this is accomplished by the actions of small muscles which lie in the palm of the hand. The bone which forms the end of the thumb nearest to the palm is so shaped that it can rotate or turn inwards and under the influence of the muscles the sensitive pads of each of the fingers can be met by the pad on the front of the thumb. This not only enables things to be picked up but as the sensitive pads are brought together we can tell by feeling alone the shape and texture of an article picked up.

An interesting point in the human hand is that whereas in the lower animals the flexors and extensors of all the fingers are combined into one single muscle so that all work together, in man and the apes the muscles of the thumb and forefingers are separate and so these fingers can move separately, with an obvious increase in skill. Such movements as tying a knot in a piece of string would be impossible if all our fingers moved together. That the other fingers move together can be seen at once by anyone who tries to make his fourth finger curl up alone. It is impossible, except for one who has long practised it, the middle and little fingers always move with it because the muscle controlling them is the same.

Much of our skill would be lost if we could only curl up our fingers under the influence of the flexor muscles. Writing, for example, would be impossible. Before this complicated and highly-skilled action can take place we must be able to keep our fingers nearly straight and yet have them bent at right angles to the palm at the knuckles. Special muscles lying in the palm have been evolved for this, their action being to bend the fingers at the knuckles and yet keep the fingers themselves straight. These are only a few of the interesting features of our hands, but sufficient has been said to illustrate their intricacies and to give an idea of how they work.

THE JOURNEY OF THE BLOOD THROUGH THE BODY

BEFORE the inter-relationships and anatomy of the various organs of the body can be fully understood a working knowledge of the system which carries blood and nourishment to every part of the body must be discussed. The vascular system comprises the whole of this apparatus, and in it are included the heart, the arteries which convey pure, nourishing blood from the heart, the capillaries (or fine veins) where the nourishment is given off to the tissues, the veins which convey blood back to the heart, and a specialised system of vessels called the lymphatics. The system is really a closed circle, or rather two circles, as we shall see later, with the heart at the centre driving blood round and round.

If we start with the impure blood returned to the heart by the veins we find that it passes successively through two chambers situated in the right side of the heart and thence by the pulmonary artery to the lungs where it is purified and saturated with oxygen. After leaving the lungs it passes by the pulmonary veins back to the heart, where after traversing two chambers in the left side of the heart it leaves by the great artery called the aorta and finally reaches the tissues by passing through the smaller arteries. After supplying the tissues with oxygen it becomes impure and is carried back by the veins to the heart and lungs for purification.

It will be seen that in the greater part of the body the arteries contain pure blood and the veins impure blood. The arteries may be compared with the clean water supply of a town, while the veins are the sewers. In the lesser circulation—that is the part in which the lungs are interposed—the reverse is the case, for the pulmonary artery contains the impure blood and the pulmonary vein the pure blood. After this general discussion we can now start on a consideration of each separate part.

THE ROUTES BY WHICH BLOOD TRAVELS TO THE HEART

IF we start with the capillaries to which blood is brought by the arteries, the microscope must be used, for they are exceedingly small. Every organ in the body is riddled with these tiny tubes which are the means of nourishing the tissues.

Their walls are excessively thin, for they are composed of flat cells which lie only one cell deep so that a kind of pavement is formed, so delicate that nourishment easily passes through it. Further on the capillaries join together, forming larger vessels which in their turn join until eventually quite a large vein is formed. Veins from all parts of the body converge upon the heart, becoming larger and larger as more tributaries enter them. Many of these veins have special names, but only a few need be mentioned here.

Blood coming to the heart from the head is carried by the jugular veins, internal and external. These join on each side with veins from the arm called the subclavian veins, forming the innominate veins, right and left. Later the right and left innominate veins join together to form the vena cava superior or great vein of the upper part of the body, which directly enters the heart.

From the lower part of the body a vein from each leg—the femoral vein—after passing into the abdomen from the thigh and receiving many tributaries, joins with its fellow of the opposite side to form the inferior vena cava or great vein of the lower part of the body. This vein lies in front of the vertebral column in the posterior part of the abdomen and runs directly upwards until, after receiving impure blood from the liver, it pierces the diaphragm and immediately enters the heart. We have now, by devious routes, brought all our blood back to the heart, so we must next proceed to describe this organ in detail.

WORK IN THE PUMPING-STATION OF THE HEART

THE heart is divided into two parts—right and left—by a partition or septum which runs down the middle. Each part is further subdivided into two cavities called auricles and ventricles. The auricles are thin-walled muscular chambers which receive blood from the veins and pass it on to the ventricles. The ventricles are thick-walled and contain very strong muscles which form the main pumping-station of the heart and drive the blood all over the body.

Starting with the right auricle, this cavity has two large openings in its right wall, namely the superior and inferior venæ cavæ. In addition there is a small opening—the coronary sinus—which conveys venous blood from the heart itself back to the right auricle. After passing through the auricle the blood enters the right ventricle through the valve called the tricuspid valve. This structure is interposed between the auricle and the ventricle in order to prevent the blood regurgitating back into the auricle when the ventricle contracts.

The valve is composed of three thin membranous cusps which meet accurately at the centre and form a completely watertight joint when the valve is closed. Each cusp is like an umbrella with the convex surface upwards so that blood can flow freely over it when the auricle contracts, but concave on its ventricular surface so that, under pressure, the ventricular blood catches under it and closes it. The working of the valve is purely automatic and is under no sort of control. It depends solely on the difference in pressure in the two chambers. The sequence of events is as follows:

The auricle is distended with blood entering it from the veins; it then contracts and the pressure rises sufficiently above that in the ventricle to force the valve open. The blood then passes into the ventricle which, in its turn, contracts, and when the pressure inside it rises sufficiently high the valve automatically closes, preventing the blood from flowing back into the auricle.

It might be thought at first sight that the valve would itself be turned inside out under the pressure. Nature has guarded against this by providing thick strands of fibrous and muscular tissue which stretch from the wall of the ventricle to the under surface of the cusps. The umbrella shape of the cusps and their inelastic nature also tend to prevent this movement which would be so disastrous.

Having been filled with blood by the contraction of the right auricle, the right ventricle contracts and drives the blood through another valve into the pulmonary artery which leads to the lungs. The muscular wall of the right ventricle is much thicker than that of the auricle, for it has to pump blood all round the lungs. Its thickness, therefore, is a response to the greater amount of work it must perform. The pulmonary artery divides into ever smaller and smaller vessels until the capillaries lying in the walls of the air sacs of the lungs are reached. Here the blood is re-oxygenated and collected into the pulmonary veins which lead the blood back to the heart by entering the left auricle and pouring the purified blood into its cavity.

The cavities of the left auricle and ventricle show no very marked differences from those on the right side of the heart.

As might be expected, however, the wall of the left ventricle is many times thicker than that of the right, for whereas the right ventricle pumps blood only through the lungs, the left must be sufficiently strong to force it through the whole of the remainder of the body.

THE VESSELS THAT SUPPLY BLOOD TO THE BODY

THE left ventricle pumps blood under pressure into the aorta, which is the great main artery that leads blood from the heart and delivers it to the whole of the system. Just from the point where the aorta leaves the heart arise two arteries of moderate size which are two of the most important arteries in the body, for they supply the heart. They are known as the coronary arteries, right and left, because they run round the top of the heart like a crown. Should one of these arteries become suddenly blocked death will ensue immediately. This is the cause of death in those cases where a man suddenly falls down dead in the middle of the street. Blockage of certain arteries in the brain will cause immediate unconsciousness and death at a later date, but there is nothing which will strike a man down and kill so rapidly as blockage of the arteries to the heart. It is indeed a sudden visitation of the Angel of Death.

After giving off branches which supply the arms (the sub-clavian arteries) and the head and brain (the carotid arteries) the aorta turns downwards and, passing down the back of the chest in front of and to the left of the vertebral column, it enters the abdomen. Here it gives off large branches which pass to supply the liver and intestines, and eventually the main stem divides into two branches which pass one to each leg, and are known as the femoral arteries.

THE PULSE: THE HEART'S SECOND GEAR

PERHAPS the best-known artery of all is the radial, for it is from this artery that the pulse rate is commonly esti-mated by doctors. It lies on the thumb side of the wrist and any-one can easily feel the pulsations that are transmitted to it from the heart. The value of the pulse can at once be seen when it is realised that it gives an immediate indication of the rate at which the heart itself is beating. Whenever the heart is working under difficulties, when it is itself diseased or when it suffers with the body in general during fever, it goes, as it were, into second gear and beats more rapidly. At each beat it need not pump out so much blood, as it is working faster. The result is exactly the same as that attained when a car goes uphill in second gear. The work done eventually is the same, but it is done with less strain on the engine. The normal pulse rate of an adult is about 70 to 80 beats per minute. Anything over 90 is usually an indication that the heart is in difficulties and must be rested by keeping the patient in bed.

The larger arteries that we have mentioned so far divide continually until finer and finer branches are reached. These lead eventually into the capillaries where the blood is at last made use of. This continual division into smaller vessels means that when the blood comes to be used the surface of the blood that is available for the interchange of nourishment with the tissues is enormously increased. Some enthusiast has worked out that the surface which the blood presents in the capillaries of a medium-sized muscle, such as the biceps, corresponds to something like ten whole pages of *The Times*.

THE VESSELS THAT CARRY FOOD TO THE LIVER

WE have now discussed the circulation in general, but we have yet to mention a small but important system of vessels known as the portal circulation. In the section on Physiology we shall see that food, after it has been digested, is absorbed into the capillaries of the intestines. These capillaries, as they do everywhere else, gather themselves into veins which form eventually a large vein known as the portal vein, which enters the liver. This vein conveys to the liver, which is the storehouse and factory of the body, the blood which contains the food.

The portal vein breaks up into capillaries again inside the liver and blood comes in contact everywhere with the liver cells which extract the food and make it up into new products. The blood is then re-collected in a further set of veins which enter the inferior vena cava, and from there it soon reaches the right side of the heart.

The liver, therefore, is an unusual organ, for it has three sets of blood vessels whereas other organs have only two. Arterial blood brings oxygen which enables it to live, and the veins carry off the impure blood. In addition the portal vein brings food from the digestive tract which serves the special functions of the liver.

THE LYMPHATICS : THE FIRST LINE OF DEFENCE

BESIDES the blood vessels there are small vessels which carry a watery fluid known as lymph. This serves quite a different purpose from that of the blood. Lymph spaces lie between the cells all over the body and they communicate with tiny vessels which collect the lymph and pass it on eventually into the veins. The lymph vessels open into a large lymphatic channel known as the thoracic duct which lies in the chest and which passes up into the neck and discharges its contents into the subclavian vein where they enter the general blood circulation. Some of the lymph vessels that enter the thoracic duct come from the intestines and they carry the fat that has been absorbed during digestion, so one function of the lymphatics is to convey food into the blood stream.

A further reason for their existence is to protect the body from the invasions of germs or bacteria. Before they enter the subclavian vein, all the lymphatics have to pass through a series of filters known as lymph glands which strain off any foreign bodies or germs which may be present in the lymph and destroy them. Thus, if a few germs gain entrance to the body through a small cut on the foot, the germs will be carried into the lymphatics and held up at the groin where the main lymph glands are situated. If the glands are sufficiently strong they will destroy the bacteria, but if the germs are numerous and virulent they may cause inflammation of the glands which will then become enlarged and inflamed or may even form an abscess.

WHAT A SWOLLEN LYMPH GLAND SUGGESTS

THE lymph glands do their best, and even if the germs are not destroyed or an abscess forms, the glands have localised the infection and prevented it from spreading all over the body where it would be much more dangerous. A swollen lymph gland will always suggest that there is some sore in the region which the glands drains. Thus, swollen glands in the neck are often the result of inflamed tonsils, swollen glands in the armpit are caused by sores on the arms or breast, and swellings in the groin arise from trouble in the feet or legs. Swellings in the groin can easily be felt under normal circumstances by anyone who searches for them, for they are much larger than the glands in any other part of the body, and are the only ones that are large enough to be felt in the ordinary way.

HOW THE BODY IS VENTILATED

WE have talked of the mechanism by which air is drawn into the lungs by enlarging the diameters of the chest, and we must now describe the passages which convey the air down to the lungs. During normal breathing air is first drawn into the nose which has a special action in warming and moistening the air and clearing it of some of its larger impurities before it reaches the delicate tissues of the lungs. When the air enters at the nostrils, it finds itself in quite a large cavity whose depth is represented on the front of the face by the distance from the nostrils to the bridge of the nose.

If you can imagine a cavity as deep as this and perhaps one and a half inches from side to side, extending directly backwards until it joins with the cavity of the mouth, you will have quite a good idea of the anatomy of the nose. This cavity is divided into two by a partition which runs from the roof to the floor and completely separates one side from the other. At the entrance of each nostril there are a large number of very stiff hairs which strain off any particles such as soot which might be breathed in.

The side wall of each compartment of the nose is thrown into a number of large folds which greatly increase the surface which is presented to the air passing over it, and as they project inwards towards the partition they take up a lot of room and in places almost touch it. The whole of the interior of the nose, including these folds, is covered with a thick, velvety layer of mucous membrane which is very thickly supplied with blood vessels. It is called mucous membrane because it is a membrane made up of cells that secrete a thick viscid fluid known as mucus. As the mucous membrane is well supplied with blood it is always kept warm and the mucus secreted keeps it soft so that the air passing over it has the chill taken off and is moistened.

In addition some of the dirt carried in with the air adheres to the mucus and is discharged from the nose when next it is blown. That this is so is well shown by the difference in the dirt on our handkerchiefs after a day spent in the smoky atmosphere of a large city and that found after a day spent in the country. It must be realised that all this filth would have entered the lungs, where it might have done considerable damage, if it had not first been removed by the nose.

The nose is, of course, one of the main places where germs enter the body, and considerable numbers are caught and held up in the mucus which covers its surfaces. Very frequently these are germs which cause trouble and a cold in the head is the result. When this happens the mucous membrane of the nose becomes swollen, so much so that the nose is blocked and breathing through the nose becomes difficult or impossible. At the same time the flow of mucus is greatly increased so that large numbers of the disease-producing germs are washed away in it.

THE SECRET OF A " NASAL " VOICE

WE have seen that the nose communicates at the back with the cavity of the mouth. The posterior part of the floor of the nose is formed by a muscular sheet known as the soft palate. When this is pulled up, it shuts off the back of the nose from the mouth so that when we swallow fluids they cannot enter the nose and flow out through the nostrils.

Leading out of the cavity of the nose are quite a number of fairly large cavities, whose function it is to make the sounds formed by the larynx reverberate, so that the voice takes on a ringing character. When we speak the nose and mouth are kept in continuity because the soft palate is kept open and air passes through the nose as well as through the mouth. If for any reason the nasal cavity is blocked, as for example when we have a cold in the head or when we pinch the nostrils together with our fingers, the voice will be flat and " nasal " in quality. The action of these cavities is exactly like that of the large cavity which is always made in the body of a violin behind the strings. One can readily imagine the flatness of the note of a violin that was made of a solid block of wood.

THE NERVES THAT ENABLE US TO SMELL

THE roof of the nasal cavities is formed by quite a thin plate of bone which separates the nose from the cavity in which the brain lies. Piercing this layer of bone are numerous tiny nerves which carry sensations of smell to the brain. Being extremely delicate structures Nature has packed them away in an inaccessible region of the nose where the least possible harm can come to them, and yet where the air warmed by the remainder of the nose and carrying the odorous substances which stimulate these nerves can easily reach them.

Owing to the close proximity of the brain to the outside wall at this point it is one of the situations in which the brain is most exposed to infection, and it is one among others at which it is supposed the germs of infantile paralysis enter the nervous system. This disease is an example of many such that are caught first in the nose, just like the common cold.

THE SOUND BOX OF THE HUMAN VOICE

BOTH the nose and the mouth lead backwards into a cavity which connects the two and which is known as the pharynx. This has two large tubes leading from its lower portion. The front one is the larynx, which produces the voice, and the one lying behind is the gullet. Leading out of the side wall of the pharynx on each side is a short tube that connects it with the inside of the ear. This is one of the danger spots of the upper respiratory passages, for quite often when these are inflamed owing to some infection, such as measles, this tube also becomes inflamed and infection may reach the cavity of the ear. This is the explanation of the relative frequency of that serious condition known as mastoid disease which so often follows otherwise trivial diseases of this region.

Leading out of the lower part of the pharynx is the cavity known as the larynx. This is like a box with its upper and lower ends open and is formed by a number of small cartilages, the largest of which projects on the front of the neck and is known as the Adam's apple.

Stretching from front to back of the lower part of this cavity are two folds of mucous membrane known as the vocal cords. When air passes over these structures during expiration and inspiration they are thrown into vibration and a sound is produced. They are well supplied with different sets of muscles so that not only can they be separated and brought closer together so that they may be made to meet completely, but also they can be both stretched and relaxed. Separation and approximation of the cords will control the volume of air passing over them so that the loudness of the voice can be controlled. Tightening and relaxation of the cords determines their pitch so that all kinds of variation in the tone of the voice can be produced. The larynx produces only the sound of the voice. It is the mouth and tongue, lips and teeth, that fashion these sounds into words and syllables.

WINDPIPE AND BRONCHI: THE SENTINELS OF THE LUNGS

THE lower part of the larynx leads directly into the windpipe which runs down through the lower part of the neck into the chest. Here it divides into two branches and these in time divide into even smaller and smaller branches until eventually they reach the air sacs of the lungs.

The windpipe and bronchi are composed of rings of cartilage separated in the intervals by fibrous tissue. The rings are incomplete behind and the interval between the ends of the ring behind is filled in by muscular tissue, thus enabling the tube to be made smaller or larger in diameter when the muscle contracts or when it relaxes. This is of little importance in the windpipe, for it is a very wide tube and only slight variations can be made in its calibre. But in the smaller bronchi it is of some importance, for it is the explanation of how asthma is produced.

There are certain substances in the air we breathe which will cause a spasm of these muscles in individuals who are susceptible to them. Such things are the pollens of certain plants and dusts from various sources. When the substances gain access to the bronchi the bronchial muscles go into spasm in an effort, as it were, to exclude the dangerous particles from the lungs. So effective is the spasm that it often makes breathing almost impossible for the unfortunate sufferer.

It is really misdirected energy on the part of the bronchi, for the condition they produce is more unpleasant and more dangerous than the one they are seeking to avoid. It is therefore justifiable for the doctor to abolish this spasm by the use of drugs, and this is usually done by inhaling the smoke from certain leaves or by giving a special injection. When the bronchi become inflamed the well-known condition of bronchitis is produced.

The mucous membrane of the windpipe and bronchi is very remarkable and forms the final barrier which tends to prevent dangerous substances entering the lungs. It is composed of a layer of tall cells fitted together like a palisade. Each cell has a number of hairs sticking out into the cavity of the windpipe, which the cell can move freely. There are small glands lying deep in the membrane which throw out quantities of fluid mucus in which foreign particles and germs become entangled.

The hairs on the cells beat always upwards so that they carry the mucus which is laden with foreign particles upwards in a stream away from the lungs. This is eventually voided by coughing, because when it reaches the sensitive larynx a reflex is set up which results in the production of a sharp cough. This same reflex is responsible for the unpleasant results that follow food " going the wrong way," for instead of being swallowed normally it is inhaled by mistake into the larynx from which it might reach the lungs if it were not immediately coughed up.

THE RHYTHMIC WORKING OF THE LUNGS

THE lungs consist of a vast number of infinitesimally small air sacs crowded together and welded into one mass so that a structure something like a very fine sponge is produced. Each tiny air sac has a correspondingly small branch of a bronchus leading into it, so that during inspiration and expiration the air lying in the air sacs is constantly being changed and kept fresh. The walls of the sacs are formed by a very thin membrane formed by flattened ends which lie only one layer deep, so that an effect like a pavement is produced.

Running in the walls of the sacs and separated from their air-containing cavities by only this thin layer of membrane are innumerable capillaries which are branches of the pulmonary artery that brings impure blood from the right side of the heart for purification. So fine and so numerous are the capillaries that an enormous surface of blood is exposed to the action of the air in the sacs, with the result that the gaseous interchange between blood and air can take place to the best advantage.

The substance of the lungs is made up mostly of elastic tissue, so that when they have expanded under the influence of the increased size of the chest during respiration, they will automatically collapse and drive out the air inside them, when the expanding force is removed. The outer surface of the lungs is covered with a smooth, glistening membrane known as the pleura. The whole of the inner surface of the chest is also lined with this same membrane, the result being that the lungs can move about inside the chest when they are expanding and relaxing with the minimum amount of friction.

THE FORTY FEET TRAVELLED BY OUR FOOD

FOOD taken into the mouth is first ground into smaller and smaller fragments by the teeth and intimately mixed with saliva and then finally swallowed. The mouth, of course, is not only concerned with eating but also with speaking and sometimes with breathing when for any reason the nose is blocked. The dangers of habitual mouth-breathing will be readily recognised when it is realised that all the good offices served by the nose that we have previously considered are eliminated by breathing through the mouth.

The saliva is produced by three sets of glands on each side, each of which discharges its secretion into the mouth by means of a duct. One of these is a gland lying on the side of the face in front of the ear and known as the parotid. This is the one which becomes enlarged during the course of the illness known as mumps. The saliva has a double function, for it is not only a digestive juice which helps to split up starch but it also acts as a lubricant and facilitates the movements of the tongue so that speech is more easily accomplished.

When the food has been ground up and mixed with saliva it is rolled up into a ball by the tongue and promptly swallowed. This simple remark has a lot behind it, for in this process many interesting mechanisms are brought into play. After being collected into a ball the food is thrown against the back of the pharynx, where it comes in contact with a very sensitive spot. Immediately a reflex is produced which accomplishes several very important acts. First the soft palate is raised so that the back entry into the nose is closed, preventing food being lost by this route. Secondly, the upper entry of the larynx is closed in rather a complicated way so that no food can enter there. Thirdly, the food is swallowed into the one remaining channel left open, namely, the gullet.

This is a tube with a very muscular wall, one layer of muscle lying longitudinally and another encircling it from top to bottom. During the action of the reflex that we have just mentioned, the muscle above the food contracts and that below it relaxes, so that the food is rapidly pushed downwards. This muscular action proceeds in a wave passing down the whole length of the gullet until the stomach is reached.

It is this mechanism which is responsible for the propelling force which causes the food to pass from one end of the alimentary tract to the other. It is known as peristalsis and is essentially a wave of contraction preceded by a wave of relaxation into which the food is pushed. All through the alimentary tract from the mouth to the anus where the food or its remains are eventually voided, the same arrangement of muscles is found, and everywhere the mechanism of propelling the food is the same.

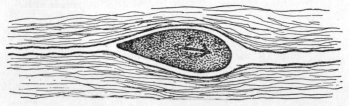

THE FOOD ON ITS JOURNEY

The food is collected into a " bolus " and forced on its journey through the gullet by waves of muscular contraction known as " peristalsis."

THE SECOND MILL THAT GRINDS THE FOOD

BETWEEN the gullet and the stomach is a ring of muscle which, when it contracts, firmly closes the upper end of the stomach and prevents the food from being regurgitated back into the gullet. This sphincter, as the muscle is called, is normally kept closed, but during swallowing it forms the lower end of the wave of relaxation which precedes the oncoming food which is thus finally passed into the stomach.

At the lower end of the stomach there is another sphincter which is called the pylorus and which works in exactly the same way as the first that we have just mentioned. There is a slight difference, however, for any solid particles in its neighbourhood have the power of making it contract and close, ensuring that food is not passed on to the next part of the bowel until it is in a more or less fluid condition and in a fit state to be digested by the special juices which are next going to work upon it.

Thus when food has entered the stomach both sphincters close and now begins a firm pummelling in which strong contractions of the stomach pass from left to right over the surface of the organ, breaking up any solid or semi-solid particles of food and intimately mixing them with quantities of juice which is secreted from the inner surface of the stomach and which helps to make the mass almost liquid in consistency.

The food remains in the stomach for about three hours in normal circumstances, so that it forms between meals a sort of reservoir which is almost constantly passing material into the bowel for digestion. Before breakfast, however, if nothing has been taken all night, it should invariably be empty. When the food has been reduced to a more or less fluid pulp a wave of peristalsis relaxes the pylorus and a quantity of food is passed through the opening. This process is repeated at intervals until all is finished.

THE LAST STAGES OF THE FOOD'S JOURNEY

THE tube which next receives the food is called the small intestine owing to its narrow width. Its upper part, next to the stomach, has a special name—the duodenum—which is of interest because quite often a serious ulcer may develop there. Leading into the duodenum are two long ducts, one from the pancreas which secretes a special alkaline juice, and the other from the liver which conveys the bile. Just after the bile duct leaves the liver where the bile is made, it sends off a large duct which passes to the gall bladder.

When the duodendum contains little or no food the bile is side-tracked up this channel and stored in the gall bladder, where it is available in large quantities for the next time it is required when the gall bladder contracts and drives the bile into the duodenum. The gall bladder has the power of absorbing water from the bile which lies in it, so that the bile is concentrated when it is ready for use. Sometimes, especially when there is infection and germs are present in the gall bladder, the bile becomes too concentrated and stones form, leading to a train of serious symptoms.

In the small intestine the food becomes progressively more and more fluid, for not only are the bile and pancreatic juice added to it, but the intestine itself secretes a juice, the three together finally breaking the food down into its last constituent parts, all of which become completely dissolved.

The inner surface of the intestine is raised into many ridges and the whole surface is covered with innumerable tiny finger-like processes known as villi which increase a thousandfold the surface available for absorbing the disintegrated products of the food. The special function of the villi we shall see later. At the lower end of the small intestine all the valuable parts of the food have been completely absorbed, but the contents are still fluid. These now take a new character and are more or less the same, apart from their consistency, as when they are finally voided at the anus. They are now known as fæces.

SOMETHING ABOUT APPENDICITIS

AT the lower end of the small intestine is another sphincter which holds back the remains of the food. At intervals, and especially when food is taken into the stomach through the reflex mechanism, the sphincter opens and the fæces are pushed down into the next part of the bowel, which is known as the large intestine, owing to its greater width. The small intestine enters the large at a right angle and a small portion of the large gut, known as the cæcum, projects down below this entrance.

It is from the lower end of the cæcum that the notorious appendix springs. This is a small tube about four inches long with a blind end, and it is when this becomes blocked for any reason that inflammation starts inside it and appendicitis, with all its serious consequences, begins. The contents of the large intestine and appendix are always swarming with highly virulent bacteria, even in perfectly normal persons. So long as the germs remain only inside the intestine no harm results, but as soon as they begin to pierce the coats of the intestine and work their way through into the large cavity in which the intestines are confined, the infection spreads all over the abdomen, with the most disastrous consequences.

The inner surface of the bowel wall is quite immune from their advances, and it is only when this becomes damaged by products which have been dammed back for any reason, that any invasion of the walls can take place. We can never tell from outside exactly how far the inflammation has progressed, although we may know that it is inflamed.

AN AILMENT THAT CAUSES UNNECESSARY CONCERN

THE remainder of the large intestine has the power of absorbing water and so concentrating the fæces and making them solid so that they can be more easily held until an opportunity arises for voiding them. It also secretes large quantities of slimy mucus which protects the wall from ulceration and lubricates the now solid fæces so that when they are voided this action is accomplished with the minimum of difficulty.

When food is taken into the stomach a reflex wave of peristalsis is set up in the large intestine which pushes some of the fæces downwards and results in a desire to void them. This is the reason why most people always have a desire to pass their motions after breakfast. If the impulse is neglected the intestine becomes accustomed to their presence in its lower part and the desire passes, perhaps not to be repeated for many hours. It is the breaking of this habit of passing one's motions at regular times that so often leads to constipation.

Constipation of itself leads to very few ill effects and much nonsense has been written of its serious consequences, with the result that an immense amount of unnecessary worry has been produced. This worry about the bowels is of much more importance than the constipation itself. However, it is obviously much more healthy to discharge the fæces at regular and fairly frequent intervals, and for this reason the habit should be carefully preserved.

We have now discussed the whole of the alimentary tract from top to bottom, from mouth to anus, and it may be of some interest to note that the journey has been a long one, for we have passed through nearly forty feet of sinuously coiled tubing.

THE BODY'S DRAINAGE SYSTEM

THE kidneys are the organs that filter off the waste products that collect in our blood, and concentrate them into the urine. We are not concerned here with how they do it; that we must leave to Physiology. Each kidney is a fleshy object that is composed of thousands and thousands of tiny tubes which secrete the urine. This passes from the kidney into a long tube known as the ureter, which leads the urine down into the bladder.

The wall of the ureter, like that of the intestine, is composed of two thicknesses of muscle tissue which by their contraction and relaxation propel the urine down into the bladder. When the ureter enters the bladder it pierces its muscular wall very obliquely so that it has an oblique course inside the bladder wall for about half an inch. While this ingenious arrangement allows urine to flow freely down the ureter into the bladder, it effectively prevents urine from passing in the opposite direction if large quantities should collect under pressure in the bladder for any reason, thus stopping the development of a back pressure upon the kidneys which might damage them. Sometimes when there is long-continued obstruction to the outflow of urine from the bladder, the bladder becomes stretched so much that this mechanism breaks down and the kidneys are inevitably seriously damaged.

The bladder is the receiver in which urine is stored until a suitable opportunity for voiding it offers itself. The ureters deliver urine from the kidneys at the rate of a drop about every two seconds, so we can readily see that if it were not for the bladder we should spend our whole day passing water continuously. The wall of the bladder is composed of muscular tissue, so that it can contract and relax at will. The circular muscle is collected into a thick ring or sphincter which surrounds the channel which carries urine away from the bladder and is known as the urethra. When the bladder muscle contracts in the act of passing water this sphincter is relaxed so that urine can escape, but at all other times it is tightly closed.

During the time that passes after the bladder is evacuated urine steadily collects inside it from the ureter. The muscle of the bladder allows itself to become progressively relaxed so that the pressure inside the bladder remains more or less at a constant level. Eventually, however, so much urine collects that it is difficult for the bladder to relax any further, so the pressure suddenly rises. The nerves in the bladder then send messages to the spinal cord complaining of the increase in pressure and asking for the bladder to be emptied. These impulses reach consciousness and we can either empty the bladder if we wish to or, if the opportunity does not arise, we can consciously relax the bladder still further and so reduce the pressure and the demand for evacuation.

This conscious control over the bladder is only learnt by experience and education, and its lack in infants explains why they pass their water at regular intervals. It is only when they become older and acquire this conscious control that they become " clean." It is never wise, therefore, to scold or punish a child for being " dirty," because it is not his fault. It is only that this conscious control has not yet developed or has been retarded by some special circumstances.

When water is passed the bladder walls contract and the sphincter closes, and at the same time the muscles of the abdomen contract under the control of the brain so that their effect is added to that of the bladder. The urethra is simply the tube which carries the urine away from the bladder. In the male it is long and opens at the end of the penis, but in the female it is very short. It is owing to the greater length of the canal in the male and the presence of a gland called the prostate which surrounds it in its upper part that it is so much more frequently diseased in men than in women.

THE ORGANS UPON WHICH NEW LIFE DEPENDS

As is well known reproduction is effected by the growth of a cell which is formed by the joining together of two cells, the ovum and spermatozoon which come from the female and male respectively. Both male and female, therefore, must produce these cells and must contain a system of tubes by which they may be led to one another, and also a place where the fertilised ovum can safely develop. When animals lived in the water it was comparatively simple, for the ovum thrown out into the surrounding water to be fertilised by the male could not be destroyed by drying, and when fertilised could continue its development unhindered except by the raids of other animals that desired it for food.

In these circumstances, therefore, millions of eggs were laid by each female and these were subsequently fertilised by millions of spermatozoa cast at random over the egg mass. Thus was it ensured that even if many were destroyed by predatory animals, a few would survive. When, however, animals left the water some new method of reproduction had to be found in order to prevent the embryo drying in the air. To accomplish this the ovum is fertilised inside the female by spermatozoa which are introduced by the penis into the passage of the female known as the vagina.

Many of the land animals have avoided the difficulty of drying by covering their fertilised eggs with a shell, the egg being laid and continuing its development outside the mother. In the mammals and man, however, the fertilised egg is retained and is developed inside the mother and is born in a state of comparative maturity. Many animals, too, produce large numbers of fertilised eggs so as to ensure the complete development of at least a few. In man, however, only one egg is produced at a time under normal circumstances, for the environment is such that the developing ovum and subsequent infant have relatively few dangers to withstand owing to their careful protection. Such have been the factors that have given rise to the rather complicated arrangements for reproduction in the human body.

THE MALE'S PART IN A COMPLEMENTARY SYSTEM

THE essentially male organs which produce the spermatozoa are the testicles. These two organs were originally formed, and in the developing embryo actually lie, inside the abdomen, but in the adult they have become pulled down into a bag which lies between the legs. It is difficult to see the reason for this, for they are obviously less protected in this position and, of course, from a racial point of view they are one of our most important possessions. However, it would appear that in the higher mammals the stimulus of relative cold is required for their proper development at puberty, for if by chance they fail to descend or remain in the warmth of the abdomen or if they are artificially replaced there they fail to develop as they should.

Each testicle contains a large number of enormously long and tortuous tubes closely coiled together and very narrow in cross-section. These tubes produce the spermatozoa, which are minute cells with a head and a very long tail which can be waved vigorously so that locomotion is possible. All the tubes of the testes are gathered together finally into a long duct which passes upwards and enters the abdomen, finally reaching the back of the bladder behind which a sac grows out of the tube in which the spermatozoa can be stored. Out of this leads a very fine tube which traverses the prostate gland surrounding the urethra into which the duct finally leads.

Spermatozoa after passing into the urethra are discharged at the proper time from the end of the penis. The prostate gland secretes a fluid which stimulates the spermatozoa to active movement. This secretion comes in contact with them only when they are about to be discharged, for although it makes them more active it materially shortens their life. In the body of the male, if they are not discharged, they can live more or less indefinitely but when passed into the organs of the female they can live at most only for about ten days. Millions upon millions of spermatozoa are discharged at one act of coitus, but it is characteristic of the prodigality of nature that only one of this huge number is responsible for fertilizing the ovum.

CONCEPTION: A MIRACLE OF NATURE'S EVOLUTION

THE essential sex organs of the female are the two ovaries which lie in the lower part of the abdomen. They are small, oval objects about the size of a large almond and consist of large numbers of cell groups, which produce the ova, embedded in a mass of supporting tissue. When an ovum ripens it bursts through the coat of the ovary and comes to lie in the lower part of the great abdominal cavity that surrounds the intestines. It lies in this cavity, however, only for a short while, for in close proximity to the ovary is the open end of a tube down which it will later be carried to the womb.

The open end of this tube has its wall frayed out into processes which more or less surround the ovary, and the inside of the tube is lined by cells which possess hairs that by their motion can produce a stream which sucks the ovum into the tube and carries it down its interior, where, if conditions are satisfactory, it becomes fertilised by a spermatozoon which has worked its way upwards from the vagina. The fertilised (or unfertilised) ovum then passes down the remainder of the tube which leads into the upper part of the womb. If the ovum is fertilised it finds the walls of the womb thickened and specially prepared to receive it and it then starts actively to burrow into the substance of the wall. Here it continues its development until it is fully mature and ready to be born.

The walls of the womb are composed of a thick layer of muscular tissue which is used at the end of pregnancy for driving the infant out of the womb. Normally the womb weighs but a few ounces, but during pregnancy it increases enormously in size and its walls become thicker and more richly supplied with blood vessels for the nourishment of the infant until the womb at full term comes to weigh two to three pounds.

The lower part of the womb leads directly into the vagina where the spermatozoa are lodged by the male in the act of coitus. The spermatozoa, after their deposition in the vagina, make their way by the active motion of their tails into the cavity of the womb and from there into the tube where they meet the ovum and fertilise it. We shall see in the section on the ductless glands how the ovary sends out its two messengers into the blood stream, œstrin and lutein, which prepare the womb for the reception of the ovum. We shall see, too,

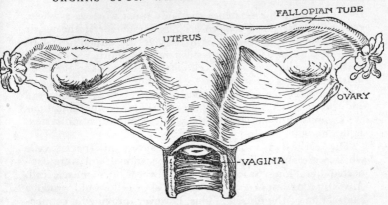

DIAGRAM OF THE WOMB

Showing the uterus or womb in relation to its connected organs

how the second hormone, lutein, is produced only after the ovum is ripe and has burst its way out of the ovary and how progestin is produced only for long periods if the ovum is fertilised.

If fertilisation does not occur then the production of progestin ceases after ten days, and with its cessation the lining membrane of the womb breaks down and is cast off with a certain amount of blood and constitutes menstruation.

TELEPHONE AND TELEGRAPH IN THE HUMAN BODY

IF we look for a moment at the single-celled creatures that form the present representatives of the beginning of life, we shall find that a stimulus attractive or repellant applied to any part of the cell will result in the cell reacting as a whole. There is little or no difficulty in communication within the cell from point to point. There is a single-celled creature known as Vorticella which consists of a bell attached by a spiral stalk to some neighbouring weed. A stimulus applied under the microscope to any part of the cell will occasion the stalk to contract and the bell to close up so that the creature takes up a defensive attitude.

When we come to the next grade of living creatures, those that are composed of more than one cell, a difficulty arises.

In the struggle for existence the body must work as a whole, each cell must react as a co-ordinated member if the whole mechanism of the creature is to survive the difficulties of its life. If a noxious chemical substance or another dangerous creature touches one single cell all the other cells in the body must react in an endeavour to flee and escape the danger. For this a service of communications between each body cell and every other cell is required. These communications are known as the nerves and the whole communicating system as the nervous system.

The earliest nervous system consisted in special cells which were situated in the skin of the animal and were connected by a long process running inwards to a muscle cell. Any stimulus applied to the special skin cell would produce contraction of the muscle. This, however, provided a connection between only two cells and each muscle would have to contract independently of the others, so very soon the specialised cells began to branch so that several muscle fibres became connected together. The next step came when the branches became large and numerous and it was necessary to provide a cell both to control them and to nourish them, so nerve cells were formed in the course of the network.

The primitive nervous system thus formed was composed of fibres leading from the special skin cells to nerve cells which were connected together by a branching network of communicating fibres which gave off branches to the muscle fibres. This system was found to be adequate up to a point and is still found to-day in certain lowly animals. But it presented a big disadvantage which had to be overcome before progressive evolution could take place. A stimulus applied to one part of the system might have to travel all round the system and by various devious routes before it could arrive at some point at a distance from where it was applied.

What was needed was a central clearing station or exchange which on receiving impulses could co-ordinate them and pass them on directly to the correct channel. The fibres leading into this central system are known as sensory fibres and those leading out of it to muscles or other organs which produce a reaction are known as motor fibres. The animal thus came to possess sensory organs situated in the skin which sent impulses to an exchange which relayed them by the motor fibres to the muscles or other organs. This central exchange, in order to suit the requirements of the animal,

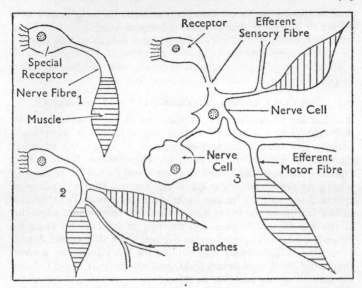

THE BEGINNING OF THE NERVOUS SYSTEM

From single cells situated in the skin and connected each to a single muscle fibre (1), the nervous system has grown, by branches linking several muscle fibres (2), to a complicated network in the higher animals (3), nourished and controlled by special cells of its own.

became formed into a long cord running the whole length of the creature and so a primitive spinal cord was formed.

The path leading from the sensory organ through the nerve cells situated in the central nervous system to the motor organ is known as a reflex arc, and the response of a muscle to a stimulus applied to the sensory organ is known as a reflex response. The earliest vertebrates (animals with backbones) and their predecessors, animals like the earthworm, were composed of a number of divisions or segments each of which contained a segment of the central nervous cord which controlled their movements by means of reflex arcs. Thus sensory organs in segment 6 of the animal would send messages to segment 6 of the nervous system and produce a response in the muscles of segment 6 of the animal.

In addition it was essential that each segment of the nervous system should be in communication with its neighbours and others at a greater distance, so communicating fibres or long tracts were formed which ran the whole length of the central nervous system and co-ordinated the whole. By these means a stimulus applied to segment 6 could now produce a reflex response in one or all of the other segments.

THE EARLY BRAIN : A "LOOKOUT" FOR THE BODY

IN the act of locomotion it was found to be of enormous advantage to the animal if that segment which went first, namely the head end, was capable of detecting in advance changes in environment, such as enemies or food. The animal must not wait to discover an enemy until he is already within its jaws. He must know beforehand that an enemy is approaching so that he can make preparations to fight or flee before his enemy is upon him. For this reason that segment of the animal which preceded the rest in locomotion came to be endowed with special sense organs, eyes that could detect variations in light, ears that could pick up vibrations, a nose that could smell and detect food, and organs that could inform the animal of his position in space.

With the development of all these special organs in the head it was necessary that the head should contain a very much larger and more efficient central nervous system than the remaining body segments. This specially enlarged central nervous system of the first segments is known as the brain, and upon its efficiency in warning and producing reactions in the remainder of the body depended the whole survival of the animal in the struggle for existence. The more useful the brain became the more chance had the animal of surviving. This is well seen if we look at the disaster that overtook the vast cumbersome reptiles that lived in the period following the emergence of animals from the sea. For a time their size and weight enabled them to overcome their adversaries and devour them. Their reaction to environment was to produce enormous muscles in their limbs which would give them power in fighting, and that part of their central nervous system which controlled these muscles—for example, the lower segments of the spinal cord supplying their legs—grew to be enormously larger than the brain itself !

They developed enormous power but their brains failed to develop the skill to use it. Their opponents, on the other hand, left their muscles to look after themselves and developed

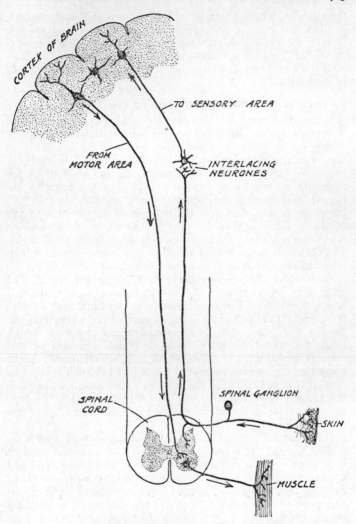

THE HUMAN TELEGRAPH SYSTEM

When trouble attacks the body machine, a warning message is flashed to the brain by the nervous system, pain is "felt," and the brain sends immediate orders for defence.

their brains, which brought with them new skill and cunning so that the great cumbersome reptiles were wiped off the face of the earth. Man's salvation in the struggle for existence has been his conservatism in leaving his body to look after itself and concentrating his attention on the development of his brain.

NERVES THAT BRING MESSAGES TO THE SPINAL CORD

IN the discussion of the anatomy and physiology of the nervous system that follows, we will start with the parts which are simplest to understand, and lead up gradually to the more complete and more difficult. Situated in the skin are many different kinds of sense organs and still others for receiving sensations of heat and cold. In the muscles are organs that detect deep pressure and tension and in the joints are organs that give information of the position of the bones in relation to one another. From all these sources nerve fibres collect information, one fibre from each organ, and these are later bound together into nerve trunks which travel to the spinal cord and there relay their information.

Just before the sensory nerve fibres enter the spinal cord each fibre gives off a small branch which passes to the cell which looks after the nourishment of the fibre and enables it to live. This cell is an integral part of the nerve and the fibres which reach it from the sense organs and those which enter the spinal cord are really only prolongations of this cell. There is thus a collection of cells which form a slight lump or ganglion on the nerve trunk just before it enters the cord. This is known as the posterior root ganglion, because the sensory roots entering the spinal cord do so in its posterior part (as opposed to the motor root which leaves the cord anteriorly).

Once having entered the spinal cord the sensory nerves do several things. The spinal cord consists of a central mass of grey matter which contains large numbers of nerve cells and a surrounding sheath of white matter that consists of fibres running up and down the cord, some travelling right up to, and down from, the brain. Some of the sensory fibres entering pass immediately into the grey matter and form connections with nerve cells in the front of the grey matter of the same segment. From these, fibres arise which leave by the anterior motor roots and pass into the nerves to innervate the muscles directly.

This is the simplest reflex path. Other sensory fibres run up or down and pass to neighbouring segments, some of them crossing over to the opposite side, forming reflex arcs with other segments. Other sensory fibres, some of which make connections with cells in the posterior grey matter and some of which go direct, turn upwards and run right through the length of the cord to various parts of the brain, carrying impulses of touch, pain, heat and cold, which eventually reach consciousness in the great sensory area of the brain cortex, which we shall talk of later.

LIFE WITHOUT THE BRAIN : THE SPINE'S ACTIVITIES

HAVING seen something of the anatomy of the cord we can now say something of what it does, but in order to study this experimentally we must destroy the brain, for this modifies the reflexes produced by the spinal cord by its controlling influence. An animal such as a frog, with its brain destroyed, is known as a spinal animal because its spinal cord only is now controlling it, and as it will live painlessly for a considerable time we can use it to excellent purpose for studying the functions of the spinal cord.

Such an animal exhibits reflex activity. Thus if the foot is pinched or if a hot instrument is applied to the foot, it will be drawn away, the whole limb being thrown into an attitude of flexion. Thus, the toes and foot are bent upwards, the knee and the hip are flexed. This reflex is known as the flexor reflex and represents a primitive activity of the nervous system in protecting the lower limb from damage. It is the simplest form of reflex, the paths used being those that we have mentioned.

At the same time as the stimulated limb is withdrawn by flexion, the opposite limb will be reflexly extended—the crossed extensor reflex. This enables the animal when standing to preserve its balance on the other foot while it draws the affected one away. Other reflexes may be briefly mentioned such as the scratch reflex in which tickling the back of a dog produces movements of flexion and extension of the hind limb in an endeavour to scratch away the offending object. Also the stepping reflex in which pressure on the sole of the foot, especially if the limb is slightly flexed, produces extension of the stimulated limb and flexion of the other. This is the mechanism of walking. As soon as the right foot touches the ground the pressure reflexly excites the muscles so that the right foot straightens to bear the weight, while the left flexes in preparation for the next step.

In addition to these reflexes which produce movement, many other reflexes are served by the spinal cord, the movements of the bowel producing peristalsis and the passing of fæces, the contraction of the bladder resulting in the act of passing water, various reflexes resulting in contraction or dilation of the vessels of a part, and a whole multitude of other reflexes which look after our well-being without ever reaching consciousness.

It must be understood that these muscular reflexes, such as the flexor reflex, are shown to their best advantage only when the spinal cord is working independently of the brain, when the brain has been destroyed or when the long tracts connecting it with the cord have been severed. The brain exercises a powerful control over these reflexes, modifying them and preventing them from dominating our existence. In the lower animals they were originally of immense value to the animal which possessed them, but as evolution progressed so have the spinal reflexes become more and more suppressed and brought under control of the higher centres of the brain.

An example of this is well shown in the case of the flexor reflex. In man, if the spinal cord is destroyed or if the nerve fibres running down from the brain which serve the voluntary control of the muscles are destroyed, a flexor reflex may be elicited by scratching the outer side of the sole of the foot. This action causes the great toe to be bent upwards, which, as we have seen, is one of the component parts of the protective flexor reflex. If, however, the sole of the foot is scratched in an individual in whom the tracts to the voluntary muscles are undamaged, the toe will bend downwards and the foot will, as it were, attempt to curl up.

The brain has depressed the flexor reflex and replaced it with a new reflex. It is only when the cord is " released " from the control of the brain that the flexor reflex manifests itself, although it is there, lying latent all the time. This is an example of what is known as the " release phenomenon " and is seen right throughout the central nervous system. It is found even in the higher centres of the brain which watch over such recently developed powers as the observance of social conventions, in fact the veneer of civilisation.

There are certain drugs which temporarily paralyse the highest and most recently developed functions of the brain and release those that lie below. A well-known example of a drug of this kind is alcohol, which is not really a stimulant at all but a paralyser of the highest centres. Under its influence those centres of the brain which supply us with our critical faculties and with the finer conventions of society are temporarily paralysed, allowing our " baser " and more instinctive natures to appear. It has often been said that alcohol is one of the finest means of revealing the true nature of a man.

THE NERVE CENTRES UPON WHICH LIFE DEPENDS

IF the spinal cord is followed upwards to its entry into the skull, it will be found to swell up into a wider mass which is known as the medulla oblongata. This is really only a specialised portion of the spinal cord and works in just the same way. Sensory nerves enter in its posterior part and motor nerves leave in its anterior part. Here, though, are situated the vital centres of the body—the respiratory centre which controls respiration and the cardiac centre which drives the heart. Sensory nerve fibres enter in a nerve, which is known as the vagus, and bring impulses carrying information from the heart and lungs. These fibres make connections with the cells in the medulla, and from them motor fibres leave, those to the heart travelling back to this organ in the vagus nerve, and those to the muscles of respiration passing down into the spinal cord and leaving it at different suitable levels. These nerve centres are absolutely vital for our continued existence, and their destruction brings about instantaneous death.

In this region, too, lie the centres which watch over our balance. Situated in the ear are special sense organs which supply these centres with information of the position in space which our head is occupying and of the movements which the head is making at any moment.

In order that a movement may be carried out in an orderly fashion, it is not sufficient for a given centre only to give orders that a movement must be made. In addition sensory nerves must inform the centre concerned of the progress of the movement from start to finish, so that it may order any modifications that may be necessary. This rule applies, of course, to all movements that are made, the sensory nerves carrying information from the muscles that make them. But, in movement of the head, information comes also from the ear, informing the centres about the balance of the head and its position in space. In all the lower vertebrates, these balancing organs are highly efficient and well developed, but in man they have regressed considerably, their powers being taken over by the eyes. They are, however, still of great importance.

Fish have balancing organs of a high degree of efficiency and so have birds, the reason being that these animals live and move freely in space, sometimes freely in three dimensions at one moment. Man, however, has had occasion, up till now, of moving only on flat surfaces. Deprived of the use of his eyes, his balance is precarious, and it is well known that airmen flying in fogs and clouds are often quite unaware of their position in space and may actually fly upside down without knowing it.

THE GREY MATTER: SEAT OF ALL SENSATION

ALL the way up the spinal cord, nerves enter from the body and limbs, carrying impulses of touch, pain, temperature and other sensations. Some of these fibres, we have seen, pass to cells in the cord and subserve local reflexes. Others, however, pass up towards the brain and, after relaying in two centres and being joined by similar nerves from the head and face, reach what is known as the sensory cortex of the brain. In their course upwards, they cross to the side of the body opposite to the one where they started, so that fibres reaching the right cortex come originally from the left.

Here we must say a few words about the structure of the brain. It is a hollow mass of nervous tissue, in the centre of which is a cavity containing fluid which circulates downwards to the medulla and then leaves by a small hole and gains the surface of the brain. The cavity is continuous with a central canal lying in the spinal cord. Surrounding the cavity is a great mass of white matter, made up of vast numbers of fibres passing in all directions and connecting together all the centres of the brain. Spread out like a thick plate over this white matter is a layer of grey matter which contains innumerable nerve cells. This grey matter is known as the cortex and is folded upon itself in convolutions in order to increase its area. The cortex of the brain is the highest and most specialised part of all, and it is this which confers upon us the powers of consciousness.

The sensory fibres, passing into the brain from the spinal cord, spread out and eventually reach a part of the cortex which runs vertically upwards and downwards just behind the middle of its lateral surface. This area is accurately localised and has been proved by the following experiment to be the site of conscious body sensations. During operations on the brain, this area has been stimulated in a conscious person by an electric current, with the result that sensations of pain have been felt in some part of the body at a distance, say in the hand, if the hand area was stimulated.

The sensory cortex is divided up accurately into areas which receive information from particular parts of the body, and which are the same for all persons. Owing to the fact that the sensory fibres cross over, as we have mentioned, before they reach this area, stimulation of the hand area on one side of the brain will produce a sensation in the hand on the other side of the body.

HOW THE BRAIN GIVES INSTRUCTIONS TO THE BODY

JUST in front of the sensory cortex is a vertical strip of grey matter, known as the motor cortex. Here are found large cells of a triangular or pyramid shape, which give off long processes passing right through the brain and spinal cord and making connections with the motor cells in the anterior part of the grey matter of the spinal cord. These are the same cells that we mentioned when we spoke of the motor cells or nerves that the spinal cord contained.

In their course downwards, these long fibres from the motor cortex cross over to the opposite side, so that a cell in the motor cortex of the right side controls a cell in the spinal cord, and through it a muscle fibre, on the left side of the body. This is the reason why a hæmorrhage in the motor area of the brain on one side (which is known popularly as a " stroke ") produces a paralysis of some part of the body on the opposite side. Just like the sensory cortex, the motor cortex has special areas for special parts of the body and stimulation of an area, say the hand area, will produce a movement in the hand of the opposite side.

We have spoken so far only of the two simplest parts of the brain cortex, where some body sensations become conscious and where volitional movement is originated. The rest of the cortex is made up of similar areas which serve their own particular function. Thus the visual area that brings to consciousness what we see with our eyes is situated on each side at the back of the brain. The hearing area is low down on the lateral surface, and a special speech area is situated on the left side of the brain. The front part of the brain is that part which is used in the processes of intellectual thought, memory and all the higher mental functions of which man is capable. All these areas are connected together by fibres which run between all the centres of both sides of the brain, so that a stimulus in affecting only one of them may produce a reaction in any one or all of the others.

THE ESSENCE OF MENTAL ACTIVITY

So far we have hinted that for any activity of the body to take place, a stimulus must be applied to some sense organ which will initiate a reflex. We have given the impression that, like a slot machine, something must be put in before anything can be got out. That this applies to the spinal reflexes there can be no doubt, but much argument and discussion have taken place over the mechanisms which lie behind conscious and unconscious mental processes. Many of our actions and thoughts appear at any rate to arise spontaneously in the brain without any previous stimulus setting them off, but on further consideration, it will always be found that there is a sequence in our thoughts and actions each depending on one that passed before.

Thoughts that spring into our minds with apparent spontaneity will always be found to have some association, often unconscious, with something previously seen or heard, a combination of circumstances or a previous thought. What constitutes the difficulty in applying our knowledge of reflexes to all grades of mental activity is not this but memory. It is difficult to see how a stimulus applied last year can produce its results to-day. If I agree to meet a friend in a certain place at a certain date and time next year, it is difficult to see how one can ascribe the performance of the visit to ordinary reflex activity. Some say that the reflex has been delayed, others that the nerve cells store up energy which is discharged at the appointed time, but these theories only beg the question by answering it in terms of another.

The best theory on which it is explained is that of the *conditioned reflex*. If a dog is given food, it will secrete saliva. If a bell is rung, and a few minutes later food is given to the dog, it will again secrete saliva in simple response to the food reflex. But after this process has been repeated a number of times, a curious thing occurs, for it is found that the dog will secrete saliva even in the absence of food, if the bell is still rung. The secretion of saliva is said to be conditioned by the ringing of the bell, and the reflex in response to which the saliva is secreted is known as a conditioned reflex. The secretion of saliva in response to the ringing of a bell is therefore a conditioned reflex.

It is known for certain that the nerve cells subserving all conditioned reflexes are situated in the brain cortex, for if this is destroyed experimentally in animals, all conditioned reflexes are abolished. It is assumed that new paths are formed between the cells of the cortex concerned and that a given stimulus—light or sound or anything else—therefore travels direct through this new path to the cells which produce the conditioned reflex. It is the laying down of new paths between the untold myriads of cells which constitute the cortex of our brain, in the course of every experience that we undergo, that is the essence of our mental and intellectual activity.

HOW THOUGHTS CARVE NEW PATHWAYS IN THE BRAIN

IN the case of memory, a new path is formed down which a stimulus travels at an appointed time, directly to the cells producing the conditioned response. In the case of a prearranged visit, when the arrangement is made a new path is formed between the sensory cells which bring to consciousness the knowledge of time and the motor cells which will set in motion all the activity needed for the visit. The combination of the date and hour when they arrive will occasion impulses which will travel along this specially made path, producing the conditioned response, in this case the visit.

It may be argued that we remember such things actually before the time arrives. This is true, but does not invalidate the argument, for some association will have brought the combination of date and time into our mind, producing in an indirect way the necessary conditioned response. Thus, in a chance glance at a calendar a week before the visit was to take place, our eyes might fall upon the date arranged. This stimulus would travel along the path specially laid down and would awake the consciousness of memory. This is only a crude example but serves to illustrate the theory and brings our mental processes into line with the general laws of nature, according to which we know that energy and matter never arise out of nothing.

THE HUMAN MACHINE AT WORK

by THOMAS ARMSTRONG, *M.A.(Cantab.)*

*P*HYSIOLOGY *is the study of how the body works under normal conditions. It is the study of the workings of the family life and the interrelationships of each of its members. It tells us how much money, or in physiological language, how much energy is required to run the house, what food must be bought and by whom it must be cooked. In physiology the actual part which each organ of the body plays in the running of the whole is accurately worked out.*

Many of these things are known definitely now, but there is still much that is controversial and much about which we know absolutely nothing. As time goes on, however, more and more of the obscurities are brought by research into the light of day, and with the progress of knowledge about the normal working of the body, more and more is understood of the abnormal working of the body, so that medicine itself also advances. Physiology is the basis of medicine, and without a knowledge of it doctors could know nothing of their job to-day.

If we start at the very beginning of our life, we were each one of us originally one single fertilised cell lying in the ovary of our mother. The ovum or egg cell is like any other cell, a tiny membranous bag containing a mass of jelly or protoplasm. In the centre of the cell is a nucleus which controls the life of the cell. During fertilisation the spermatozoon or male germ pierces the envelope of the egg cell and joins with the nucleus, the two forming one cell. This cell is the fertilised egg and represents our earliest beginnings.

Almost immediately after fertilisation has taken place, the cell starts to divide into two, the nucleus first dividing and the cell then following suit. Each of the two cells so formed is exactly like the one from which it originally arose. In a short time each of these two cells again divides into two, so making four. This process continues, first eight, then sixteen, then thirty-two cells being formed, until the egg comes to look something like a mulberry and is now called a morula.

This process of division goes on continuously until eventually certain parts of the mass begin to take on a definite function of their own. After this, one or two cells become different from the others and " differentiate " into a rudimentary liver, one or two others differentiate into a lung, and some more start to form a brain.

From this time on these cells are destined to form their respective organs and can only form this kind of tissue. Finally, a complete and perfect individual emerges, an individual composed of thousands of millions of tiny cells, each performing its own special function and working harmoniously with the whole.

This process has been studied to the greatest advantage by means of cinematography. A developing egg is placed under the microscope and supplied with a nourishing medium and a photograph is taken, say once every half-hour. When the photographs are thrown upon a screen, one after the other in rapid succession, the movements and method of division of the cells and the formations into which they arrange themselves can be studied in the minutest detail. The leg of a chicken can be seen to grow from a shapeless mass of protoplasm into a useful member with all its intricate parts, and this even when it has been cut away completely from the main part of the developing egg.

LIFE THAT GOES ON AFTER DEATH

NOT only have quite separate parts of a developing individual been kept alive and studied under the microscope, but organs and separate cells of a fully-grown organism have been kept alive for long periods of time, existing quite separately from their parent mass of body tissue. Thus there is a strain of fibrous tissue which has been kept alive and constantly growing for twenty or thirty years. Some tissues are easier to culture than others, this depending to some extent on the food requirements of the tissue cultures.

All cells, however, are potentially immortal. There is no real reason why they should ever die, provided they are constantly kept supplied with nourishment. Under natural cirumstances the cells of the body die only because they are deprived of their nourishment, for the circulation of the blood and respiration, which are vital processes depending on the activity of the whole body, cease when the individual dies. Life continues for a considerable time in the cells themselves after death of the body as a whole has taken place. If the body of a frog is opened ten minutes after death, the heart will still be found to be beating. In the same way an animal which is incapable of moving its legs because it is dead can be made to do so some time after death if a nerve passing to the muscles is stimulated by an electric current.

This life after death need not dismay us, for it lasts at most for a few brief hours, and in spite of it, the animal as a whole is dead, for it is capable of no sensation and no movement. Consciousness, of course, is lost immediately, for the brain, being one of the most delicate mechanisms the body possesses, ceases to function instantaneously and dies very rapidly.

Loss of power to function must be understood to be quite different from death. From real death, death of all the cells, there is no recovery, but from loss of function recovery is possible. If the arteries supplying the brain are clamped, consciousness is lost immediately for they cease to function. If the clamps are removed quickly enough, consciousness is regained, for the cells were only temporarily paralysed. If, however, the clamps are left on for six minutes, the brain will never function, for the cells will have died.

Some tissues die more rapidly than others, and it is always the vital tissues that are most differentiated, like the heart and brain, that die most quickly. Others, like the humble fibrous tissue which only supports, may take some hours, and if removed within this period, may live and grow indefinitely if placed in proper surroundings.

We have said that some cells are more differentiated or specialised than others and that these die much more rapidly than their humble, unspecialised brothers. The special cells of the brain and heart and of the liver and kidneys may be compared to the intellectual members of society, such men as scientists, doctors, Cabinet Ministers, and artists, without whose services the community would collapse but whose natures and constitutions are so delicate that they withstand the strains of hardship very poorly. If deprived of their ideal surroundings, they first fail in their work and then in their bodies. The supporting structures of the body, however, such structures as fibrous tissue and fat, may be compared to those humbler but no less important members of society, the manual workers, who being less pampered and less sensitive to their environment are more capable of withstanding ususual hardships.

We have said enough to illustrate how the body is composed of elements which, under ideal circumstances, are capable of a separate existence, but which must for their proper functioning depend on the integrity of the individual as a whole.

THE PHYSIOLOGICAL INCOME

BEFORE we can understand the part that food plays in the workings of our inner man, we must know something of the chemistry and composition of the food we eat. For practical purposes we may divide our food into four great classes, each of which, as we shall see, has its own particular use. First and most important of all are the proteins. These substances are the essential basis of all living matter, and, as one might expect, their chemical composition is extremely complex. The proteins are found throughout nature in all types of living matter, both plant and animal.

Some of the simpler ones the animal body is capable of elaborating for itself, but others must be obtained by the food, and these will come either from other animals or from plants. If a protein, for example the white of an egg, is digested in a test tube with some juice from the stomach and some hydrochloric acid, after a time the composition of the digest will change. The complicated protein molecule will be split into many simpler parts. If the process is continued until the protein is split into its simplest components, it will be found that, instead of egg albumin, we are left with a large number of substances called amino acids. Here we cannot go into the structure of the amino acids, but we will simply say that they are acids which always contain atoms of carbon, hydrogen and nitrogen, and sometimes also sulphur, phosphorus and other elements. They also have the power of combining together under special circumstances and forming chains.

It must be understood that the proteins are a large class of substances, the individual members of which may have many differences, but they all have certain properties in common. We have seen that a particular protein, egg white, can be broken down into various amino acids. It remains now to reverse the process and synthesise the protein from its constituent parts.

It may be said at the outset that this has never been done completely, but so much of the road has been explored that the remainder is certain. If amino acids of different kinds are made to join together in sufficient numbers, a substance known as a polypeptide is formed. Many polypeptides joined together in chains form a peptone, and numbers of peptones joined together form primary and secondary proteoses. These latter when joined together make up the complete protein.

Each of these substances, amino acids, polypeptides, peptones, proteoses and proteins have their own special chemical reactions so that they may be identified. The composition of the proteins has been shown by digestion and each stage has been worked out. The road backwards has been fully explored. The road forwards from amino acid to protein has progressed so far only to the polypeptide stage, but the last part may be inferred from the backward journey, which is known. If we remember that there are a large number of amino acids, that they can be combined in any way and any number that nature chooses, and that in a protein molecule there may be hundreds of thousands of amino acids, we shall realise how many proteins Nature can make in her workshops. We shall also realise how extremely complicated their structure is.

SUGAR: A CONSTANT SOURCE OF ENERGY

THE next class of substances are the carbohydrates or sugars. The simplest of these is glucose or grape sugar, and it contains six atoms of carbon, twelve of hydrogen, and six of oxygen. Its chemical formula is $C_6H_{12}O_6$. Glucose belongs to the class of monosaccharides because it is composed of one sugar molecule. If two monosaccharides are combined together, a disaccharide is formed, of which the ordinary household cane sugar is an example. If many mono- or di- saccharides are combined, a polysaccharide is formed, and the most important of these are starch in the vegetable kingdom and glycogen in the animal kingdom. Starch and glycogen may be resolved by digestion with hydrochloric acid into their component monosaccharides. The carbohydrates are one of the main sources of our energy, for they can be readily burnt up in the body with the resulting evolution of heat or energy.

FATS AND SALTS: THE ECONOMICAL FUELS

THE fats are composed of carbon, hydrogen, and oxygen, like the carbohydrates, but they contain a larger proportion of carbon and hydrogen and less oxygen so that when burnt up more heat is generated than when the carbohydrates are burnt. The fats, therefore, are the most economical of fuel. They give us the best money's worth. As found in nature, the fats are combinations of a fatty acid and glycerine, a so-called neutral fat. Digestion will result in resolution into the two component parts.

The fourth class of substances are the salts. The simplest example of these is common household salt which, as is well known, is composed of an atom of sodium and an atom of chlorine. Its formula is NaCl. Many other mineral salts enter into our food, but they are not of much interest here, for digestion has no effect upon them and they are absorbed unchanged into the circulation. Their use is a complicated biochemical one and they are certainly essential to life, but we are not concerned with them in this connection.

THE DIGESTIVE MACHINERY

THE object of digestion is to break down the constituents of the food into the simplest parts, so that the food is more readily absorbed. Also the proteins must be broken down first, so that they may be built up later into proteins characteristic of the animal that uses them. Mutton protein as such would be useless to man. It must be absorbed in pieces so that he can make his own peculiar protein for himself.

Digestion is accomplished by means of certain juices which break up the constituents of the food. These juices are secreted by glands. A typical gland is composed of a number of cells arranged to form a flask or retort, from the opening of which a duct leads. The cells have the power of taking substances from the blood and converting them into juices or secretions which are carried down the duct to the place where they are used. Each gland is supplied with nerves which control its working.

When food is taken into the mouth, it is broken up into small fragments and intimately mixed with the saliva which is secreted by certain glands in the neck. This saliva has the power of breaking down the starches and polysaccharides into disaccharides. The stimulus which makes the glands secrete is not only the presence of food in the mouth, but even the sight or smell of food. It is a well-known fact that the " mouth will water " even at the sight of some tasty morsel.

When the food is swallowed, it reaches the stomach, and here it comes under the powerful influence of the gastric juice, which breaks down the proteins into proteoses and peptones and has some small action on the sugars. The mechanism of the secretion of gastric juice has been well shown by Pavlov's experiments with dogs. He cut the gullet in the neck and brought each end to the surface, so that food swallowed by the dog did not go into the stomach but was discharged from the cut end. He also brought a small part of the stomach to the surface of the body, so that he could directly watch how much juice was secreted.

He found that the sight or smell of food, even if it was not given to the dog, would start the stomach secreting. If food was swallowed, the stomach would secrete, even if food did not reach it. Also if food was introduced into the stomach without the knowledge of the dog, as could easily be done, the stomach would secrete, but the amount of secretion depended on the character of the food. Meat was more potent in producing a flow than bread, for example. Here, laid before us, is the whole mechanism of glandular secretion. First comes the psychical secretion at the sight of food, then the mere presence of food in the stomach from its mechanical action, and thirdly the chemical stimulus from the nature of the food.

HOW THE FUEL IS BROKEN UP

AFTER the food leaves the stomach it enters the duodenum, which is the next part of the bowel. Into this open two ducts, one the bile duct from the liver and the other the pancreatic duct from the pancreas. The juice from the pancreas contains several ferments which act in conjunction with the bile. This, though it contains no ferments itself, is a powerful assistant to the pancreatic juice. Between them these two juices break up the remains of the proteins into polypeptides and amino acids, the fats into fatty acids and glycerine, and the sugars and starches into monosaccharides.

Some few of the food constituents will have escaped the breaking-down process, and these are acted upon by a juice, the succus entericus, which is secreted by the small intestine itself. The result is that the contents of the intestine now consist of a fluid mass containing amino acids, fatty acids, glycerine and monosaccharides in such a condition that they are ready for absorption.

HOW FOOD GETS INTO THE BLOOD

THE intestine is well supplied by blood vessels and lymphatics into which the products of digestion can be taken. The mechanism by which this is affected is by no means certain, and the probability of its exact working being discovered is remote, for the process is an obscure and essentially vital one that would require a knowledge of the deepest secrets of the cells themselves. It may be stated that during absorption work is performed by the cells, for they have to work against a definite pressure. The contents of the intestine are more concentrated than the blood, and therefore water will tend to pass out of the tissues into the bowel.

This tendency to equalise concentration on both sides of a membrane is known as osmotic pressure, and the cells have to work against it in absorbing material into the blood. One thing, however, we do know, and that is that the finger-like processes known as villi, which cover the inside of the intestine, are contractile elements. Their function is to increase the effective area over which the absorption can take place and also to assist it mechanically.

A villus is a minute structure, like the frond of a sea-anemone, covered on the outside with absorbing cells and filled with soft, connective tissue. Running up the centre is a lymphatic vessel and blood vessels into which the products are absorbed. There is also a muscle which can increase and decrease the volume of the villus, so that suction on the contents of the bowel can be applied. This suction sucks the bowel contents through the cells and not through any opening. Under certain circumstances the villi can be seen contracting rhythmically under the microscope, proving the action. This is all that we know of the mechanism of absorption, and it is by no means the whole story.

The fats, which have been re-synthesised in the villi after their splitting in the bowel, are absorbed into the lymphatics, and later enter the blood stream. The sugars and amino acids are absorbed into branches of the portal vein, and pass from there to the liver, as we know from our anatomy.

THE LIVER : CHEMICAL FACTORY OF THE BODY

WHEN the sugars reach the liver, they are converted by the activity of the liver cells into glycogen, which, as we have mentioned before, is a complex starch made up of many monosaccharide molecules. The glycogen is stored in the liver and later, as required, split down again into glucose and passed into the circulation, where it is used directly by the tissues. The liver, thus, is a storehouse for sugar and prevents its too rapid use.

Of the amino acids absorbed, some are burnt up in the same way as the sugars are, in order to provide warmth and energy, and the liver plays a large part in this process. Before they can be burnt, they must be converted into sugars, and this action is performed by the liver, which removes the nitrogen from their molecules so that it can be excreted by the kidneys. Those amino acids which are not burnt up for energy escape the gauntlet of the liver and pass to the body cells in general, where they are built up into complex human proteins.

This is the part of our food which replaces the wear and tear of the body and is so essential for the well-being of an adult and the growth of a child. We require actually only sufficient protein in our diet to enable us to replace our wear and tear. Sugar and fat can supply the energy, but they can never be of use in this particular way. This, too, is why growing children require so much more protein than adults.

The fats also eventually reach the liver by way of the general blood stream. Some of them after absorption are taken up by the fat cells under the skin and in other parts of the body, and stored there until they are wanted for the production of energy. Before they can be burnt, however, they must pass through the liver, which changes them slightly and so makes them more readily combustible.

The liver is one of the important workshops in which sugar is converted into fat. That this is possible in the body is interesting, for it is the cause of fatness in many people to-day. It was for long considered that excessive eating of sugar could lead to obesity, and it was proved conclusively by feeding two pigs of the same litter, one with and one without sugar. The weight of fat in the pig fed with sugar greatly exceeded the fat in the body of the one who had gone without. The majority of people to-day who are unduly fat could reduce comfortably by cutting down their diet, especially that part containing sugar.

INSULIN: THE MATCH THAT LIGHTS OUR FIRES

THE story of insulin is a fascinating one, but we can deal with it only very briefly here. Our warmth, energy and muscular activity depend upon the amount of fat and sugar which is burnt inside our bodies. Before fat can be burnt, sugar must be burnt, too—the fat is, as it were, burnt up in the heat generated by the carbohydrate fires. If sugar is not burnt at the same time as fat, the fat is incompletely burnt and the products of its disintegration are poisonous. They are known as ketone bodies, owing to their chemical composition. This unhappy result takes place either when there is no sugar to burn with the fat, as during a prolonged starvation, or when the sugar, though present in abundance, cannot for some reason be burnt itself.

Insulin is a substance secreted into the blood stream by the pancreas, which makes it possible for the body to burn sugar. Without insulin no sugar can be burnt nor, of course, can the fat be completely used up. The result of this is that sugar accumulates in the blood and overflows into the urine, while poisonous products of fat metabolism, the ketone bodies, appear in the body and may eventually cause death. The cure for this condition which, of course is diabetes, is the injection of insulin under the skin. The insulin puts a match, as it were, to the fires of carbohydrate metabolism in which the fats are completely burnt without leaving a trace of poisonous ash.

THE CHEMICAL MESSENGERS OF THE BLOOD

WE have seen how the ordinary glands of the body produce their secretions and how the latter pass down particular ducts to the sites where they act. We have now to deal with those glands which have no duct and pass their secretions direct into the blood stream. These glands are therefore known as ductless glands.

In those humble forms of life, in which the organism contains only one cell, any movement or reaction which the cell undergoes must be due to physical or chemical stimulation by its environment. Single-celled organisms will be attracted or repelled by heat or cold or by chemical substances present in solution around them. In those animals, which contain not one but many cells, a similar response takes place, for certain glands throw out into the blood stream substances which act as messengers, producing reactions in those cells with which the blood comes in contact. These chemical messengers are known as hormones.

THE THYROID GLAND: SPEED REGULATOR OF OUR LIVES

PERHAPS the best known of the ductless glands is the thyroid, which lies in front of the windpipe or trachea in the neck. This gland is composed of a number of more or less spherical

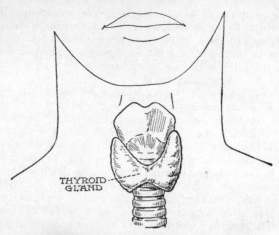

POSITION OF THE THYROID GLAND

The gland embracing the Adam's apple, whose secretion affects growth and exercises a profound influence upon all the body cells.

bulbs or alveoli. They are like flasks but there is no opening. The interior of the alveolus is filled with a transparent mass of material called colloid, which is secreted by cubical cells lining the alveolus. Between the alveoli are numerous blood vessels into which the secretion is absorbed to be distributed all over the body. The active principle of the thyroid gland is a substance called thyroxine which has been completely investigated chemically, whose formula is known, and which has been synthesised in the laboratory. It is the only ductless gland secretion which exerts any effect when taken by the mouth, for it is unaffected by digestion. All the others are completely destroyed by the processes of digestion so that they must be taken by injection to exert any effect.

The rôle played by the thyroid has been worked out by studying the effects of the removal of the gland from animals and by injecting extracts of the glands into animals from which it has been removed. Also, certain individuals, known as cretins, have the misfortune to be born with insufficient thyroid secretion, while others suffer from a disease known as exophthalmic goitre in which the gland secretes excessively.

The cretin presents a picture of under-development both

mental and physical. Stunted, pot-bellied and ugly, a cretin of twenty may have the appearance and intellect of a child of four. If treated sufficiently early, by feeding them with thyroid tablets, these creatures may be turned into intelligent and useful members of society.

WHEN THE FIRES OF LIFE BURN LOW: A STRANGE DISEASE

IN adult life, if the thyroid undergoes regression, a condition known as myxœdema is produced. The unfortunate person becomes slow and dull of intellect and so forgetful that it is quite impossible to cure his condition by giving him a bottle of thyroid tablets to take home, for he will forget to take them when relapse occurs. The skin becomes coarse and dry and the hair falls out. The whole aspect of the individual changes and he sinks into a purely vegetative existence. The temperature and pulse rate fall, and he will complain bitterly of cold, owing to the lowered rate at which the fires of metabolism are burning. The appetite goes and there is little desire for food, and with it falls the amount of waste products secreted in the urine. If the basal metabolic rate, which is the measure of the warmth and energy given out by an individual at rest, is measured it will be found to be enormously below par. This condition is completely curable by feeding the patient with thyroid tablets, but they must be administered for the rest of his life and never given up, and it must be seen that he takes them regularly.

THE PATIENT WHO LIVES TOO FAST

AT the opposite end of the scale is Graves's disease, in which the thyroid exhibits a high degree of over-activity. The condition is often precipitated by a nervous shock, and the patient presents a picture of great excitability. He is exceedingly restless and always fidgeting, worrying incessantly about trivial matters of the least consequence. Sweating is profuse and the heart beats at a greatly increased rate. The temperature is raised and, owing to the rapid rate at which food and body tissues are burnt up, the patient becomes very thin. The basal metabolic rate will be found to be greatly increased. The surest method of curing this condition is to remove the greater part of the enlarged thyroid gland by an operation, the results of which are sometimes almost miraculous.

It is therefore clear that the thyroid regulates the rate at which we live. It is like the tap on the side of a gas oven which controls the temperature inside. In addition to this, it is responsible in part for growth and mental development.

Some years ago, when the parathyroid glands were insufficiently understood, it was noted that patients who had their thyroid gland removed for Graves's disease sometimes went into a condition known as tetany. Their nervous systems became enormously over-excitable and, at the slightest provocation, their hands and feet would go into a painful spasm. Later it became known that this was because some small glands, situated inside the thyroid but differing from it in function, had been removed with it. These were the parathyroid glands.

It was found in addition that the people who suffered from tetany had less chalk in their blood than normal people. In contrast to this, if a normal animal was given injections of an extract of the gland, it was found that the amount of chalk in its blood went up until eventually it collapsed and died of vomiting and diarrhœa. It will be quite obvious, therefore, that the parathyroid hormone regulates the amount of calcium or chalk in the blood. Exactly how this is done is not quite certain, but there is strong evidence to show that the hormone in some way makes the calcium leave the bones and enter the blood.

This suggestion is supported by the fact that people who have tumours of their parathyroids, causing them to secrete too much hormone, have a curious condition of their bones which, because they have too little chalk in them, are rarefied and brittle and break under the slightest strain. When the parathyroid glands are removed, the bones return to their normal condition, showing clearly that the glands were the cause of all the trouble.

THE GLAND THAT DEFENDS US IN EMERGENCY

LYING on the top of the kidney on each side of the body is a gland known as the suprarenal. It consists of two quite separate parts which have nothing whatever to do with one another. There is an outer shell or cortex of a yellow colour and an inner dark-brown mass known as the medulla. The cortex is essential to life, for if it is diseased or removed the animal becomes pigmented and its blood pressure falls until eventually it dies. Sometimes when the cortex is over-active, the individual reverts apparently to the opposite sex. For example, a woman will develop a coarse beard all over her face, like a man. This is often the cause of the so-called bearded women sometimes seen in circuses.

The medulla, however, is quite different, for it secretes a substance known as adrenalin, which is now well known and has actually been made in the laboratory. The action of adrenalin may be summarised by saying that it makes the animal alert and puts it in the best position to defend itself when attacked. Thus if adrenalin is injected into an animal, it makes all the blood vessels contract in those parts of the body which are not useful in fighting and drives the blood into more useful channels. The blood vessels of the intestines are emptied so that more blood can go to the brain and muscles. At the same time, adrenalin increases the force and rate at which the heart beats, so that more blood is available for rapidly-working organs. The effects of adrenalin are exactly similar to those produced by the sympathetic nervous system, for the suprarenal actually is a part of the sympathetic nervous system and is actuated by it. One other action of adrenalin is of interest, and this is its effect on the muscles which control the hairs. Each hair has a minute muscle attached to its base which, when it contracts, will make the hair stand on end. Both stimulation of the sympathetic nerve and the application of adrenalin will result in contraction of the muscle so that the hair is erected.

If this happens all over the body, as it does, for example, in the cat, the animal will be bristling with hairs all over and will appear much larger and more formidable to its enemies. The same action is seen in the hedgehog, only here it produces not only an apparent but also a real protection, for with the spines erected the animal presents an almost impregnable fortress. In man, goose-flesh is produced by some shocking or revolting sight, and excessive fear will result in our hair standing on end.

The proof that adrenalin is secreted under conditions of fear and can cause these effects is experimental and very interesting. A cat, under anæsthesia, had a long glass tube passed into a vein in its leg and running right up into the abdomen to a point where blood was returned into the inferior vena cava from the suprarenal glands. Blood from the suprarenals could thus be drawn off directly whenever desired. After a time, when the cat had recovered from the anæsthetic, it was frightened by a dog barking in the same room and some of the blood from the tube was drawn off. When this was used for perfusing an isolated heart, the rate at which the heart was beating was increased. In addition, when this blood was injected into another cat, all the effects of adrenalin were produced.

THE GLAND THAT CONTROLS OUR GROWTH

SITUATED at the base of the brain and hanging down from it is a gland known as the pituitary. It is divided by a septum into two parts, known as the anterior and posterior lobes, which have quite different functions. The anterior lobe is one of the main organs which control growth in young animals and keep it in check in older ones. If the pituitary is experimentally destroyed in young animals, they fail to grow and they also fail to exhibit sexual development—that is, the organs of sex remain in an infantile condition.

Overgrowth of the gland has been shown to give rise to gigantism, a condition in which all the bones of the body show a more or less harmonious overgrowth, with the production of a giant instead of an individual of normal proportions. In the same way, rats may be caused to grow to enormous sizes by giving them injections of the anterior lobe of the pituitary when they are young.

If the overgrowth of the gland occurs when the individual is already fully grown, it produces the curious condition known as acromegaly. Here only a few of the bones undergo unusual enlargement, these being the hands, which are large and spade-like, and the lower jaw, which becomes heavy and projects forwards unduly, so that the lower teeth come to lie in front of the upper when the jaws are closed. The face grows long and heavy, and the nose becomes very accentuated, the whole facial expression being changed to one of extreme ugliness such as is best described by the expression " lantern-jawed."

The posterior lobe secretes several hormones, one of which makes the blood vessels contract and another which has a special influence on the muscle of the womb during labour. For this reason it is much used during childbirth when the womb contracts only feebly. This substance goes by the name of " pituitrin."

THE GLAND THAT CONTROLS MENSTRUATION

IN addition to producing the ova or egg cells, which we shall consider later, the ovary has several very interesting and important functions. In childhood it secretes a substance known as œstrin, which is responsible for growth and develops the secondary sexual characteristics. In fact it makes a girl into a woman and is responsible for all the differences between men and women that appear at the age of puberty. At this age a woman commences to menstruate, that is, she bleeds every month from the womb. This process, which has caused so much trouble, is really a mechanism by which an egg cell, which is discharged from the ovary every month, may, if it becomes fertilised, find a new and clean home in which to develop. When the ovum does not become fertilised, the womb casts it out, as it were, and repairs itself in readiness for the next opportunity.

The ovary contains certain structures, known as follicles, which produce the ova each month. Before the ovum is ripe and is ready to be thrown out of the ovary, the follicle produces œstrin in fairly large amounts. The action of this substance is to prepare the inside of the womb for the reception of the fertilised egg. Later, when the ovum has been cast out of the ovary and is ready for fertilisation, the remains of the follicle produce a new substance known as lutein, which keeps the womb in good condition and assists the implantation of the ovum.

If the ovum is fertilised, it becomes imbedded in the womb and pregnancy ensues. The lutein secreted by the ovary helps in this process and prevents menstruation occurring. It also produces enlargement of the breasts, so that the infant can suckle when born. After eight months it begins to disappear and allows labour and the birth of the child to take place. If, however, the ovum is not fertilised, the follicle, which is still producing lutein and stopping menstruation, begins to disappear after ten days, so menstruation takes place in preparation for the next ovum which the ovary will discharge the following month.

CAN MONKEY GLANDS GIVE NEW LIFE TO MAN?

THE testis, the organ which produces the male germ cells or spermatozoa, elaborates also a hormone which is responsible for the secondary sexual characteristics that appear in man. If deprived of this organ, man fails to grow hair upon his face and body, and the voice remains high-pitched and " unbroken," owing to under-development of the larynx. Eunuchs, too, are invariably fat.

Voronoff has claimed that many of the manifestations of

old age are due to the fact that the testis runs out of secretion and fails to keep the body in good repair. He grafted the testes of monkeys into patients who were growing old and claims that they became rejuvenated. Whether his results are as good as popular opinion would lead us to suppose is uncertain, but it would seem to be a dangerous experiment, for it is, as it were, driving too hard a dying horse. The last years of life may be made more exciting and the patient may feel younger, but the machine will probably run down more rapidly and life come to an end sooner and in a more spectacular manner.

It must not be supposed that the ductless glands work separately and independently of one another. Each affects the others, and any upset in one will lead to corresponding upsets in the rest. A balance is normally effected between all the hormones circulating in the blood, and on this balance our well-being depends. Some people place disturbances of the ductless glands as the cause of many of our obscure conditions of ill-health, others say that they are responsible for all the differences in personalities and psychical qualities that exist between each one of us. However much truth there is in these theories, one thing is certain and that is that we know very little of their relationships one to another, that much will be found out in the next few years, and that meanwhile we should be wary in upsetting the balance by dosing people with products of the ductless glands without adequate cause.

THE HEART: VORTEX OF CIRCULATION

IN the section on Anatomy, we learned that the heart consists of four muscular chambers, and we considered the main points in the anatomy of the circulation as a whole. Here it is our business to discuss the mechanisms by which the circulation is kept going and under what circumstances it varies.

If we cut out the heart from an animal immediately after death, we shall find that it will continue to beat rhythmically for a short period of its own accord. If we now supply it, through the openings of its vessels, with a nutrient fluid, we can keep it going for a longer period, and we can study it as simply as we could study any other purely mechanical machine.

We shall find that the heart of itself has an inherent power of beating rhythmically and that the direction of the blood flow through the heart is always the same and is determined by the valves. The first thing that happens is that the auricles fill from the veins and then contract, driving the blood through the auriculo-ventricular valves into the ventricles. Both auricles contract simultaneously. One-tenth of a second later the ventricles contract, again simultaneously, and drive the blood into the arteries. Regurgitation of blood, as we have seen, is prevented by the valves.

LAWS THAT THE HEART MUST OBEY

THERE are two " laws " which govern the working of the heart as a machine and which are of the greatest importance and interest. The first is that each muscular fibre of the heart always contracts to the very best of its ability at any one moment. A fibre can give only one kind of contraction at any moment, namely the maximal. A fibre contracts completely or not at all. This is known as the " All or None Law." The maximal contraction will vary from time to time according to circumstances, but each contracting fibre is always bound to do its best under the circumstances existing at the moment.

The second law is known as " Starling's Law of the Heart," and states that within certain limits the longer a muscle fibre becomes, owing to stretching, the better and more forcibly it will contract. The best that a fibre can do is increased if the fibre is lengthened.

The vast importance of this is that, if a larger than usual amount of blood comes to the heart via the veins, the heart will be unusually distended with blood and its muscle fibres will be lengthened. They will therefore be capable of more vigorous contraction, and the heart will consequently be able to pump out the extra amount of blood without becoming dilated or actually bursting.

It is a defence mechanism, preventing the heart from being disabled and automatically ensuring that the heart responds at once to the work required of it. In exactly the same way if the pressure in the arteries is increased for any reason, as in exercise, the heart must do more work in pumping out blood against a greater resistance. Temporarily blood is dammed back into the heart, but immediately the fibres become lengthened owing to the distension by the blood dammed back, and they contract more forcibly enabling the heart to cope with the increase in work required of it.

THE NERVES THAT CONTROL OUR HEART-BEATS

IN the wall of the right auricle is a collection of nerve cells which start the contractions of the heart. From this point the contraction spreads over the heart like a wave. It is by virtue of this collection of cells that the heart is enabled to beat when it is cut out of the body. These nerve cells are known as the sino-auriculo node, and in the body they are controlled by two nerves coming from the central nervous system—one, the vagus, from the brain : the other, the sympathetic, which comes eventually from the spinal cord.

These nerves influence the rate of the heart. This can be proved if the nerves are cut one by one. If the vagus is cut, the heart will beat more rapidly, for its slowing influence is removed. If the cut end which leads to the heart is stimulated by an electric current, the heart will beat more slowly. If the sympathetic is cut, the heart will beat more slowly, and if its cut end is stimulated, the heart will beat faster. The vagus, therefore, slows the heart and the sympathetic quickens it.

In the walls of the great veins entering the heart are certain nerve fibres which are sensitive to stretching when the veins are dilated by a large volume of blood. These nerves collect themselves into a bundle of fibres, which pass to the central nervous system and form connection with the vagus and sympathetic. They subserve a reflex known as Bainbridge's Reflex, and their function is to drive the heart faster in order to cope with an extra amount of blood coming to it. When the veins are engorged, these nerves are stretched and impulses pass to the nervous system which inhibit the vagus and stimulate the sympathetic so that the heart beats faster.

On the other side of the heart, in the wall of the aorta, are some nerve fibres which join to form the depressor nerve which subserves the depressor reflex. If the pressure in the aorta is increased, these nerve fibres are stretched and impulses pass up them to the nervous system, where the vagus is stimulated and the sympathetic inhibited so that the heart is slowed. This, of course, is a defensive mechanism to prevent the blood pressure from becoming too high. Both these reflexes act purely automatically, of course, and we know nothing about it when they are brought into play, for their activity never comes into consciousness.

HOW THE BLOOD IS SENT BACK TO THE HEART

At first sight it would seem difficult to understand why blood returns to the heart from the capillaries without anything to drive it. The heart itself drives the blood to the capillaries, but there is no heart to drive it back. There are three things that assist the return by the veins, the first being the fact that there are valves interposed in the course of the veins, preventing the blood flowing backwards—away from the heart. This can be demonstrated quite clearly by choosing any vein which stands out sharply in the arm and running a finger firmly down it towards the hand, finally compressing the vein with the finger so that no further blood can enter it. The blood will flow backwards from above until a valve is encountered, where it will be held up. The vein below the valve, and between it and the finger, will remain quite empty so long as the pressure is kept up.

The flow of blood back to the heart is greatly assisted by the contraction of the muscles which under normal circumstances is continually taking place. The muscles squeeze the blood along the veins and help to counteract the influence of gravity. The third factor of great importance is the negative pressure—i.e. pressure less than atmospheric—which exists in the thorax and which is greatly increased when we inspire. This negative pressure which surrounds the great veins entering the heart is constantly tending to suck blood into them, thus returning it to the heart.

WHAT HAPPENS BETWEEN HEART-BEATS

The pressure which the blood exerts in the arteries is, of course, dependent on the amount of blood which the heart pumps out on each beat. If the arteries were rigid tubes, this pressure would fall and rise with every beat of the heart, or would fall almost to zero between each beat when no blood was leaving the heart or entering the arteries. Nature has guarded against such an untoward result by making the arteries elastic, so that they expand when blood is forced into them and store up the blood.

When the heart finishes its beat and is resting in preparation for the next, the arteries rebound by their elasticity, so that the pressure is kept within reasonable limits and blood is forced into the capillaries in a continuous stream, instead of in an intermittent one. In old age the arteries become degenerate and hardened and lose their elasticity, so that the blood pressure becomes higher and fluctuates more when the heart beats.

THE COMPLICATED PROCESS OF RUNNING A RACE

WE have seen briefly how the heart works by itself and how it works when controlled by its nerves. In order to see it in action in relation to the body as a whole, let us see what is the effect upon it of exercise, say the running of a strenuous hundred-yards race. The muscles all over the body, but especially those in the legs, are working much harder than normal, so that they will require a greatly increased blood supply in order to enable them to work efficiently. This extra blood must be supplied by the heart which pumps blood round the circulation more rapidly.

Because the muscles are working and contracting, they will squeeze more blood back to the heart, and this effect will be helped by the increasing rate and depth of breathing, which will suck the blood back into the thorax. Respiration is increased, of course, so that the blood may become more oxygenated and therefore be of more use to the hard-working muscles. The increasing venous return, both because it elongates the muscle fibres of the heart and because it sets the Bainbridge reflex in operation, results in the heart doing more work and throwing out more blood into the circulation at each beat.

Meanwhile the suprarenal glands secrete adrenalin into the blood stream, and this substance increases the force of the heart beat, adding its support to all the other mechanisms. Adrenalin, however, has quite a different action as well, for it has the peculiar property of making the blood vessels of the structures inside the abdomen contract and squeeze out their blood, which then becomes available for a more important purpose. Adrenalin ensures that no blood is wasted in supplying organs that do not need it at the moment. It sends it to organs whose need is greater.

Such are the provisions that Nature makes to enable us to work without undue strain being put upon our hearts or muscles. Such a system works to perfection so long as the strain is not too great. The heart, however, being a vital organ, must be protected from overstrain, and it will always happen that the muscles will become too tired to work before any dangerous strain is placed on the heart. Work will always cease and allow of a breathing space before the vital structures are endangered.

It follows from this that a person with a perfectly healthy heart cannot possibly strain it by doing too much exercise, whether by road-breaking or by playing a hard game of football. It is only in those cases where the heart is already diseased and where the staying power of the muscles exceeds that of the heart that any damage can be done. The muscles may then outwear the heart and subject an already diseased organ perhaps to breaking strain. This is the reason why people who really suffer from heart disease must be extremely careful in the exercise they take. But the heart is far less easily damaged than is generally supposed.

THE VITAL STREAM ON WHICH LIFE DEPENDS

MILLIONS of years ago, when the first living creatures made their appearance in this world, they were composed only of one single cell which extracted its nutriment and life-giving oxygen from the water in which it lived. In those far-off days, nothing could live outside the water which prevented it from drying up and dying and which provided a surrounding always constant in composition. As time went on and more living things developed, certain cells began to form a skin which prevented drying and enabled the organism to live in the air and to be independent of the water which previously nourished it.

Before this could happen, however, a substitute for water had to be found, and it was necessary that this substitute should bathe every cell in the body with its life-giving properties, so that each cell could continue to live. The substitute which the animals developed was blood, and the functions it serves are those which we have mentioned.

Blood is a fluid which, between the narrowest of limits, is always of the same composition ; it has the peculiar property of being able to carry oxygen from the lungs and pass it on to all the living cells, no matter where they are situated, and it carries food substances for the cells, which enable them to carry on their various activities and to repair the wear and tear which work imposes on them. In addition, it carries the chemical messengers which we have discussed already, and also certain substances which the body produces for its defence against various germs.

THE RED MILLIONS WHICH BRING LIFE TO THE TISSUES

IF we place a drop of blood under the microscope, we shall find that floating in a straw-coloured fluid are millions upon millions of tiny cells. These cells can be divided into two great groups which serve quite different functions. The first group are the red cells, whose rôle is to carry oxygen from one part of the body to another. Each red-cell is a tiny circular disc, so small that its diameter is only seven-thousandths of a millimetre and its thickness only one-thousandth. The red-cells are so numerous that in one cubic millimetre of blood, which is a quantity considerably less than the size of a pin's head, are no less than five million red-cells. If the number falls to three millions, we complain that we are suffering from anæmia.

The cell is composed of a thin membrane outside, with a sponge-work of the same material inside, holding in its meshes a solution of hæmoglobin. This chemical substance is responsible for the oxygen-carrying properties of the red-cells. Hæmoglobin has the property of combining with several substances if these are presented to it in sufficient quantity. At a given moment, it will take up large quantities of certain substances, if present in excess, and give them up when they are present only in small quantities in its surroundings.

Let us suppose that we have a single red-cell in one of the small arteries leading to the tissues. This red-cell is saturated with oxygen. When it reaches the tissues, its surroundings are nearly devoid of oxygen but highly impregnated with carbon dioxide, a gas which is produced by the tissues when they burn up food substances. The red-cell is forced to give up its oxygen, which is greedily seized and used by the tissues, and at the same time it takes up the carbon dioxide which the tissues have produced and must get rid of.

The red-cell then continues on its journey through the veins and heart and eventually reaches the lungs. Here, because the lungs are filled with air, the concentration of oxygen is high and that of the carbon dioxide is very low, so the red-cell exchanges its load of carbon dioxide for a further load of oxygen and goes upon its beneficent round once more. The function of the red-cell, therefore, is to provide the tissues with oxygen and to carry away their waste products.

TINY CELLS THAT ARE SCAVENGERS OF THE BLOOD

IN each cubic millimetre of blood are about nine thousand white cells of several different kinds. The functions of some of these are quite unknown, but others have been seen to do their work under the microscope, and we know a great deal about them. One of the best-known, and one which is fairly typical of the others which do the same work, is known rather grandiosely as the Polymorphonuclear Neutrophil Leucocyte. This name describes it, for it is a white cell (Leucocyte) which takes up neutral dyes when stained (neutrophil) and its nucleus is usually divided up into several lobes and may take on many different shapes. It is known for short as a polymorph.

These cells behave in the blood and tissues exactly as does the single-celled amœba which lives in the water of our country ponds and is taken as the prototype of the commencement of animal life. If an amœba or a polymorph finds itself in close proximity to a small particle of matter, it will throw out long processes of its substance, surround the particle, engulf it and digest it. This procedure cannot be described as a voluntary one on the part of the cell ; it is merely the reaction which is forced upon the cell by chemical substances exuding from the particle in question.

The amœba and the polymorph are not free agents in the matter, for they have only two courses open to them. Faced with a body which produces any reaction upon them, they will either move away from it if the substance repels them, or will engulf it, if it attracts them. It is the chemical composition of the body which determines their reaction and not any voluntary process on their own part.

The amœba engulfs a particle in its surroundings only for the purpose of supplying itself with food, but, while the polymorph may do this, its main function is to eat up and digest and destroy foreign bodies, germs and the like which might prove dangerous to the body in general. Very often the germs are so virulent that they may multiply inside the body of the polymorph instead of being digested, and in this case the cell will die in the performance of its duty.

If polymorphs from the blood are placed on a microscope together with disease-producing germs, this process can be watched directly and a graphic record may be taken by the cinematograph which will show it up to perfection. The polymorphs will engulf the bacteria and, under favourable circumstances, they will be seen to disappear under the influence of digestion. The polymorphs are thus the scavengers of the blood and represent the first line of defence of the body against disease-producing germs.

WHEN THE BLOOD CLOTS FOR OUR PROTECTION

INCORPORATED in the blood are a third group of tiny bodies, smaller even than the red-cells, which are known as platelets. Their job is to assist in the formation of a clot, when this proves necessary. When small blood vessels are cut by accident, blood will pour out and, unless something is done to stop it, the bleeding will continue indefinitely until no more blood is left in the body. Clotting of the blood is the first defence which the body puts up to prevent severe bleeding after an accident, and it is also one of the ways in which the spread of infection is stopped in severe cases because, through it, the circulation is stopped in the infected area, with the result that the infecting organism dies and is cast off without the infection becoming generalised.

Clotting, therefore, is essentially a reaction to damage, and only this may start the processes which lead to clotting. How disastrous it would be if all the blood in our body were liable to clot for no apparent reason! Nature has arranged therefore that severe damage, and only this, shall lead to a clot forming in the vessels of the affected part. The whole chemical mechanism is a very complicated one and cannot be gone into fully here, but we may briefly say that three substances, including calcium, are always present in the circulating blood. When tissues are damaged and bleeding takes place, the platelets also become damaged and from the tissues and platelets is produced a substance known as thrombokinase which works upon the three chemicals we have mentioned until a clot is produced.

When a vessel is cut, clotting is the first defence against severe bleeding. Soon, however, cells begin to wander into the clot which becomes organised later into solid, immovable living fibrous tissue which ensures that no further bleeding can take place. What disastrous consequences can follow inability of the blood to clot can well be seen in the condition known as Hæmophilia. This disease is a rarity and no one yet knows the exact cause of it. The essential trouble is that the blood will not clot in the normal time, with the result that the unfortunate victim will bleed to death after the most trivial of injuries—for example, if a tooth is removed.

HOW THE TISSUES DEFEND AND REPAIR THEMSELVES

IF the tissues are damaged in any way, either from violence or as the result of infection by germs, a definite train of events follows. First, as there is much work to be done by the cells in defending themselves, the blood supply must be increased. This is accomplished by dilating the blood vessels which supply the infected part, the dilation itself being the result of a reflex which is set in motion at the site of damage.

After a time the circulation slows and large quantities of fluid from the blood escape into the tissues through the damaged vessel walls in order to dilute the poisons which the infection is producing and to carry substances which will destroy these poisons. At the same time, polymorphs actively make their way through the walls of the vessels and creep into the tissues, attracted by the chemical substances produced by germs and damaged tissues. Here they eat up and remove the germs and any tissues that may be dead. Later fibrous tissue grows into the wound which is thus replaced by a fibrous scar.

Everyone knows the signs of inflammation. These are heat, redness, swelling and pain. All these are explainable on the basis of the facts we have just mentioned ; because more blood is arriving at the part, it becomes hot and red. Fluid exuding into the tissues makes it swell and stretches the delicate nerves which produce pain. Because the part is damaged, it ceases to work, and loss of function results. Thus an inflamed joint is not moved and an inflamed muscle will not contract. Rest is essential for repair, and this is automatically secured.

THE FORCES THAT KEEP US BREATHING

WE have seen how the respiration of each cell of the body is effected by the red-cells carried in the blood, and we have discussed in the section on Anatomy how the lungs expand and relax with the chest when breathing takes place. What we have not yet explained are the forces which keep breathing going on—why in fact we breathe at all. Situated in the lower part of the brain, just where the spinal cord joins it, are a number of nerve cells which control respiration. These cells are connected by nerve fibres directly to the muscles which raise the ribs and to the diaphragm.

These cells, just like the heart, have the property of sending out at regular intervals impulses which travel down the nerves and activate the muscles. They exhibit, in fact, rhythm. Moreover, they are exquisitely sensitive to the composition of the blood which bathes them. We have seen that the blood takes up the waste products of combustion, namely carbon dioxide, from the tissues, and we have seen also that it carries a large quantity of oxygen picked up in the lungs. These two substances are the factors which control respiration, and they do it quite automatically. They control, increase and decrease, and even abolish the inherent rhythm of these cells which have been called the respiratory centre.

Primarily, the centre depends on the amount of carbon dioxide in the blood for the impulses it sends out to start breathing. Increase in the carbon dioxide will increase the number of impulses sent out in a given time and will increase the frequency of breathing, so that more carbon dioxide is washed out of the lungs and more will leave the blood. A decrease in the carbon dioxide of blood will result in depression of respiration, until the carbon dioxide increases once more sufficiently to stimulate the cells again.

A simple experiment that anyone who is sufficiently interested can do for himself will prove this. Breathe very deeply and at a rapid rate for, say, thirty breaths. You will then find that you will stop breathing and not recommence for quite a long while. The explanation is that by voluntary forced breathing, you have washed out so much carbon dioxide from your lungs and blood that your respiratory centre is no longer stimulated and ceases to function until the carbon dioxide content of the blood rises again to a sufficiently high level.

Oxygen has rather a different effect upon the centre, for when its blood content is low, it makes the centre more sensitive to the existing content of carbon dioxide, so that a deeper and more rapid breathing results. Lack of oxygen has only an indirect effect ; carbon dioxide has a direct effect. When we climb a high mountain or go up in an aeroplane to a great height, we breathe automatically faster, for there is less oxygen in the air and therefore less in the blood, with the result that the respiratory centre is stimulated. It will thus be seen that the respiratory centre tends to keep the amount of oxygen and carbon dioxide in the blood always within the limits which are best suited to the body. An increase or decrease in either will result in immediate and automatic compensation. Thus is the blood always kept properly ærated, and thus is the removal of some of its waste products automatically ensured.

We have spoken so far only of the automatic control of breathing. We can, of course, regulate our breathing at will. The rib muscles, like any other muscles of their kind, are under the voluntary control of the brain. This mechanism, however, ensures that we shall always breathe, and enables us to breathe without having to devote our attention to it.

CLEARING OUT THE WASTE: THE KIDNEYS AT WORK

THE purpose of the kidneys is to remove from the blood those waste products which have resulted from cell activity in all parts of the body ; the kidneys remove and secrete the "ash" left over from the fires of life, which, if it accumulated, would clog the delicate mechanisms and eventually kill us owing to its poisonous effects. Urea and uric acid are the main substances which the kidney removes from the blood.

The tiny blood vessels which result from the division of the kidney arteries pass to an enormous number of structures which are known as glomeruli and which are situated only in the outer layers of the kidney. A glomerulus may be likened to a ball made of a very thin filtering membrane to which is attached a tube which opens into the inside of the ball. One side of the ball is deeply indented by a mass of capillaries which are coiled upon themselves and continually branch, forming a densely-packed network. Under the influence of the blood pressure a large volume of the fluid part of the blood containing the waste products is forced through the glomerular wall and filters through into the interior of the ball.

This fluid is, of course, identical with the blood fluid, and not only contains the waste products but also many substances which are valuable to the body and must be reabsorbed. The only substances which cannot get through the glomerular wall are the proteins contained in the blood fluid, for these are formed, as we have seen, of very large molecules and it is by virtue of their size that they are retained. The glomerular filtrate, therefore, is identical with the blood fluid except that it contains no proteins. This has been actually proved, for fluid has been drawn off under the microscope from a living glomerulus and has been analysed.

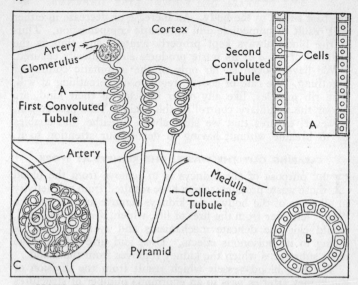

HOW BLOOD IS FILTERED BY THE KIDNEYS

Blood brought to the kidneys by the kidney arteries first passes into numerous tiny structures known as " glomeruli " and then, leaving its proteins behind, it filters through the glomerular walls into long coiled tubules where all except its waste products are absorbed. In the diagram, A is a section through the tubule at the point marked A on the main drawing ; B is a section across the tubule at the same point. In the inset C a glomerulus is drawn greatly enlarged to show the network of capillaries forming its core.

From the glomerulus the filtered fluid passes into the tube which leads out of it and here it starts on a long journey. The glomerulus is situated in the outer layers of the kidney and the first part of the tube remains too in this layer coiling and twisting upon itself amongst the glomeruli. Then it starts to move straight towards the centre of the kidney and having gone about half-way it turns back upon itself, forming a loop, and returns again to the outer layers where it becomes coiled and twisted for the second time. After this it turns again towards the kidney centre and joins up with many similar tubes which are each coming from a similar glomerulus and passes its contents eventually into the ureter.

During this long journey the glomerular filtrate becomes greatly changed. It is changed, in fact, from blood fluid into urine. All the substances which the body requires and must not waste are absorbed into the blood by the cells of the tubules through which it passes. At the same time an enormous volume of water is also reabsorbed by these cells so that the urine which leaves the kidney is greatly concentrated and contains only waste products and nothing which could be of value to the body. A great deal of work is therefore done by the cells lining these tubules, even if we consider only the water which has been reabsorbed. It has been estimated that, in the cat, if the glomeruli filter off twenty-four pints of blood fluid, twenty-three and four-fifths pints of water is reabsorbed and that only one-fifth of a pint of urine is produced.

Many people say that this simple account is not the whole story of how the kidney produces urine. They say that in addition to absorbing water and some solids the kidney tubules also actively secrete waste products into the fluid passing down them. Some even go so far as to state that the tubules only secrete and do not absorb water, and that it is this secretion only which concentrates the urine.

The problem of how the kidney works is one of the most vexed questions in physiology and perhaps more ink and paper have been wasted and more wordy battles have occurred on it than upon any other subject in the whole of physiology. We will leave the matter here and say only that there is good experimental evidence that both processes occur, and therefore that both parties are probably in a measure right. Anyhow it is not a matter of the greatest importance for we have made for ourselves a theory which, if not absolutely correct, is sufficient to explain the main workings of the kidney both in health and in disease, and from it many excellent methods of treating kidney diseases have been worked out.

SOME BOOKS TO READ NEXT

BOOKS about these two scientific subjects, Anatomy and Physiology, are of necessity inclined to be technical, but there are some works which may be tackled with interest and profit by the layman as well as by the medical student. Far and away the best work to read on Anatomy as a reference book is Gray's *Anatomy*. It is, of course, technical, but is profusely illustrated. Three books of great interest to the student of human anatomy are : *Human Embryology and Morphology* by Sir Arthur Keith, *History of the Human Body* by Wilder and F. Wood, Jones's *Man's Place Among the Mammals*. These three books, although containing a number of technicalities, are much more interesting than those dealing only with pure Human Anatomy.

Physiology, like so many sciences to-day, has many different divisions, and as many different books have been written about them. An interesting, simple and well-written book on the chemistry of the body is T. R. Parsons' *Elements of Biochemistry*. Bainbridge and Menzies' *Textbook of Physiology* is an elementary book which covers the whole field of Physiology, but being condensed makes somewhat difficult reading. For those who want to learn more about advanced Physiology Starling's *Physiology* is the standard work.

HEREDITY: THE STREAM OF LIFE

by ELDON MOORE, lately Chief Officer of the
Imperial Bureau of Animal Genetics

HEREDITY is not, as some people seem to think, a little imp that perversely upsets all human calculations. And there is nothing mystical or mysterious about it either. It is simply the greatest force in life, being, in fact, the life-force, the stream of life itself.

The old saying that " all living things come from an egg " is rather misleading. It should run " All living things spring from living parents." You are alive because you are sprung from living parents ; the same is true of your dog, or the sparrow picking up the crumbs outside the window, of the potted fern on the dining-room table, of the goldfish in the bowl—in fact, of every living thing you can mention, from amoeba to man.

St. Francis, when he called the birds his " brothers," probably thought he was talking good theology, while modern humanitarians seem to consider it a metaphorical statement of how we should treat the birds. They may both be right in their way. But St. Francis was more literally correct than he realised. In pure, unmetaphorical science, the birds are our relatives—so are dogs, monkeys and apes, in nearer degrees, so are fish, spiders, lettuces, and oak trees in more distant degrees.

You yourself came from human parents, and if you could trace back to *their* parents, and so on, you would ultimately arrive at the common stock from which both men and apes are sprung. A little further back, the monkey branch joins the main stem ; further back still is the common ancestor of all mammals, including your dog. Another big step, and we come to the ancestor of all mammals and some reptiles, yet further back is the ancestor of all reptiles and birds, including your sparrow —and so on, through the amphibia, such as the frog, the fish, like your goldfish, back to the common ancestors of land insects, spiders, and lobsters. And so the great trail runs right back to a single-celled creature [1] which had not quite made up

---

[1] See page 156 *et seq.*

its mind whether to be animal or vegetable. One of its children became the ancestor of all plants ; another started the great Noah's ark procession of the animals.

All this is evolution. You have climbed down your own family tree from the topmost shoot called Man, down the main trunk past the places where the different great branches shoot off, to the bole at the bottom, from which spring not only the plants and animals we know, but also the germs that sour the milk and improve the Gorgonzola, that give us typhoid and tuberculosis, the putrefaction of meat and our essential manures. But, since plants and animals (including men) all take their life ultimately from the first living thing, it is essential to grasp the fact of evolution if the principles of heredity are to be understood.

THE IMMORTAL CELL

ONE-CELLED creatures and their ways have already been described in detail. Here we will look at one of them that is, in essentials, a representative of them all. We will take the " Slipper " (*Paramecium*). Its precise shape and other etceteras do not matter to us, and we can also disregard its real size, and suppose that it is under the appropriate power of the microscope.

This funny little thing, looking like the white of a raw egg with specks in it, swims into the field of the microscope just at the moment it is going to " breed." It does not need any partner in the business, since its " breeding " consists in pulling itself in half.

Both these two little new " Slippers " now start to feed and grow, each re-forming whatever organs it has lost—one, for instance, has no mouth, because that organ was stolen by the other. The second has to re-form the primitive stomach—and so on. Both of them soon succeed in becoming exactly like their " parent," and in growing to the same size. Each " child," in its turn, becomes a " parent " in the same way, so that there are now four " Slippers," instead of the original one— and so on indefinitely.

In fact, setting aside accidents, there is no such thing as death for a " Slipper," and the one we are looking at now is, in a very real sense, identical with the first that lived, aeons before the earliest fossils in the rocks. That great desire of so many men, Immortality, was and is the normal possession of the simplest known creatures. Death is the inevitable

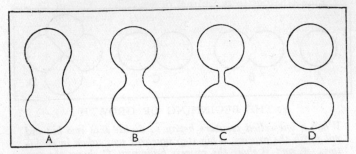

1. THE BREEDING OF A ONE-CELLED ANIMAL

The Paramecium or " slipper " is a one-celled animal which reproduces simply by pulling itself in half. In the diagram A *represents the single adult cell ;* B *shows the cell beginning to " pinch together ". In* C *the process has gone a step further, and in* D *the division is complete, giving two separate cells.*

penalty only of complicated creatures like a cow, a man, or a cabbage. Why ?

That question is answered by the next step upwards in evolution, when some single-celled creature started to split into two halves, but did not quite finish the job, so that the halves remained stuck together, like the cells of a honeycomb. These two cells split again, in the same incomplete way, making four cells all joined together. The process went on until the growth of the organism was ended. Cell-division of this incomplete kind is known as " cleavage." Diagram 2 puts the whole process pictorially.

REPRODUCTION WHICH GIVES DEATH A MEANING

THIS colony of cells all joined together had decided advantages over the old single-celled type of creature, since one group of cells could specialize in making an efficient mouth, another a high-capacity stomach, while those all round the surface could give themselves whole-heartedly to forming little oars to row the colony through the water, or to fan floating bits of food into the communal mouth.

This is the beginning of the creatures we commonly see, such as lettuces and oak trees, animals and men—highly organised colonies, in which each little group of cells has one particular job to do for the common good. The story is rather

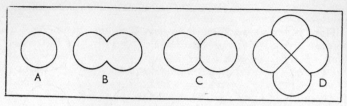

2. THE BEGINNING OF GROWTH

When a one-celled creature began to divide into two but did not finish the process, a big step upwards was taken in evolution. A and B show the process beginning, C shows the two resulting cells joined together. In D each of the two cells has divided again to make a small colony of four. This incomplete cell division is known as cleavage.

like that of the mediæval carpenter, who used to do everything from cutting up the tree-trunk to inlaying and polishing the finished cabinet ; and who has now been replaced by an organised factory, with one man cutting the planks, another smoothing them, a third laying out the joints—and so on up to the last touch of polish. One man, one job—specialisation.

And just as a factory has to have a manager, who is not necessarily good at any specialised job, so those early cell-colonies kept a few unspecialised cells which had no work to do except to pinch off halves of themselves. Those free-swimming halves became the founders of whole new colonies. When life had reached this stage of budding off the beginnings of a complete new colony, there was no longer any need for the parent colony to go on living. In fact, it had better die, to prevent over-population. Natural death therefore arrived as the cure for too much birth !

THE BEGINNINGS OF SEX

AT a very early stage in evolution these free-swimming halves became divided into two distinct sorts—a rather large, well-fed cell that floated quietly, the *ovum*, and a more compact, active little cell which swam vigorously about, the *sperm*. When these two half-cells met, they united into one, forming the fertilised egg, which thereupon started to multiply, in the usual fashion, into a new colony. At one evolutionary stage—there are many living creatures still in it—any cell colony would produce both ovum and sperm. A little later came the next step, when one colony of the species produced only ova, another only sperm.

Here is sex as we know it to-day, with the members of a species divided into two—the females who produce the ovum kind of cell, and the males who produce the sperm kind. We can now summarise the beginning of life into three stages :

1. A single-celled creature which, when it grows too big for comfort, divides into two separate creatures.

2. Its descendant, which divides into several attached cells, each specialised for some particular job, but which occasionally throws off separate half-cells that multiply into new colonies.

3. A similar sort of colony, but rather better organised, which throws off only the sperm type of half-cell—a male colony—and a corresponding female colony that throws off only the ovum type of half-cell. Ovum and sperm thereafter combine into one whole cell, the fertilised egg, that becomes the founder of a similar colony, male or female.

There are many minor variations of this essential process, but none of them is important. The main thing is that the stream of life flows unbroken from parent to child—and the child " takes after " the parent in more respects than that of merely being alive.

THE BEARERS OF THE HERITAGE

Now that we have seen how life is handed on, we can go on to discover how all those things that distinguish horses, men, and marigolds from each other are passed on from generation to generation. To do this, we must switch on the high power of the microscope and take a look into the very private life of the cell. With this great magnification, the cell becomes quite different—just as the ground looks different when you are flying at 500 feet from what it does when you are flying at 5000.

Let us suppose that, under this magnification, we are looking at a fertilised egg—the single cell that, made out of the union of the father's sperm and the mother's ovum, is the starting-point of the new colony. A short time after the sperm and the ovum have united to form the fertilised egg, you will see, more or less in the middle of the egg, a pattern that looks rather like two old-fashioned armies forming up in battle array opposite each other. The two armies, though, are exactly like one another. The first company of each is a straight line, the second company of each a half-moon, the third is curly, the fourth a sort of blotch—and so on.

These companies are known as *chromosomes*, and you may fairly look upon them as the all-important organisers of cellular activities. You can here disregard the rest of the cell (cytoplasm), and fix your attention solely on these chromosome armies, particularly remembering that they are exactly the same size, shape, etc., and that one of them is the father's contribution to the new individual, the other the mother's. This is important because, as you will see, it is one of the things that show that father and mother play exactly equal parts in the making of a child.

Now, if we were looking at a human egg just after the union of sperm and ovum, we should see 24 chromosomes in each of the two " armies "—48 in all ; if it were the egg of a certain kind of fly (Drosophila), the numbers would be 4–8, of the green pea 7–14. The numbers, shapes and sizes vary with each species—of which, in fact, they are the cause. We, however, need not consider these specific differences, and can pretend that each army is composed of one company only— that on the right from the father's sperm, that on the left from the mother's ovum. See diagram 3 (A).

The next thing to happen is rather startling—each chromosome splits neatly in half all the way down the middle (B). After that, the halves separate completely (C) and, following this, the rest of the egg starts to pinch together (D), finally becoming two separate but attached cells (E). The last stage is exactly the same as that of our one-celled creature just before it splits completely in half ; but this time the greater magnification has enabled us to see the chromosomes.

We are not now looking at a one-celled creature, however, that splits into two entirely separate individuals, but at the first stage of a many-celled creature's life. So the two cells, each the identical twin of the other, remain stuck together ; and the next step is for each of them to divide again in the same way. Thus one cell becomes two, two become four, four become eight—and so on until, when the number has reached many millions, the fully grown human being (or other creature) is perfected.

This is a compressed description of cell-division, which is the basic principle of both growth and breeding. The main characteristic (setting aside some exceptions that are momentarily unimportant) is the behaviour of the chromosomes,

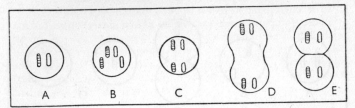

3. THE DANCE OF THE CHROMOSOMES

A shows the fertilised egg-cell with two Chromosomes, the shaded one from the ovum, the outline one from the sperm. In B each Chromosome has split into two, and in C the halves have separated to opposite ends of the cell. D shows the cell beginning to pinch in between the two pairs, and in E two cells with identical Chromosomes have been formed from the one fertilised egg-cell.

since, though the rest of the cell is very often unequally divided, those dictators of development are always halved with great precision—each of the two joint managing directors of the firm splits into two whenever a new branch is to be started. This means that in every cell of your body and brain there lives and moves that fatal pattern your parents stamped in the egg from which you sprang.

HOW WE HALVE OUR HEREDITY

Now return to the beginning. The chromatin (chromosome-stuff) of a one-celled creature splits neatly in half, and the rest of the cell makes a very bad attempt at doing the same. The badness of the attempt, though, does not matter, since the chromatin, like any good board of directors, can soon collect and organise local supplies ; so that before very long the two new creatures are exact duplicates of each other and of their joint parent.

The growth of a many-celled creature differs only in that the cells remain stuck together, instead of swimming apart, and that the cytoplasm (but not the chromosomes) of each cell specialises in one particular job—forming the chalky substance of a bone or of a lobster's shell, the soft, porous substance of our lungs, the elastic quality of a muscle fibre, and so on.

Now if a one-celled, a-sexual creature splits in half in order to " breed," it must obviously give exactly half its

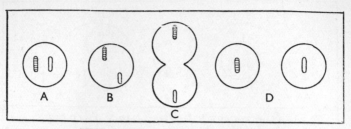

4. THE MECHANISM OF BREEDING

A shows the parent's cell with two chromosomes exactly like the egg-cell in fig. 3a. In B, the chromosomes instead of splitting have separated whole to opposite ends of the cell. In C the cell begins to pinch in between the two chromosomes, finally giving two half cells, or gametes (D), one with the shaded chromosome from the mother and one with the outline chromosome from the father.

chromatin to each of its two " children "—splitting both of its chromosomes. But what would happen if many-celled, sexual creatures did the same ? The ovum would carry two chromosomes, so would the sperm, and if the two united, the resulting egg-cell would have *four* chromosomes. In the next generation there would be eight, in the one after, sixteen, and so on until the egg-cell was carrying an infinite number of chromosomes. Many-celled, sexual creatures had therefore to invent some way of cell-division different from the " breeding " of the one-celled creatures or from their own body-building process.

Instead of doubling the chromosomes, as in ordinary cell formation, they divided them in making *gametes* (a convenient term, meaning " marrying cells," to cover both ova and sperms). Now switch the microscope on to the reproductive organs of any of the higher creatures, male or female, just as ovum or sperm is being formed. The first picture you will see is the familiar one of the chromosomes " setting to partners," (A) of diagram (4), but from this point the dance is different. Instead of each chromosome splitting neatly in half, the two waltz away from each other (B), then the rest of the cell pinches in between them (C) and finally, the two halves of the cell become completely divided (D). There are thus two " marrying cells " or gametes, each with half the number of chromosomes of its parent.

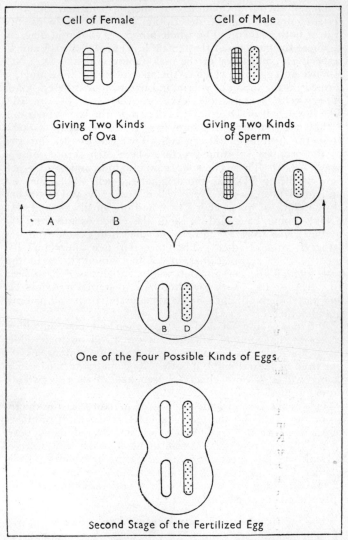

5. HOW THE CHROMOSOMES ARE HANDED ON

Showing why a new individual bears in every cell of its body and brain a chromosome contribution from each parent.

Though ovum formation and sperm formation differ in certain minor ways, the description just given is in essence true of both of them. The whole process is shown in diagram 5, where the gametes of the female (ova) are labelled A and B, respectively, and those of the male (sperms) C and D.

Since an egg-cell, which is the start of a new individual, is formed by the union of sperm and ovum, four different kinds of egg-cells are possible—AC or AD, and BC or BD. The lower half of Diagram 5 is drawn on the last supposition —that the mother's B-ovum has united with the father's D-sperm, forming a BD egg-cell. That cell divides into two by the ordinary splitting process, where each chromosome is neatly halved. Those two split again into four, and so on—each new cell being BD, like the original egg-cell. Thus the new individual possesses in every cell of his body and brain one chromosome of his mother's two, and one of his father's two.

Now going backwards a step, the chromosome from the mother came from *her* father, and the chromosome from the father from *his* father. Therefore our new individual has inherited the chromosomes of its two grandfathers in this case, though the combination might equally well have been AC, AD, or BC—both grandmothers, maternal grandmother and paternal grandfather, or maternal grandfather and paternal grandmother.

And now going forward a step, when our new individual comes to the point of breeding, it can hand on to its child either the chromosome it received from its mother, or the one from its father; but not both. Its gametes or " marrying-cells " will each be a chance-chosen half of its two parents' chromosomes.

This is the essential mechanism of heredity, as the microscope shows it. But the *theory* of heredity, a sort of prophecy of the microscope's revelations, was discovered many years before (in 1865) by the Austrian monk Mendel, who deserves to rank with his great contemporary Darwin. Unfortunately neither knew of the other, and Mendel's combination of careful breeding experiments with sound reasoning was un-appreciated for over thirty years.

HOW MENDEL SAW HEREDITY AT WORK

MENDEL actually worked on the green pea, but since he chanced on a minor complication (only later understood) it is easier to understand his theory by taking an example

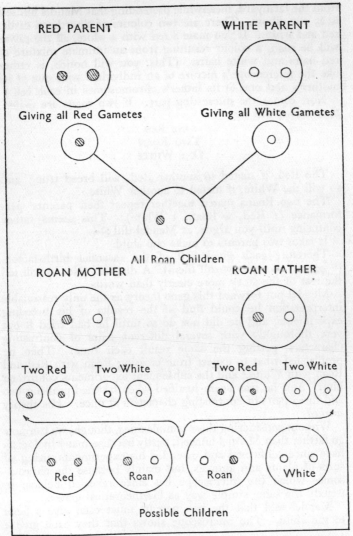

RED PARENT WHITE PARENT

Giving all Red Gametes Giving all White Gametes

All Roan Children

ROAN MOTHER ROAN FATHER

Two Red Two White Two Red Two White

Red Roan Roan White

Possible Children

6. SIMPLE MENDELISM

*Shown in red, white and roan cattle. Note that any of the
mother's ova may unite with any of the father's sperms.*

from the farmyard, meanwhile pretending that Mendel himself is at our elbow. There are two colours of Shorthorn cattle, red and white. If you mate a red with a white, all the calves will be roan, a colour resulting from an intimate mixture of red hairs and white hairs. (This, you will notice, is rather like the microscope's picture of an individual with one of its mother's and one of its father's chromosomes in each cell.)

Now comes the interesting part. If two roans are mated, *their* calves will be :

ONE RED

TWO ROAN

ONE WHITE

The Red, if mated to another Red, will breed true ; and so will the White, if mated to another White.

The two Roans mated together repeat their parents' performance (1 Red, 2 Roan, 1 White). This seems rather confusing until you argue, as Mendel did :—

It takes two parents to make one child.

Therefore each gives half of the essential birth-factors (" genes " as we now call them). A diagram (No. 6) will tell the rest of the story more clearly than words.

Mendel put forward this gene theory as the only reasonable interpretation he could find of the results of his breeding experiments, and he did not do so until he had tried it out very thoroughly with several different pairs of contrasting characters, getting the same result each time. Then he prophesied what to expect from crossing Roan with Red and Roan with White,[1] and the subsequent experiments confirmed him. And he was again justified when he tried crossing two and three pairs of contrasting characters at once. His theory *worked*.

Without considering these complexities, though, we can now go farther than Mendel himself, partly because many biologists have since confirmed and extended his experiments, using all sorts of plants and animals, but mainly because the chromosomes which the microscope has since revealed behave in exactly the same simple way as his theoretical genes.

Mendel said that the two parents must each give a gene to the child. The microscope shows that they each give a

---

[1] The results are 2 Roan : 2 Red in the first case, and 2 Roan : 2 White in the second. If you will spend five minutes with pencil and paper working out these two " riders " for yourself, you will find that the whole business of simple mendelism has been clearly impressed on your mind.

chromosome. Mendel said that the two genes do not get mixed up together, but part company when the child breeds. The microscope shows that the chromosomes do retain their individuality, and that each passes into a different gamete.

In fact, if you will compare the picture of chromosomes in this section with Mendel's pictures of genes, you will find that they are interchangeable (though Mendel, of course, did not even touch on what happens to the genes in the business of body-building. That is purely the discovery of the microscope).

We can now put the whole thing in a nutshell :—A living thing is, in a very real sense, a dual personality, since each of its cells contains one chromosome from its father and one from its mother. Its method of breeding is to break off a living fragment of itself, a half cell containing *either* its mother's chromosome *or* its father's—a matter of chance—but never both. That living half-cell unites with one from the other parent, and the new individual thus formed starts on its career with the full complement of two chromosomes, one from each of *its* parents.

If the characters of the parents contrast, like red and white, then they will struggle for mastery in the child, as it were, and produce an apparent blend such as roaning. But they never effect a *permanent* blend ; and they part company when the child itself breeds. A roan cannot hand on roan to any of its children, but only a red gene or a white. The roan child of roan parents does not inherit the colour from either of them ; it takes red from its father and white from its mother (or *vice versa*), and so compounds the mixture afresh.

There are a great many simple mendelian characters known in all forms of life. In men, for instance, if a pure blue-eyed man mates with a pure dark-eyed woman, their children will all have eyes of the hazel or light-brown type. And two hazel-type people will have one blue-eyed child, two hazel, and one dark. Curly hair mated to straight hair produces wavy ; and two wavy-haired parents will have one curly-haired child, two wavy-haired, and one straight-haired.

This " simple mendelian ratio " of $1 : 2 : 1$, by the way, only holds when large enough numbers are bred, since the shuffling of the chromosomes is a matter of chance, which only works out evenly in the long run. If you and a friend, for instance, tossed pennies a hundred times, you would get this result—as near as no matter :

> 25 both coins Heads,
> 25 both coins Tails,
> 50 one a Head and the other a Tail.

This is exactly the same as the ratio of one Red : two Roan: one White. But if you only tossed four times, you might very well get quite different proportions. It is the same with parents who only have four children. So do not count on these averages to enable you to prophesy the result of any one mating. They are useful mainly in revealing the mechanism of heredity, and next in allowing accurate forecasts of a large series of matings—for instance, in most kinds of practical breeding.

THE CHROMOSOME'S ULTRA-MICROSCOPIC PASSENGERS

Before going any further, it is as well to get a clear idea of what genes and chromosomes really are—since they are not the same thing. A gamete (ovum or sperm) is a rather compact living jelly of complex chemical nature. The chromosomes in it are tougher, more opaque, and even more complex chemically. If the cell is killed and stained, they show up like worms of various shapes and sizes.

Genes are, strictly speaking, theoretical, since they are too small for the most powerful microscope. But we know not only that they exist and behave exactly like the visible chromosomes, but also that they are carried in the chromosomes— many genes in one chromosome. And sometimes we are even able to say, for instance, that some particular gene is carried seven-tenths of the way down the third chromosome. The chromosome is a railway carriage, and the genes are its ultra-microscopic passengers.

It is also worth noticing that the chromosomes of an egg-cell bear no more resemblance to the red or white hairs of a cow than the directors of an aircraft company look like an aeroplane. These tiny bundles of chemicals are not animals or plants in miniature. They are the directors of a firm that builds such creatures.

DOMINANCE: THE SECRET OF "SKIPPED GENERATIONS"

When Mendel experimented with his green peas, he had the bad luck to happen on the minor (but very common and important) phenomenon called Dominance, which confused him and later biologists for a long time. He mated a tall pea to a dwarf. But, instead of the first generation being intermediate in height—as one would expect—they were all tall. When these were interbred, they produced the following offspring :

> One Tall that bred true
> One Dwarf that bred true
> Two Talls that repeated their parents' performance.

To us, looking at things with our present knowledge, the explanation of this result is obvious, since it is in essence exactly the same as the grandchildren of the red and white cattle—

> One Red (true-breeding)
> One White (true-breeding)
> Two Roan (hybrids who, like their parents,
>   therefore do not breed true).

The same diagram of breeding performance would fit either cattle or peas equally well. The sole essential difference between them is that, in peas, the tall gene completely dominates the " dwarf " when they come together in the same body-building cells, whereas in cattle the opposing characters are of equal strength.

Mendel found several other instances in peas alone of one character dominating its opposite number (yellow over green, smooth over wrinkled), and a multitude of them have since been found in almost every kind of plant and animal. In the Aberdeen-Angus cattle, for example, the normal black colour is dominant to the unfashionable—but no worse—colour red. In man the " Hapsburg lip " (which is really a slightly over-grown lower jaw) that has characterised the Spanish and Austrian royal families, is dominant to the normal mouth.

And, generally speaking, useful normal characters are more common than defects, for the very good reason that defective individuals do not usually live long enough to breed, while healthy individuals do. Indeed, the only kind of defect that has much chance of survival is a " recessive " that can be handed on by apparently normal " carriers." But for the moment, the chief practical importance of Dominance is the explanation it gives of " skipping a generation," and of the sudden appearance of a child that is not the least like its parents or any other near relative.

RED-HAIRED CHILD FROM BLACK-HAIRED PARENTS

To take an instance that must have happened innumerable times, especially in Ireland. A black-haired man marries a flaming red-haired woman, and all their children are black-haired, since pure black is fully dominant to pure red. One of these children finds a pure black-haired mate and produces a third generation of black-haired children. One of these, who has inherited the concealed red gene also marries a black-haired mate—but one who is like herself (or himself) in having a concealed red gene inherited from an equally remote ancestor.

Few people keep records of their ancestors' hair-colour, especially not farther back than the grandparents, so these two black-haired young people are absolutely astounded by the sudden, apparently inexplicable appearance of a red-headed child.

In fact, they have only seen an example of the sort of thing that is familiar to every practical breeder and experimental geneticist. The re-appearance of an ancestral character after several generations, due to the junction of two underground streams, is a commonplace to people who keep proper pedigree records.

A recessive (as the opposite number to a dominant is called) may, of course, get lost at the very first mating. But if there are four children in each generation, the chances are decidedly in favour of it being handed on to at least one of them. This re-appearance of a recessive from the mating of two impure dominants is the most usual (though not the only) cause of the children of any species " throwing back " to some remote ancestor, or even *appearing* to bear no resemblance to *any* member of the family!

In the examples given here, dominance is complete ; and that is why they (and others) misled many early biologists into thinking that dominance was an essential part of heredity. In fact, it often does not occur at all, and at other times is far from complete. Dominance may range from the completeness shown in the Tall-Dwarf pea example to the semi-dominance of dark eyes over light and the absolute lack of dominance in the Red-Roan-White cattle—with many degrees in between.

Indeed, dominance is not strictly a matter of general genetical principles at all—of the way the chromosomes behave in the actual breeding process. It is an affair of physiological detail—of the way the chromosomes struggle or co-operate with each other in the development and functioning of the body. And these details naturally vary greatly from species to species and character to character.

In peas, for instance, tallness is certainly dominant to short-ness. But in human beings, shortness normally *tends* to be dominant to tallness. Short parents, you will notice, often have tall children ; but the reverse only occurs if there has been some developmental accident, like infantile paralysis. The white of English Park cattle is dominant to other colours, though in Shorthorns white is equal to red. In man and the Aberdeen-Angus cattle, black is dominant to red, but not in horses, which have such a complication of colour genes that the only certain thing is that chestnut is recessive to every other colour. Chestnut, consequently, is the only one that invariably breeds true.[1] In rabbits, the wild colour, which is really a sort of " dazzle " mixture of several colours, is domi-nant to everything else.

OUR MIXED INHERITANCE

So far, we have pretended that there is only one pair of chromosomes, each of the pair carrying merely one gene. In fact, every chromosome carries a great many genes—it is a large railway-carriage packed full of passengers—and most organisms have many more than one pair of chromosomes.

For the moment, we need not concern ourselves with what happens when a pair of chromosomes carries more than one pair of genes ; nor with the possibilities arising from 24 pairs of genes each in a different one of man's 24 pairs of chromo-somes. But it is impossible to understand one of the most important things about heredity if we look only at a single pair of chromosomes, so now we will take three of the human pairs for an example. It is easiest if we name them after playing-cards, so, in diagram 7, the first chromosome is the Ace, and then come the King and the Queen, and we can suppose that one parent comes from a pack with Black backs, the other from a pack with White.

[1] This is a useful rule to remember : A recessive always breeds true, since it has no hidden genes. A semi-dominant, or anything like a roan, never breeds true, since it is a hybrid with a mixture of different genes. A full dominant is doubtful, since it may be either a hybrid or pure—and that can only be decided for certain by experimental breeding (though pedigree, of course, is a valuable pointer).

The child of these parents—call it a girl—must inevitably have a Black Ace, King, and Queen, and corresponding White cards. And we must suppose that she grows up and mates with a boy of similar parentage.

Now, when we were looking at only two chromosomes, we saw that in the " reduction division " that precedes the formation of gametes, the two chromosomes always separated from one another. And the same thing happens this time—if the Black Ace, that is, goes to the top of the cell, the White will go to the bottom. The Kings likewise will separate from each other, and so will the Queens.

But all the Black cards do not go to one end of the cell, all the White to the other. Each pair sorts itself out independently of the other pairs, so that in one gamete there may be a Black Ace, and the two other cards White; in the next a White Ace and King, but a Black Queen. There are obviously many other possible combinations. The bottom half of diagram 7 shows two of them—an ovum (large letters) from this daughter, and a sperm (small letters) from the man she is marrying. They unite to form the child at the bottom of the diagram.

And now, to round off things, let us find genes and characters to fit these chromosomes:

Ace contains a gene governing eye-colour (Black = dark; White = light).
King contains a gene governing hair-form (Black = curly; White = straight).
Queen contains a gene governing jaw-bone (Black = Hapsburg; White = normal).

This grandchild, therefore, has hazel eyes, taking light from his maternal grandfather, dark from his paternal grandmother ; pure curly hair, taking the genes from each of his grandmothers ; and a normal chin, taking the genes from each of his grandfathers. He is a chance assortment of all the factors which his four grandparents handed on to his two parents. In the dance of the chromosomes, not only are opposite numbers bound to separate completely, but the different companies of the same " army " are liable to do so.

THE CHANCE THAT DECIDES THE NEXT GENERATION

THIS is very different from the vague idea that most people have of the relation between parents and children. They wrongly tend to look upon father and mother as rather like

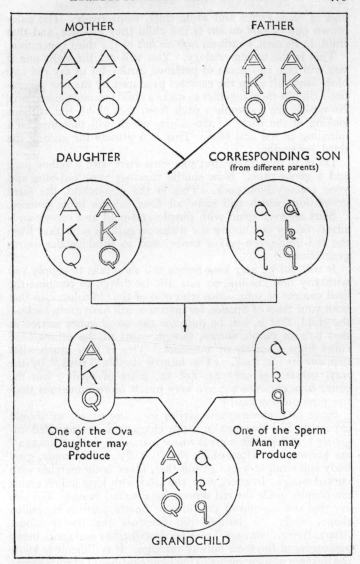

7. OUR MIXED INHERITANCE

jugs of black coffee and white milk, respectively. The pale-brown cup of *café au lait* is the child they produce, and that child, in its turn, hands on *café au lait* to the third generation.

This is the wrong analogy. You will get the right one if you will take two packs of patience cards—let us say red and blue—and call them the gametes produced by the first generation. Shuffle them together to make a child (second generation). Now pick out a complete pack from that child, but without looking at the backs of the cards, which will therefore be a mingling of red and blue. This is a gamete for making the third generation.

Do it all over again, but this time start with a yellow pack and a green pack. Now shuffle together your red-blue and your green-yellow pack. This is the grandchild, the third generation, which will show all four colours in its gametes.

Start all over again with purple-and-gold and orange-and-silver, finally combining the ultimate gamete with that from the red-blue-green-yellow series, and so produce the fourth generation.

It will not be very long before the shop fails to supply you with any new colours, so you will be driven to combine the final gamete of your series with one of the old colours, so that both your Aces of Spades, for instance, will have green backs—the child, that is, will be pure for the set of genes carried in that pair of chromosomes, though most of the others have come from a variety of ancestors. This is very much what happens in life itself. (The human double " pack," by the way, consists of only 24, not 52, pairs of cards ; but the genes in a chromosome are very much more numerous than the pips on any card.)

Since each chromosome carries so many genes, we should expect to find that two or more characters are inherited together ; and in fact a great many instances of this " linkage " are known. In Drosophila, the fruit fly, for example, grey body and straight wings go together, black body marches with curved wings. In sweet peas, the kind with long pollen grains are purple, while the red flowers have round grains. You can say that the top pip of the three of hearts controls the pollen shape, while the bottom pip controls the flower-colour. Alternatively, " linkage " may be described as two genes being passengers in the same railway-carriage. It is difficult to know the linkages in man, owing to the large number of chromosomes and the impossibility of experimental breeding.

SOME PUZZLES OF HEREDITY EXPLAINED

FOR the sake of lucidity, we have so far considered only well-known or easily visualised characters, such as tall and short, black and grey, and have stuck to those that depend on a single pair of genes. But obviously such big and important characters as milk-yield in cattle, health or intelligence in man, or disease resistance in plants must usually have a much more complex hereditary basis. Most of them, indeed, depend on many pairs of genes, each perhaps in a different pair of chromosomes. One simple example (that has been several times known) will explain how this works.

A White and Negro married, producing mulatto (*café au lait*) children. One of these married another mulatto and had a large family—one child much whiter than either parent, one much blacker, and the rest an assortment of varying coffee shades. Evidently there has been no blending (or all the children would be the same colour), and you can see what has happened if you suppose that there are six pairs of genes involved (the exact number is not known) in as many chromosome-pairs.

Both the mulattoes, therefore, have six black genes and six white ; but each of their children is likely to get a different assortment—one with eight black genes and four white ; the second, the opposite ; a third, half and half (like the parents) ; a fourth, eleven white genes and only one black—and so on. Straightforward cases of this sort are called cumulative genes.

The " rose-pea-walnut " series of comb-shapes in chickens is a simple example of another very common kind of complication called complementary genes, which you will find explained in the books mentioned at the end of this section.

A whole large complex of such complementary and cumulative genes, spread out over many chromosomes, must be responsible for such complicated things as the different varieties of the normal human brain, the fitness of certain plants for various soils and climates, the excellence (or otherwise) of some dogs for driving sheep, and similar characters.

Let me hastily beg you not to be discouraged by this complexity of the hereditary machine. It was necessary to mention the wheels within wheels. Now you can put those details to the back of your mind, and only keep clear about the simple main principles. After all, you do not need to understand the theory of electro-magnetics in order to turn on the radio, nor even to be a practical wireless engineer. And complicated characters can be understood (and developed or eliminated) with no more than the outline of genetical principles. The great improvement in English livestock and in most cultivated plants was achieved by men who had never heard of genes and chromosomes.

HEREDITY VERSUS ENVIRONMENT

THIS is a convenient place to deal with the layman's perennial question, "Which is the more important, Heredity or Environment?" So general a question is irrelevant; the biologist's answer is on these lines : A living thing starts individual existence as an egg-cell—a tiny packet of chemicals, and the precise amount and nature of those chemicals decides whether it shall grow up a frog or a snapdragon, a fly or a man. That is heredity. But it would never grow up at all unless it had the appropriate environment.

The lesser differences between a pink and a yellow snap-dragon, a cart-horse and a race-horse, a negro and a white man are just as much due to heredity as the larger specific differences. The general question about heredity or environment therefore breaks up into a hundred little questions of detail, such as :

Does the seed or the soil determine a good wheat crop ? The answer to this is : " Both."

Does heredity or environment make one frog bright yellow and its brother dark greenish-brown ?—Environment (temperature and moisture).

Does heredity or environment make one man energetic and able, another a comatose mental defective ?—Heredity (bar a few cases caused by accident or disease before or shortly after birth).

Each character presents its own set of problems, and there can be no general answer. But there are certain general methods of investigating all of them, and the simplest of these is to find out whether a character occurs more often or more fully after inbreeding. If it does, then you can feel fairly certain it is hereditary in the strictest sense—like eye-colour in man—since inbreeding intensifies all the hereditary qualities.

If the strength of a character varies in brothers and sisters (like the skin-colour of the mulattoes' children) then, again, it is probably hereditary, since brothers and sisters have much the same environment, but not, thanks to the chromosome dance, the same heredity. If a character suddenly crops up " out of the blue," the odds are in favour of heredity, that it is a deep-buried recessive that has at last come to the surface.

But if the character you are investigating appears *consistently* in all the members of a family, or only varies step by step with the circumstances, then you must suspect the preponderance of environmental influence. The chief scientific trouble, though, is not so much disentangling heredity and environment, as defining and measuring " quantitative characters," as they are called, such as intelligence, vigour, disease-resistance. The attempts to do this are discussed in the books mentioned at the end.

WILL IT BE A BOY OR A GIRL?

" WILL it be a boy or a girl ? " is a question that has been asked by so many anxious parents that there has never been a lack of prophets, or even of people who claim to control sex—some honest, some otherwise, but all equally wrong. But since " Boy or Girl " is the same as " Heads or Tails," half the answers are pretty well bound to be right, and the other half can always be explained away !

The real controllers of sex are, again, the chromosomes, which have so far been described as being ranged in one, two, or more pairs. This rule has one exception. There is one chromosome in the cells of a male which, though a sizeable, rod-like body itself, has a partner that looks, in comparison, no larger than a blotchy full-stop. The big one of this odd pair is called the X-chromosome, the little one the Y-chromosome. In the cells of the female, however, the X-chromosome is partnered by another X in every respect like itself. Now, disregarding all the other chromosome-pairs, see how the sex-chromosomes (as the X's and Y's together are called) behave in the breeding process.

The female cell is XX and can therefore only give rise to X ova. But the male cell is XY and can therefore give rise to two kinds of sperm—X and Y. If an X-sperm fertilises the X-ovum, the result will be XX, a female ; and if a Y-sperm does so, the result will be XY, a male. Thus chance, and chance alone decides, at the moment of conception, whether the child is to be a boy or a girl.

When this discovery was first made, biologists thought that it completely explained the approximate equality of the sexes

—since equal numbers of X and Y sperm should result in the birth of equal numbers of boys and girls.

The facts, though, are not quite so simple, since boy babies consistently outnumber girl babies by about 105 to 100. Moreover, counts of dead embryos show that in man—and probably in most mammals—nearly twice as many males as females are conceived, but that the male type of organism is inherently more likely to die. After birth, the male death rate of humans is consistently higher than the female, except during the short period of puberty, and over the age of 80 there are nearly twice as many women as men. The reason for the much higher male conception rate is still a mystery. But it is believed to be due to the Y-sperms being lighter and faster swimmers than the X's, and being therefore more often successful in reaching and fertilising the ova.

In many species—cattle, for instance—the X-chromosome in male cells has no partner at all. A bull, that is to say, is XO, instead of XY, while the cow, of course, is XX. This fact (plus some more intricate evidence) makes us think that the little Y-chromosome, when it exists at all, is a mere " dummy," which plays no part at all in the life of the cell.

Essential maleness therefore consists in having one dose of the little bunch of chemicals called X, while essential female-ness consists in having two doses. There is an intriguing exception, not yet understood, to this general rule of sex-determination. All the birds, all the moths, and a few other species are exactly the opposite. The male is XX and the female XY.

CRISS-CROSS HEREDITY: THE CURIOUS FAMILY OF " BLEEDERS"

CRISS-CROSS heredity is the useful, old-fashioned term for something that puzzled everybody until the mechanism of sex-determination was discovered. An example explains it best, and the human disease called hæmophilia is a good one, since most people have heard of hæmophilics, who are popularly called " bleeders."

A true bleeder is a man who may easily bleed to death from the slightest little cut, while anything like a large wound is almost certain to be fatal. One of the sons of King Alphonso of Spain died thus, having received some slight internal injury in a motor accident. The feature of this disease that was first noticed was that it only occurs in men. Next it was observed that *all* the children of such men were completely free from

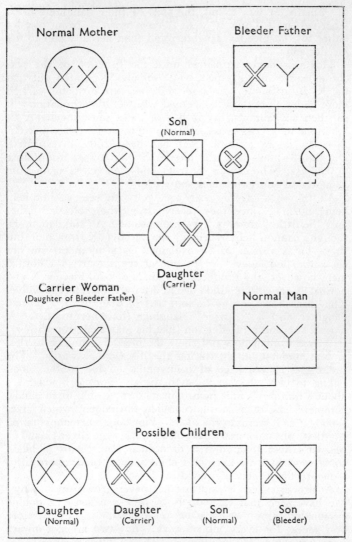

8. CRISS-CROSS INHERITANCE OF " BLEEDING "

The diagram shows how hæmophilia is passed on. The X
drawn in outline represents the disease chromosome.

it. Finally, it was found, the sons of their daughters often inherited it. Thus it went " criss-cross "—from bleeder father to non-bleeder daughter, and then across again to *her* bleeder son.

This was never explained until the function of the sex-chromosomes was grasped, when somebody pointed out that the X-chromosome was large, and therefore probably carried more genes than those concerned with sex-determination. If so, then any abnormality in one of them must inevitably be inherited in a criss-cross fashion ; it must be " sex-linked." Bleeding is an example that has been fully investigated. Diagram 8 shows how the bleeder X goes across from father to daughter (who cannot show it), and then across again from daughter to son (who does show it).

All the sons of this marriage, you can see, cannot help being normal, since they receive from their bleeder father only the little " dummy " Y-chromosome. All the daughters, though, cannot help receiving the bleeder X from him, but they—for a reason to be explained in a moment—do not show the deficiency. When one of them marries a normal man, however, she produces two kinds of ova, bleeder X and normal X, and four kinds of children are therefore possible. They are shown in the bottom half of diagram 8, a normal daughter and a " carrier " daughter (like her mother) ; a normal son and a bleeder son (like his maternal grandfather).

Why a woman does not show the bleeder gene she carries, is best understood by tracing the disease backwards. The prolonged hæmorrhage of hæmophilia is due to the blood failing to clot when exposed to the air (normal blood takes about a minute). This failure, in its turn, is due to an almost complete lack of a substance called fibrinogen, which gives " body," as it were, to the blood. Fibrinogen is manufactured by that physiological maid-of-all-work, the liver ; and a bleeder's liver, though it is of normal size, seems to be in some ways like the liver of a child a good time before birth —before fibrinogen is needed or developed.

A bleeder's liver is one that has never grown up ! Why ? We have seen that each of us is, in a real sense, a double personality, since we have two chromosomes (and therefore two genes) for every job of work. But two are not always necessary, since one is often enough. A normal woman, for instance, clearly does not need both of this particular pair of genes, since one is all a normal man possesses. And a woman with only one of them is no worse off than any normal man. But if a man gets that defective X, he is lost, inevitably a bleeder, since he has no normal X, as a female " carrier " has, to compensate for the deficiency. From the word " go " his liver completely lacks one of the chemicals essential for full development.[1]

This instance, by the way, is a good example of the long chain of complex reactions between gene and character—from gene to pre-natal liver, from pre-natal to post-natal liver, from the last to fibrinogen, from fibrinogen to bleeding. And there must be many intermediate stages as well. Every gene, you may say, does its work in the same sort of indirect way. Tracking it down is like trying to trace in detail the activities of secretary, paper-makers, printers, carters, etc., when the manager of a firm gives a simple order for a new kind of notepaper !

SEX-LINKED CHARACTERS IN CATTLE

SEX-LINKED characters are not always confined to males. One of great commercial importance, recently discovered, appears only in females—milk-yield in cattle. A medium-yielding cow carries the gene with the " kick " in it in one of her X-chromosomes ; a high-capacity cow has it in both. Taking the latter, she hands on a single dose of the character to every one of her children. The bulls, naturally, cannot show their dose at all, though they carry it (in their single X-chromosome). The cows will only be medium-yielders, *unless their father is of the same grade as their brothers*, so that they receive a dose from him as well as one from their mother.

To put it in another way, a cow inherits her milking qualities not only from her mother, but also, through her father, from her grandmother. Up till this discovery, a great many breeders had never bothered about the sire's effect upon the milk-yield of his daughters—and consequently were always failing to breed champion milkers.

Since sex-determination in moths and birds is exactly the reverse of what it is in other species, sex-linkage is also topsy-turvy—a fact to be remembered by anyone interested in poultry-breeding.

[1] Do not be misled by any of the several hæmorrhage diseases that superficially resemble hæmophilia. They are not due to lack of fibrinogen, and they are inherited differently from hæmophilia.

THE HALF-BREED: VICTIM OF
FACT AND FICTION

THAT " half-breeds have the worst qualities of both races,"
is, perhaps, the commonest saying about hybridisation,
and nothing could be farther from the truth. Cross the wild
Drosophila with the stumpy-winged variety, and the offspring will be decidedly longer-lived than either parent
stock. A mule has the toughness, disease-resistance, and
sure-footedness of its donkey father, with the intelligence, size,
and strength of the horse. Mate the English meat or dairy
breeds of cattle with the zebu-type of India and East Africa,
and the hybrids will inherit their native parents' " thriftiness "
and hardiness in difficult conditions, with a large share of
the size and other qualities of their English ancestry.

The hybrid usually inherits the *best* qualities of both stocks,
for the reason that useful qualities are generally dominant to
their opposite numbers, and the offspring of a cross is therefore the fortunate exhibitor of a double set of the characters
that evolution has found valuable. The phrase " hybrid
vigour," indeed, was a commonplace among practical breeders
for many years before the science of genetics started to explain
it as the result of dominance.

On the other hand, hybrids are often sterile, like the mule,
and for the very same reason that they are vigorous ! Look at
it in terms of chromosomes, and you will see why. The egg-
cell of the horse-donkey cross contains two sets of chromosomes which are complete strangers to each other ; and since
two heads are better than one, the members of a chromosome-
pair tend to remedy each other's deficiencies. But when
partnerships are hastily, not to say violently, formed, there
are apt, from time to time, to be quarrels between conflicting
temperaments.

The chief quarrel that occurs when the chromosomes of
two different species are forced into intimate co-operation is
over the rates of growth of the various parts of the body.
The donkey, in some ways, matures earlier, and in other ways
later than the horse. The result is that the two sets of chromosomes, each insisting that its own is the better way, between
them manage to bungle the delicate mechanism of the reproductive organs.

If the two species are only very distantly related, egg and sperm will refuse to unite, or will quarrel fatally at an early stage. If they are very nearly akin—as, for instance the red and white Shorthorns—perfect harmony will prevail. But hybrid vigour will not then be noticeable, since neither parent variety has any particularly useful dominant qualities that the other does not possess.

Beyond this general rule, hybridisation is a matter of detail. Each kind of cross is different from the others, and every new one is to a large extent a gamble. The really big gamble comes, however, when the hybrids (if fertile) are crossed in their turn—or mated back to one of the parent stocks, as is often done—for an immense number of new combinations of chromosomes thus becomes possible. Think of ringing the changes on the 28 pairs in cattle, for instance! Here is the point where only the breeder of genius can rise to the occasion :

(1) by breeding large numbers, to give him a wide choice ;
(2) by knowing which two or three beasts among them have just the right combination of grandparental qualities to enable him to use them as the parents of a new variety.

" But surely," a critic may interject, " there must be some foundation for the prejudice against human hybrids ? " There certainly is ; but it is not intrinsically connected with genetics. Man is the only creature with a social tradition, and that tradition is very much opposed to racial crosses. Usually, therefore, only the social outcasts of each race are willing to break so important a taboo, and you can scarcely expect such parents to produce a good type of child. Secondly, again owing to the social tradition, half-breeds find themselves from the very outset the objects of suspicion and dislike. Whatever good qualities they may possess have little chance to show themselves.

On the few occasions when proper studies have been made of crosses that carry no social stigma, the children have been found to be as sound and normal as their pure-bred companions. The English-Chinese community in Liverpool is an example, and another is the extraordinarily mixed population of Kisar, an island in the Dutch East Indies, where the people are a mixture of Native, English, French, Dutch, and German, with a sprinkling from India, the neighbouring islands, and some negroid types !

The " quarrelling " between the opposing sets of chromosomes in a hybrid, by the way, often makes itself felt in other parts besides the sexual organs. When the Canadians tried, for instance, to cross the native bison with English cattle, the disharmony between mother and child was so great as to cause high mortality at parturition. The double experiment that followed, though, was successful. The Asiatic yak was crossed with the bison and with English cattle (Hereford), yielding healthy offspring in each case. What is more, they were fertile. But there was about them all a comic clumsiness, a disproportion of one part with another, that betrayed their hybrid origin. When the two kinds of hybrids were mated together, the combination of cattle, yak and bison in the same animal had an effect that was at least equally odd.

The same sort of disproportion occurred when the Russians crossed yaks with zebus (the humped Indian cattle). The males of this match were sterile, too; though the females were fertile when crossed back either to yak or zebu.

One biologist (Bond) has gone so far as to say that in a hybrid the two sets of chromosomes tend to keep themselves to themselves, so to speak, and each to take charge of a different side of the body—so that the left side takes after the mother's family, for example, the right after the father's. He has produced much sound evidence, from birds, animals, and humans, to support this view. But human racial crosses are nothing like as drastic as the animal ones mentioned; and any disharmonies are too slight and dubious to be mentioned here.

A MAN MAY MARRY HIS COUSIN—WITH CAUTION

INBREEDING is the opposite of outbreeding—there is more in that truism than meets the eye—and the object of quite as much prejudice. Cousin marriage is said to be the cause of mental deficiency, insanity, tuberculosis, and most of the other ills in the medical dictionary. And, it is true, they very often follow it.

On the other hand, our cattle, horses, swine, sheep, and other domestic animals have all been brought to their present state by a system of inbreeding much closer than an occasional cousin marriage. Moreover, the Pharaohs usually married their sisters; their successors, the Ptolemies, did much the same; and there were several cousin marriages in the Wedgewood-Darwin-Galton group of families that gave us some of our greatest Victorians.

What is the explanation of these discordant results ? There is nothing either vicious or virtuous in inbreeding in itself. To repeat the truism, " Inbreeding is the opposite of Out-breeding." Instead of mixing widely different characters, it combines two sets of chromosomes whose genes reinforce each other in every way. If the stock is healthy, strong, clever, inbreeding will intensify those qualities. If it is weak and foolish, or has a number of recessive or semi-recessive defects, the results will be disastrous. The whole point about inbreeding is that it intensifies all the qualities of the stock, good and bad, known and *unknown*.

IF HEREDITY PERSISTS HOW DOES LIFE CHANGE?

CHROMOSOMES have been shown here as the mechanism of heredity, the mechanism that makes species breed according to their kind, dogs producing puppies, cats kittens. This may seem a little difficult to reconcile with the accepted theory that *all* species spring from the same parent, the first living thing. Lamarck, the earliest full-fledged evolutionist, thought that the ascent of species could be explained by the " inheritance of acquirement." The primitive giraffes, he suggested, had to stretch upwards to eat the leaves of trees, and their children's necks were therefore a little bit longer— and so on. Even Darwin tended towards a modified form of this apparently reasonable hypothesis. But both of them worked in complete ignorance of mendelism, the theory, and of chromosomes, the mechanism, of heredity. They could not know the impossibility of their hypothesis.

Since then many biologists have tried, in all possible ways, to induce the inheritance of acquirement. And every one has failed. Practically all have now given up the attempt, since modern knowledge has shown how unlikely it is to succeed. The reason is a simple one—parents do not *make* their children out of the stuff of which their own bodies are made. They simply hand on, unchanged, an assortment of the genes which they themselves received.

Very shortly after the egg-cell has started to multiply, one of the cells so formed gets set aside, so to speak, and there-after pursues its own career, regardless of the body which is developing round it.

It multiplies and ripens into the mature sex-cells, male or female, and it is these closely secluded cells which eventually give rise to sperm and ova.

Instead of looking on a parent as the manufacturer of its child, therefore, we should rather regard parent and child as different branches of the same tree. Lopping a lower limb off the family tree will have no effect on the upper branches. The point is that a parent does not hand on to its child a fully developed character, " acquired " or otherwise, but only a gene, a chemical *factor* that will later organise the development of a similar character—just as Britain, when she founds a new colony, does not transport a fully built town overseas, complete with drainage system and boulevards. She sends out only the men who can build a town from the raw material at hand. So the renovation of London's Mansion House is not likely to cause a magical spring-cleaning in the colony's Mayor's Parlour.

You will see the point best by glancing at the honey-bee, with its marvellous group of highly developed faculties for collecting honey and doing the work of the hive. The worker, the bee who does these things, never breeds. The parents of each fresh hive are the drone, who does nothing, and the queen who lays eggs. How can the lessons learned and the muscles developed by the worker in doing her job, be handed on to the next generation through the sex-cells of queen and drone ?

The hive is a good analogy, not to the ideal Socialist State (to which it is often likened) but to a single plant or animal. The workers are the mortal body-cells, while the queen and the drone are the secluded sex-cells that hand on to the next generation the immutable qualities of the hive. In the old phrase, the " germplasm," the seed of the race, is immortal and unchanging, though it builds round itself successive generations of mortal, changeable bodies to nurse, protect, and diffuse it. The stream of life flows direct from egg to egg, not from egg to parent egg. Thus the parent's experiences can have no effect on the children.

How, then, *does* one species give rise to another ? The trouble is that this, like most other questions in life, has no single answer. Cross-breeding, to start new types by combining the best of both parent varieties ; inbreeding to develop useful qualities ; natural selection, that weeds out the inefficient and forces the survivors to inbreed ; sexual selection

that will only permit the vigorous and attractive to mate—
these are three-quarters of the answer ; and very few people
realise how large a part is played by natural selection alone.
But neither one nor all of these can explain how variations that
are fundamentally new arise in the first place. The beginnings
of an explanation have only been found in the pictures the
microscope has shown us during this century.

EVOLUTION AN EFFECT WITH MANY CAUSES

SOMETIMES the chromosomes do not behave. Two opposite
numbers may stick together, so that in the gametes of a
species that normally have 8 chromosomes, one has 9 and the
other 7. At other times all the chromosomes of both armies
stick together, so that one resulting gamete has double the
chromosomes it should have, the other none.

A variety of similar aberrations are known ; and their
possessors all depart, in one way or another, from the parent
species. The *gigas* variety of evening primrose, for instance,
which is twice the size of the ordinary type, has also twice
the number of chromosomes.

There is another type of " sport " which is probably more
important, a " gene-mutation "—an ultra-microscopic change,
that is, in some single gene. Occasionally (about one in ten
thousand times), for instance, Drosophila (the fruit-fly) will
produce an egg that develops into a fly with mere stumps of
wings. This breeds true when mated to its like, and is recessive to the normal type. Mutations of this sort have been
found in practically every plant and animal studied, though
their causes are still a mystery. All that we know at the
moment is that bombardment with X-rays will make them
occur more often. Nothing short of that seems to have any
effect at all on the " germplasm ".

But biologists have now amassed enough evidence to justify
summarising their general opinion thus :—

Gene-mutations and (to a lesser extent) changes in chromosome number provide new variations.

Isolation, sexual selection, and inbreeding intensify them.

Outbreeding spreads them, mixes them, and provides new
combinations.

Natural selection completes the process by wiping out the
older, less efficient species, and leaves only the new, better
adapted varieties to breed.

In some such way, during the æons of evolution, a single-celled creature gave rise to one of many cells, fish produced amphibia, amphibia reptiles—and so on down to our not-so-distant ancestor who fathered both the apes and all mankind.

SOME BOOKS TO READ NEXT ON HEREDITY

BREEDING, as I have hinted in this article, is very closely allied to the other activities of the living creature. So if you want a bird's-eye view of the whole, but with greater detail than I have here been able to give to breeding alone, you will find it in highly readable (and reliable) form in the following three small books—read in the order I have given:—

1. *Life*, by Sir Arthur Shipley (C.U.P.).
2. *Evolution, Heredity, & Variation*, by D. Ward Cutler (Christophers).
3. *Living Organisms*, by E. S. Goodrich (O.U.P.).

Alternatively, read Shipley first, and then either *Heredity* (very short), by F. A. E. Crew (Benn) or *Heredity—Mainly Human* (rather long), by Eldon Moore (Chapman & Hall). Each of these five books gives a full list of others on the subject.

More technical are F. A. E. Crew's two books, *Animal Genetics* (Oliver & Boyd) and *The Genetics of Sexuality in Animals* (C.U.P.). Both of them, though, are especially useful to the poultry-farmer.

BIOLOGY FOR AMATEUR AND PROFESSIONAL

by W. E. SWINTON, Ph.D., B.Sc., F.R.S.E., F.G.S.,
of the British Museum (Natural History)

NEARLY four hundred years ago Pierre Charron wrote " *La vraie science et le vraie étude de l'homme c'est l'homme,*" a phrase which Pope translated and used in his famous essay as " the proper study of mankind is man." This statement, like most other generalisations, is too narrow to be entirely correct ; there can be no proper study of man unless the whole of his history, his background and his contemporaries and even their ancestors are included. That is to say we believe the proper study of mankind to be man and his world, their origin, growth and development. Surely there is no more close or fascinating theme to us than this, the history of our own selves and surroundings, a history so varied and great that there can be no one who cannot find some subject to his taste if only he seeks.

Enough has already been said to indicate the manifold fields of natural knowledge comprised in those common terms Natural History and Biology. These two terms originally meant the same thing though they have now for practical purposes acquired a slight modification of meaning. The student of natural history is usually named a naturalist, a term that at present connotes an enthusiastic (and usually amateur) worker or collector in the field. He is essentially the practical man who primarily searches for the facts and specimens and only secondarily arranges and examines them in detail. Fortunately, in England, until very recently, the race of naturalists has always been strong, and such enthusiastic workers have made remarkable and valuable contributions to science, have founded some splendid journals, and are virtually the fathers of some excellent museums. Such societies and museums, the fundamental " pillars " in the scientific edifice, were made by men inspired by Nature ; men who loved the fresh air, the trees and flowers, and who, literally, found " sermons in stones and books in the running brooks."

While there is nothing to prevent the naturalist from also being the biologist the latter term has gradually come to mean something a little more professional. While the naturalist, as we have said, is usually an amateur, the biologist is generally a man who is paid to follow his bent and who has spent years in training for his own particular branch of science. He, too, may love the wind in the willows, the flash of a bird's plumage, or the song of the stream as well as any naturalist, but his label more often denotes, or seems to imply, rather the quiet investigation of the laboratory or the scratch of pen on paper in the book-lined study ; and there are many different and apparently unrelated branches to which the biologist may belong. He may be a research worker interested in cancer, a bacteriologist busy with his microscope, a geologist looking at the amazing complexity of some of the early forms of life, or some worker on mosquito control.

BIOLOGY THE KEY TO MAN'S ENDEAVOURS

HOWEVER great a subject one appreciates biology to be few fully realise its wide ramifications. Its followers in one way or another are multitudinous, and the work and industries they are concerned with equally large. Brewing and Biochemistry, Mining and Medicine, Prospecting and Publishing, Trawling and Tailoring are only a few of the widely scattered groups which are dependent in some degree upon the work of the biologist. It is important to appreciate this, for the love of nature that the naturalist has, and which some consider to be merely a hobby, has gradually grown into the great science of biology with many branches, some of which, as has been indicated, are necessities of modern civilisation and commerce.

Without a knowledge of insects and of the measures for their control, great areas of the earth now prosperous could not be inhabited, and such a gigantic and time-saving enterprise as the Panama Canal could not have been carried out. Without a knowledge of the microscopic forms of life the conquest of disease would be reduced almost to a farce. The palæontologist with his detailed and tabulated information of fossils and their range in time has helped the prospector to track the riches of the mineral world and to tap the reservoirs of oil. The brewing of beer, the distillation of whisky, and the making of dyestuffs, depend on a knowledge of many botanical and zoological facts. Cloths and clothing depend on investigation of the breeding of animals just as paper and books require the results of botanical research.

The making of furniture and the building of houses have followed upon a knowledge of wood and trees.

Every object we use, our health and the drugs with which we preserve it, the food we eat and the clothes we wear are all based fundamentally upon the processes of nature. The work we do in office, laboratory, or industry can all be thought out to its basic necessities, and it will be seen that natural science, and generally a biological branch of it, is at the root. Our pleasures too are constantly advancing through such research.

Thus, as one might really suspect, however busy and spectacular the business and industrial powers may be, they cannot with impunity disregard the quietly working biologist. The vast superstructure that we have evolved and erected on our ancient mother earth is part of ourselves, and surely the proper study of ourselves must take notice of all the natural factors past, present, and, as far as possible, future.

THE VALUE OF MAKING CONTACTS

Now, as we have already indicated, many may be attracted to the study of natural things for the very present pleasure such study affords. Others may see in the wide importance of the subject an outlet for professional ambition and the chance of a useful and pleasant career. Both groups will naturally wish to know how further knowledge, on more or less organised lines, may be obtained so that the pleasures of the hobby or the prospects of the career may be increased or made more certain.

In the following pages we shall therefore attempt to outline the sort of education that will best suit these two divergent groups of naturalists, and we shall indicate where and how this training may be obtained.

For the non-professional person who is interested in natural history as a hobby, there are several ways in which he (or she) may develop a wider scientific knowledge out of working hours and either free of expense or at very little cost. They are so well known to many that it would seem needless to mention them here, yet some appear to remain unconscious of the great treasure houses of information that are open to them.

Sooner or later the individual naturalist will tend to specialise or, at least, to prefer one subject to the others he may still enjoy. To develop his general knowledge the most useful thing to do is to join the local Natural History Society, or any particular branch of such a society which may be desired. In this way the naturalist is brought into touch with people of similar tastes, quite apart from the fact that most of these societies possess suitable premises with a library from which the member may borrow. The society may even manage a small museum, and above all it is certain to arrange lectures on a diversity of appropriate subjects and to organise excursions. It is wise to join such a society even if it is not close at hand, for the annual subscription is usually low and the ability to borrow books is a great convenience and soon recompenses for the annual contribution.

Many such societies have their own journals and the facility of having one's ideas and observations published is not to be regarded lightly. However obvious this advice may be, it is an unhappy fact that even among the most famous of such bodies, the membership is declining, even although so many persons appear to be interested in the subject they encourage. Perhaps, after all, too few recognise the advantages that accrue from so little expenditure and how useful the strength of combined effort and interest can be.

Every naturalist, whether amateur or professional, should belong to one such society. If the eminent biologist may not gain much from membership at least he has the satisfaction of being able to advise, and to guide the footsteps of those who will eventually fill his place.

TREASURE HOUSES OF KNOWLEDGE: THE MUSEUMS

ANOTHER fruitful source of assistance is the local museum, and nowadays the country is well supplied with such institutions. Most museums have a library accessible under certain conditions to the bona fide student. The exhibited collections give an indication of local or general knowledge systematised. Education can be obtained by examining the series and reading the labels, and especially by comparing one's own specimens with the material on show.

The larger museums have additional facilities of considerable value, perhaps the most directly useful of which is the series of lectures given by the guide-lecturer, or someone acting in this capacity. The Natural History Museum in London, for example, has a guide lecturer, scientifically fully qualified, who gives a lecture each morning and afternoon during the week, while on Monday mornings and Sunday afternoons members of the Museum Scientific Staff give more advanced lectures. In this way, and free of charge, a very good outline of any special branch of natural history can be obtained. Many of the other museums have somewhat similar arrangements, the Horniman Museum in London, for example, running an excellent series of lectures on Saturday afternoons throughout the winter season.

These helpful features are fortunately not confined to London. Museums in Folkestone, Bexhill, Leeds and Sheffield, to mention only a few, give series of lectures at times to suit the average amateur, and much assistance can usually be obtained in this way. It should not be forgotten that the curators of museums are enthusiastic men only too ready to assist those of an inquiring mind and who show some desire to take the subject seriously.

There are hundreds of museums in this country alone, and the museum is a public university, without age or time limit for its students, and above all free. No amateur (or professional) biologist can afford to neglect these storehouses of knowledge which are the results of the work of generations of enthusiastic men.

THE EVER-OPEN DOOR TO LEARNING

OTHER sources of information are the extra-mural, or extension, courses arranged by various universities. Mention will be made of these later and generally they are held only in the more populous places. If the amateur is bent on a really scientific foundation for his studies he can, of course, attend some university lectures. Nearly every university and college in the country has occasional lectures by distinguished men to which the public are admitted. Further, there are numerous evening schools where a first-class training in a subject may be had usually for quite a small fee. Summer schools in various branches of biology are frequently held at some English universities. They may last for a week or a fortnight and are not expensive.

These university and college activities will be mentioned again later, but from what has been said it will be seen that the person who is a keen naturalist has plenty of strings to his bow. The local natural history, scientific or philosophical society, however it may be named, will be delighted to welcome him, encourage him and be pleased to have his observations and reports. The same is true of the museums. Their

libraries will help his studies, and even if he is so unfortunate
as to have no such aids in his locality the National Central
Library in Malet Place, London, W.C.1, will allow him to
borrow the books he desires through his nearest public
library.

It can truly be said nowadays that there is no bar in this
country to those who wish to learn. All the seeker after
free knowledge needs is energy and sincerity. Given these
elementary qualities and the advice of his librarian and museum
curator he can draw upon the richest stores of knowledge at
a purely negligible cost. Supplementing reading, writing, and
listening to lectures by his customary work in the field, any
man will find a hobby that will never fail and that presents
a new problem every day. He will soon learn that Nature is
ever changing, ever attractive and always accessible. Here is
a hobby, a pursuit, for all, of all ages, and of an allurement
that will persist.

HOW TO STUDY IN SPARE TIME

THERE are many followers of this hobby who may desire
to serve more fully in its cause than can be done in their
leisure, and it may have occurred to them that a certificated
education, or the attainment of a diploma or degree may
place them in a position to give full time to their desires.

There are few universities in Great Britain which allow
evening or outside students to proceed to their degrees. The
most notable exception is London, where external students
are admitted to its examinations and where evening education
leading up to the degree standard is quite easily obtained.
While it is no light task to work commercially by day and to
study by night, hundreds of degrees have been obtained by
this method, and the recipients now occupy splendid positions
in the scientific world. As examples of affiliated colleges in
London which give such training we may cite the Battersea
Polytechnic, Birkbeck College, Chelsea Polytechnic, and
Northampton Polytechnic.

The fees in these institutions are moderate and the tuition
excellent, but they are in London. Those who desire further
particulars of them should write to the Registrar of the individual college or institute, or better still to the Registrar of
the University of London, S.W.7, for information as to the
most suitable evening class.

Outside London there are no fewer than 135 technical

colleges in England, 3 in Ireland, 1 in the Isle of Man, and 4 in Scotland. The addresses of these institutions can all be found in *Whitaker's Almanack*, and the Registrar or the Secretary will willingly furnish the applicant with information as to costs and courses. Not all of these colleges or institutes deal with biology, but many of them will provide all that the student needs. A course of one or more subjects will lead, by examination, to a certificate which is always useful.

In addition to this form of education, advantage should be taken wherever possible of the university extension lectures. These courses are arranged by certain universities and are conducted by highly competent lecturers. Attendance over a few years will give an excellent education along the selected line, and again certificates are awarded under certain circumstances. Such courses are conducted in England under the auspices of the universities or colleges at Birmingham, Bristol, Cambridge, Durham, Exeter, Hull, Leeds, Leicester, Liverpool, London, Manchester, Newcastle, Nottingham, Oxford, Reading, Sheffield and Southampton, and by each of the four University Colleges in Wales. Information concerning the nature and scope of the various lectures can be obtained on application to the Director of Extra-Mural Studies at the university concerned.

DEGREES FOR THE PART-TIME STUDENT

THE summer schools run by one or two universities and the facilities occasionally obtainable at marine biological stations are again useful, but these are intended for people who have some acquaintance with the subject, and are more in the nature of refresher courses. The announcements concerning them are to be found usually in the advertisement pages of the scientific weekly *Nature*.

By a judicious selection or combination of these methods the part-time student will be able to obtain some sort of certificate, if, indeed, he does not take a degree, which will help him towards a biological career.

The claims of the various correspondence schools should not be overlooked. The whole theory of the subject is adequately taught and arrangements are made for practical work, so that by this means alone the student can proceed at a moderate cost to an external degree in Arts or Science of London University, no matter in what district he lives or how he is employed. The examinations, of course, have to be taken in London under the very strict university regulations. The path of the part-time student is therefore fairly clear, though it will never be easy and it demands an amount of determination and hard work, which is itself an eloquent testimony to the character of the student.

We must say something, however, for the young man or woman who wishes to take up biological work as a career, and who is prepared to devote his or her whole time to the study. A certain amount of biology is now taught in the schools, so that at a comparatively early stage the student has perhaps decided on the subject that is most attractive. It need hardly be pointed out, however, that early decisions are not infrequently regretted or changed, and since most of the biological sciences are interrelated there is ample opportunity for the development of new interests.

THE BEST TRAINING FOR THE PROFESSIONAL

WHAT then is the best method of procedure ? If the student definitely decides at school to go in for Natural Science then the immediate problem is the entrance examination to a selected university and the determination on the course to be pursued there, for there is no doubt that a university education and a degree are essential. The matriculation examination may usually be taken at school, though the form and conditions vary with the different universities. From a general point of view the natural science degrees will include the same subjects, the only difference being the emphasis on certain subjects that the student's taste dictates.

It is perhaps too seldom realised that the best biological education for those with the time and money to spare is the medical degree course. Medical men spend four years or so in the study of one particular animal from all aspects, and this study is preceded by one or two years' study of zoology, botany, chemistry and physics. A medical degree is a splendid general biological education with the additional advantage that the student has two strings to his bow. First, one of the purely biological avenues he sees in the course of his studies, and, secondly, the practice of medicine. The professional aspect of this study will be mentioned later when we deal with the question of remuneration.

Usually, however, the student will enter a university or college to study zoology, botany, geology or anthropology, and a word or two of advice and caution may be given. In the first place the ultimate object must be a good honours degree ; a pass degree, though a sign of a good general education, is almost useless in the competition for an attractive post, so that an honours standard should be the student's goal. What class of honours he attains ultimately will depend on his natural aptitude for the subject and his industry, but a first- or second-class honours degree will see him well on the way towards congenial employment.

Then, however much one subject may be admired, the others should not be neglected. In the first place degrees are not given for three or four years' study of one subject alone, and in the second place, there is no subject that cannot be amplified by, or is unconnected with, another. The embryo zoologist should therefore not neglect some botany which will tell him of the conditions of life in another kind of medium, while the comparison of reactions of the two types of life are interesting. To understand the working of living things some knowledge of chemistry and physics is essential and, indeed, the first science examination, by whatever name it passes in the different centres, usually makes such a combination of subjects obligatory.

In his later studies for his final examination the student of zoology will have his principal subject and one or more subsidiary subjects, which might be botany, geology (or palæontology), or physiology. There are often also special facilities for a greater study of insects since quite a number of universities now have a chair of entomology, and the subject is one of great commercial and professional importance.

Those who are interested in botany should follow a somewhat similar course, giving, of course, more attention to their chief subject, and perhaps less to geology, for it is exceptional for much palæobotany to be taught in the Geological Departments nowadays. The importance of the study of fungi should not be forgotten, for mycologists are much in demand at present.

Geologists, and that includes those who study palæontology, must modify their studies according to the side they prefer. Those interested in minerals and rocks need to understand a great deal of chemistry and physics, while for palæontologists, botany, zoology and anatomy are most valuable subsidiaries. Further, while the student of invertebrate palæontology cannot do without zoology he will find anatomy of little use, while the vertebrate palæontologist will find a study of human anatomy both fascinating and of constant usefulness.

Of the other sciences which have to do with biology, anthropology is an interesting study with a strong zoological and anatomical background.

WHEN THE STUDENT SHOULD SEEK ADVICE

COMPLETE information of the facilities available and of the recommended courses of study for the appropriate degree will readily be furnished on application to the Registrar of the selected university, while the student's tutor will always give the best possible advice on the particular case. Some advice is often very necessary, for as the education develops and interests widen, new attractions come into view and the first love may be deserted. This may be a wise move but it needs reshaping of studies and an abandonment of preconceived ideas. Here it is that the experienced teacher can advise and help the student not only as to the immediate changes involved but also as to the ultimate possibilities.

As no good house is ever built on poor foundations so it is most unwise to confine one's studies or interests within too narrow walls. Speed in graduation and a limitation of outlook are often attractions for an undergraduate, but the result is apt to be regretted later on. All the biological sciences are interwoven and a knowledge of something of them all is ultimately desirable if not absolutely necessary. Wide studies, ample experience of the different laboratory methods and *above all* an acquaintance with the literature of natural history and its accessibility are of great importance. Equally so is a knowledge of, or at least the ability to read, German. Scientific work without this ability is almost an impossibility.

Happy is the student, young or old, who can add to these accomplishments and qualifications the ability to write good English and the gift of drawing. His publications will be natural and valuable, and his fame more easily achieved.

Besides the degrees in Arts, Pure Science, and Medicine suitable for the persons we have in mind, several universities have additional diplomas or certificates which may prove desirable. Such for example are the diplomas in Agriculture, Archæology, and Anthropology, of Cambridge ; the diploma in Animal Biology, of Leeds ; the diplomas in Anthropology, Archæology, Biology, Biochemistry, of London ; the diploma of Bacteriology, of Manchester ; and somewhat similar diplomas and certificates of Oxford and Reading.

A full list of these subjects and qualifications can be obtained from the Yearbooks or Calendars published by the various universities and also from *The University Yearbook* (Bell).

THE PROSPECTS OF EMPLOYMENT

WHEN eventually the undergraduate becomes a graduate, after a period of research, or perhaps immediately on qualification, the question arises as to the professional possibilities of his studies. He wants to know what outlets exist for the educated and fully qualified biologist.

First of all there are the schools. As we have already mentioned biology is coming, at last, into its proper place in the modern curriculum in both boys' and girls' schools. Thus teachers are required and a congenial and useful career is therefore available for those who have a liking for teaching and not averse to exercising their art upon young persons. At any rate this opportunity does now definitely exist, though it is of recent growth. Especially good work in natural science has been done in recent years by the science masters and staff of such boys' public schools as Marlborough, St. Paul's, and Winchester. The salaries, of course, vary with the different class of school but are generally, from the present-day point of view, satisfactory. The positions are more or less permanent, and provide facilities for pensions on retirement.

Then there are posts in the technical colleges to which we have referred earlier. These consist in demonstratorships, lectureships, headships of departments, and professorial chairs with a salary scale of roughly £250 to £1000 per annum. Promotion is by merit and selection, and it is possible to become even the principal or director of the institution, although it must be remembered that biology is not the only subject taught there. In these technical colleges, where evening teaching is also done, there is probably less time for original work than in a college with a less onerous syllabus, but the work presents many opportunities and the staff meet keen students.

The universities offer similar positions to those in technical colleges, but the salaries and the professional status are higher. There are quite a number of vacancies every year for which those with a first- or second-class honours degree will be serious applicants. Obviously those with post-graduate research work to their credit will be more suitably equipped, and the opportunities for this should not be overlooked nor its value underestimated. Most of the large universities are well endowed with Fellowships, Scholarships and various research-grants which are usually sufficient to maintain the student for a year or two and to permit him to do some useful piece of work under the supervision of the head of his department. In this way lies perhaps the best approach to academic life. The ultimate end of such a career is usually a professorship with a salary of £1000 to £1200 a year. Riches will, therefore, not lie much in the biologist's path, but it will be a pleasant life among quiet ways.

CONGENIAL POSTS IN THE MUSEUMS

IN addition to academic lines of employment there are numerous other opportunities for biologists. The museums, for example, employ many botanists, zoologists and geologists. The British Museum (Natural History) has a scientific staff of fifty-two who are qualified in this way, the salaries running from £350 or so to £1700 per annum. The entrance regulations and the competition are naturally rather severe. The principal museums throughout the country have similarly qualified persons and pay salaries of between £250 and £800. Within recent years, thanks very largely to the efforts of The Museums Association, conditions of employment in museums generally and salaries have greatly improved. The museum man has come to be regarded rightly as a well-qualified friend and adviser of the public, and consequently the applicant for a position is expected to have a good degree and a good all-round interest in his work. The Museums Association has recently put a diploma scheme into operation whereby persons who have entered the profession can be examined and granted diplomas on museum competence which, with the additional scientific qualifications the curator has, forms a very important testimonial. No longer can museums be regarded as dull institutions and the larger of them must be looked on as affording congenial employment which is suitably paid, close contact with interesting and enthusiastic people, and ample opportunities for work in the open.

In the same way some of the larger libraries call for qualified biologists, and nowadays the libraries form a very important factor in public education so that they must quite definitely be considered among the possible sources for appointments. Museums have usually a good library which needs a scientifically-minded librarian, but there are several large libraries and special information bureaux where a biologist is necessary.

SOME ATTRACTIVE BYWAYS OF A BIOLOGIST'S CAREER

APART from these obvious forms of employment, there are many government appointments at home and abroad. The Ministry of Agriculture and Fisheries has numerous departments where those qualified in natural science are wanted. Those trained in entomology might find an outlet in the Imperial Institute of Entomology at home or as entomologists abroad, where this subject is of immense importance in agriculture and public health. Some excellent appointments are available in these fields. In botany, and especially in mycology, there are similar opportunities at, for example, Kew Gardens, the Imperial Institute of Mycology, and as government mycologists in the colonies.

For geologists and palæontologists there are many openings in the Geological Survey and the Museum of Practical Geology, in colonial geological surveys, or with the great oil companies, and with many mining and prospecting ventures.

The hospitals, too, require trained biologists for work in zoology, botany and bacteriology. Biochemical work is now much to the fore. With so much attention now paid to cancer research there are great possibilities in hospital work both for research and for teaching.

Finally, there are many who have made comfortable incomes by writing books or articles on natural history. This work, of course, requires the special gift of writing, but it is a pleasant occupation whose conditions are settled largely by the author himself. For all biologists there is the possibility of increasing their income by writing and lecturing, so that a biological education does not merely sharpen the appreciation of beauty, it is also a definite training for a career with many attractive aspects and many compensations. Even in these days of unemployment the trained biologist is comparatively secure. His work is necessary for many purposes in universities and schools, in fishing grounds and museums, in the oil or cotton fields, in the breweries and the hospitals, and behind his work in all the positions available is ever the delightful background of beautiful Nature itself.

INDEX AND PRONOUNCING GLOSSARY

Compiled by L. M. MONT-CLAR *and* C. H. KNOWLES, B.Sc.

HOW TO USE THIS INDEX.—In order to facilitate immediate reference to the principal entry on a particular subject, the page number for this entry is set in italics, thus : *258*. Subsidiary references to the subject which occur elsewhere in the book are indicated by numerals in roman type, thus : 387. References to illustrations are indicated by numerals in roman type surrounded by square brackets : [156]. Cross references given in the index refer only to the index pages.

THE PRONOUNCING GLOSSARY.—Where the pronunciation of proper names and technical terms is not immediately understood from the spelling, or where the spelling may be misleading, a separate pronunciation is given after the first index entry. In simple cases a hint may be considered sufficient ; in all doubtful cases a complete phonetic re-spelling is given. The word is broken into syllables as it is spoken, and an accent mark (´) follows the syllable on which the stress is placed. The notation used for the phonetic re-spelling is as follows :

ā	m*a*te	ė	th*e*re	th	*th*in
ē	m*e*te	à	f*a*ther	TH	*th*ine
ī	m*i*te	e	h*e*r	zh	lei*s*ure
ō	m*o*te	aw	*aw*l	ch	*ch*ur*ch*
ū	m*u*te	oi	*oi*l	g	*g*et
ōō	b*oo*t	ow	*ow*l	j	*j*am

The French nasalised *n* is denoted by italicising the vowel and the nasal concerned, thus : *un, bon, vin.*

Printed by H. Henderson at the Villafield Press, Bishopbriggs